Silent Boundaries

Silent Boundaries

Cultural Constraints on Sickness and Diagnosis of Iranians in Israel

Karen L. Pliskin

Yale University Press
New Haven and London

Designed by Nancy Ovedovitz and set in Bodoni type by The Composing Room of Michigan, Inc. Printed in the United States of America by Thomson-Shore, Inc., Dexter, Michigan.

Library of Congress Cataloging-in-Publication Data

Pliskin, Karen L.
Silent boundaries.
Bibliography: p.
Includes index.
1. Jews, Iranian—Medical care—Social aspects—Israel. 2. Medical personnel and patients—Israel. 3. Somatoform disorders—Israel. 4. Jews, Iranian—Mental health—Israel. 5. Israel—Emigration and immigration—Psychological aspects. 6. Health behavior—Israel. 7. Medical anthropology—Israel. I. Title. [DNLM: 1. Acculturation. 2. Cross-Cultural Comparison. 3. Delivery of Health Care—Israel. 4. Ethnic Groups—Israel. W 84 JI9 P7s]
RA418.3.I75P57 1987 362.1'089915'05694 86-32492
ISBN 0-300-03792-9

Table 7.1 is printed from *The International Journal of Social Psychiatry*, 1963, vol. 9:276, by permission.

The paper in this book meets the guidelines for permanence and durability of the Committee on Production Guidelines for Book Longevity of the Council on Library Resources.

10 9 8 7 6 5 4 3 2 1

Contents

Acknowledgments

By the mid-nineteenth century, European travelers in Iran had reported that the city of Shiraz, with hundreds of silver-engravers, was renowned for the delicate three-dimensional designs and pictures hammered onto silver trays, bowls, and urns. But by the 1970s only a few engravers remained, and of these only one or two had apprentices. I wanted to document this dying art and the lives of the artists engaged in it before it would be left to art historians to decipher the craft's demise. So in the fall of 1978 I set off for Iran, ready to study Shirazi silver-engravers.

But the Islamic Revolution closed the bazaars, and xenophobia ran rampant. Knowing such a study of Iranian arts and artists would be nearly impossible, I left Iran for Israel with the intention of studying Iranian culture abroad. In Jerusalem two months later, I met Eileen Basker at the annual meetings of the Israel Anthropological Association. Eileen, hearing that I had been in Iran, told me about a medical anthropology problem she was working on, the problem of "Parsitis" (Basker et al. 1982), and asked if I would be interested in working on it too. At that time I was desperately looking for a new research topic to replace the craftsmen study, and I gladly accepted Eileen's suggestion. Accordingly, my first thanks for the production of this work go to the late Eileen Basker.

I am also grateful to the doctors, psychiatrists, psychologists, social workers, nurses, staff, and patients at the different mental health clinics, primary care clinics, and hospitals in Jerusalem. I mention no one by name, in order to assure the anonymity of the places where I did my research. I am thankful to all my Iranian friends in Israel for sharing their lives with me. To Suleiman Mottahedeh I owe a special thanks for his special help in Jerusalem. And to my Israeli friends and acquaintances, I am appreciative of their help, comments, questions, suggestions, and information that came to me as cultural commentaries through ordinary conversation and socializing.

While I was in the field changing topics and pursuing new ideas, correspondence with Michael M. J. Fischer helped spur me on, and his comments on different chapters, as well as his help throughout my graduate school career, are well appreciated. I am especially grateful to Arthur Kleinman, whose careful and critical readings of previous versions of the manuscript helped me mold my thoughts and analyses into the form presented here. I also appreciate the help of Byron Good, whose work on medical anthropology in Iran influenced my research, and whose insightful comments on earlier drafts prompted me and inspired me. Nur Yalman's support and encouragement, as well as his suggestions regarding publication, have been reassuring and thought-provoking. In addition, Mary Jo DelVecchio Good's remarks on various chapters raised questions about problems that I had taken for granted, and I thank her for her help, too. And for comments on the nearly final version of the manuscript, I am grateful to Amnon Netzer, who as an Iranian and an Israeli read with a very critical eye (and I apologize to him for not using an official linguistic system of transliteration of Persian and Hebrew).

The research in Iran and Israel was funded by a Fulbright-Hays Doctoral Dissertation Research Abroad Grant, and the writing, back at Harvard University, was partially supported by a Foreign Language and Area Studies Fellowship. The final editing of the manuscript was completed during my tenure as a postdoctoral fellow under a National Research Service Award of the National Institute of Mental Health, in the Medical Anthropology Program at the University of California, San Francisco. It was there that Lynn Kelly, at SIMA of the UCSF library, helped me borrow a CP/M card from Bruce Payne, so that I could edit my manuscript on their computer. And it was a long-term colleague, Jim Moore, who gave me his time and let me use his word processor printer to print off the manuscript for publication.

Ultimately, the most support—the unquestioning and fundamental kind—has come from my family. If it were not for their confidence in my journeys and projects, my academic and artistic and adventurous pursuits would have been nearly impossible. And so, it is with gratitude and affection that this work of mine is dedicated to Miriam and Bill Pliskin, my parents.

San Francisco
July 1986

Notes on Transliteration

The transliteration of Persian is based upon common colloquial speech patterns, primarily of central Iran, and is here spelled phonetically (and simplified, that is, without diphthongs). This differs from official transliterations of formal literary Persian, where spelling is based upon certain codes to enable the reader to back-transliterate into Persian.

In order to pronounce the Persian words, the following sounds are distinguished:

Sound	*In Iranian word*	*Pronunciation*
a	kam (few, little, insufficient)	as in "that"
ā	bād (wind)	as in "father" or "bald"
e	cheshm (eye)	as the "e" in "sell" or the "i" in "sit"
i	pārti-bāzi (pull, influence)	as the "ee" in "feet"
o	chādor (tent)	as the "o" in "cope"
u	ākhund (cleric)	as the "oo" in "moon"
kh	khun (blood)	as the "ch" in "Bach" and in the Hebrew and Yiddish "chutzpah" (the "kh" is also used in Hebrew transliteration and is pronounced the same way)
'	za'if (weak)	glottal stop, as in the pronunciation of "bottle" in Brooklyn

The Hebrew vowel sounds, also transliterated phonetically, are simplified here by the following pronunciations:

Sound	*In Hebrew word*	*Pronunciation*
a	adam (person)	as the "a" in "ah"
e	aretz (land)	as the "e" in "bet"
i	kibbutz (collective farm)	either as the "i" in "fit" or the "ee" in "feet"
o	aliyot (immigrations)	either as the "o" in "horn" or "hope"
u	ulpan (intensive language course)	either as the "oo" in "soon" or the "u" in "put"

Silent Boundaries

Introduction

On the first day of February 1979, Khomeini arrived in Iran after a fifteen-year exile. During the five months before his return, I lived in Shiraz, a city distinguished for its roses and poetry, its polite people and its pleasant climate. Yet the months of my sojourn were marked by protests against the Shah in the streets, soldiers standing with bayonets at street corners, strikes of all kinds (electricians, bazaaris, school teachers, Iran Air employees), trepidation among the Shirazis about future strikes—that there would be no gas, no kerosene, no oil, no bread. Tension pervaded the city streets as Iran embarked on a path to the unknown. While there I couldn't help thinking how fortunate I was to have lived in Shiraz four years earlier, studying Iranian arts. The ambience then—calm and amiable—had seemed to me and my acquaintances to be that of a society entering modernity. Four years later, that budding modernity had sown the seeds of its own downfall.

I left Shiraz teary-eyed on the same day Khomeini returned. My Shirazi friends, concerned and kind, uncertain for their future, afraid that the impending Islamic Republic would stimulate the kinds of anti-minority riots they heard their parents and grandparents talk about—for most of my friends were Jewish—lived these months in anxiety and apprehension, and were relieved that I was going. Because of the anti-American course of the Revolution, some were afraid to be seen with an American on the streets. Others, knowing that I was unable to carry out my intended research on the handicrafts industry and noticing that I was asking many questions about other aspects of Iranian society (on orphans, politics, religion, women, dietary regulations, herbal medicines), must have found my probing foolish in the face of the political turmoil that everyone, including myself, was experiencing. As an outsider, I was free to leave. They—attached to their families, homes, and businesses—were not. My reaction to the daily events was to talk about them, find out what was happening, showing, at times, the disquietude I often felt. Their reactions were to create a semblance of normalcy, to listen to the radio but not discuss the news in the way I would, to enact their roles as family members the ways they did before the downfall of the shah began. Although they were afraid, although they could not play music or have parties for fear of provoking reactions among the revolutionaries, who consider music anti-Islamic, although they spoke about the events with friends, although some quietly planned what they would do, as Jews, if the situation should get worse, although they prepared to send their teenage children to the United States or Israel, many parents refrained from speaking about their fear in front of their children, and children avoided voicing their fear in front of their parents. Such was the atmosphere when, with a heavy heart, I said good-bye to my Shirazi friends and the city whose scents, sounds, and sights I still dream of perceiving.

From Shiraz I went to Israel where, having had my original topic aborted by the Revolution, I intended to study Iranian Jewish immigrants and refugees. As a researcher uprooted from my prearranged plans and immersed in yet another, and altogether different, sociocultural system, I perceived a common bond of cultural confusion with refugees and immigrants who experienced movement from one country to another. But as an anthropologist I was equipped with the analytical tools of social and cultural dissection—and also with the knowledge that my stay in Israel was temporary. In that situation of cultural confrontation, I was at once the analyzer of my own American cultural background as well as the backgrounds of Iranians and Israelis.

The cultural confrontation between different religious and ethnic groups in immigrant societies such as Israel (and the United States, Canada, the countries of South America, and lately Europe with its migrant labor force) engenders an unwilling kind of reflection about "us" and "them," in that one's own being and background come to be seen in a different light. Reflecting on cultural and behavioral contrasts can create a new level of understanding of self and other, or it can revert into the impasse of misinterpretation and stereotyping. Making sense of the cultural confrontation and the resulting misconceptions that the Israelis and Iranians have of one another became the object of my analysis. Specifically, the subject I examined pertained to the interpretive dilemma that comes about when social and cultural patterns of behavior and beliefs differ between clinician and patient. The clinicians here were Israelis, or people who had immigrated to Israel in the past, and the patients were Iranians; the site of my research was Jerusalem.

Jerusalem is a mosaic of neighborhoods, each with its own name, each with its own cultural milieu, from the Islamic, Christian, Armenian, and Jewish quarters of the Old City to the Jewish and Arab districts built outside the Old City walls beginning in the late nineteenth century. Its inhabitants, locked in economic interdependency, religious differences, political discord, and cultural diversities, interlace the city's streets with a motley representation of humanity: Palestinian peasant women in long embroidered dresses; Hassidic rabbis; secular university students; religious young married women with covered hair; old Moroccan Jewish women whose earlobes are lengthened from heavy earrings;

priests of all denominations; Holocaust survivors with blue tattooed numbers on their arms; black-garbed yeshiva students; Arab high school girls in matching kerchiefs and long coats, indicative of Islamic revivalism; ubiquitous self-assured bright-eyed children; insecure adults; Israeli soldiers with Uzi submachine guns; middle-class men and women dressed in the latest French styles.

There is a building regulation in Jerusalem, although lately contractors seem to be ignoring it, that the façades of all structures must be made of Jerusalem stone, the rough-hewn pink, beige, and gray rocks which change color with the position of the sun. So in spite of the differences of neighborhoods, whether of different ethnic groups, classes, religions, or terrain, Jerusalem stone is a leitmotif. In West Jerusalem, the Jewish section of the city, the different styles of housing denote not only the era in which they were built but for which people, for which immigrants, they were constructed. The older neighborhoods built before 1948, before the independence of Israel, have a charm of their own that cannot be replicated; several of these old neighborhoods are the homes of some of Israel's most religious people, whereas others are occupied by old-time socialists and atheists from Russia, Poland, and Germany who helped establish the country at the turn of the century. When the immigrations of the 1950s created a massive housing shortage, the apartments that were built to accommodate the mostly Middle Eastern immigrants were prefabricated, more cement than stone, and these neighborhoods today are some of the poorer areas of city. After the Six Day War, new housing was erected in the areas that had been uninhabited—the vacant no-man's-land that separated Israel from Jordan. Now, outside of the borders of pre-1967 Jerusalem are numerous new neighborhoods whose residents are a mixture of East and West, religious and secular, immigrant and native-born.

I lived in three different neighborhoods during my two and a half years in Jerusalem. The first, where I resided for three months, was in an area where pine trees grow, where prefabricated apartment buildings of the 1950s face modern, large, expensive apartments of the late 1960s. Few Iranians lived there. I then moved to one of the post-1967 neighborhoods where I lived for twenty months. This neighborhood, a middle-class one, was inhabited by people from various countries and by native-born Israelis. Among the inhabitants were Iranians who immigrated before 1948, between 1948 and 1977, and after 1977 as refugees from Khomeini's Revolution. Living there and walking to the local shopping center to buy groceries at the supermarket, have coffee in the cafe (owned by an Iranian family who immigrated in the late 1940s), go to the bank (a daily activity for Israelis who continuously monitor their money because of the high inflation rate), I would meet Iranians.

As a Persian-speaking American, I became an object of interest for the

Iranian immigrants. Those living in Israel since the 1950s befriended me quickly. They had become Israeli-ized and would invite me to their homes to converse over instant coffee and cake. The others, those who immigrated in the 1960s and early 1970s, still more formal, some less open, curious about my adventures in Iran, were more guarded. And the refugees, those who left Iran around the same time I did, welcomed the opportunity to express their sorrow to someone who was neither Iranian nor Israeli and who would understand.

The third neighborhood in which I lived was one of the older ones in Jerusalem, an area known for its ultra-Orthodox population, an area closed to traffic between late Friday afternoon and Saturday evening for proper observance of the Sabbath. Several blocks from my apartment was a neighborhood where Iranians, Bukharians, and Afghanis, all of whom speak various dialects of Persian, settled at the turn of the century. That neighborhood, known as Bukharim, houses Iranian synagogues, produce markets, bread-bakers whose flat loaves stick to the side of the stone oven until they puff off, an herb and spice seller whose business attracts Middle Eastern immigrants from all over the city, and sidewalk venders, such as Yemeni women from farms outside Jerusalem who, early Thursday mornings, sit with burlap bags filled with fresh herbs and fragrant plants for the Sabbath.

The Sabbath in Jerusalem begins late Friday afternoon. Because public transportation stops in Jerusalem on the Sabbath, people rush to get home on Fridays before the siren wails, signaling that the candles should be lit to begin the Sabbath observance. Although Israelis estimate that roughly 20 percent of the population is religious or traditional and observes the Sabbath as well as other holidays, proscriptions, and commandments, the Sabbath is welcomed by everyone as a respite from work and the profane happenings of the financial and political world. Many families, whether religious or not, have their Sabbath meal together. Children and grandchildren visit parents and grandparents. Friends visit friends. The secular have parties, and the religious pray and worship. Shops are closed, and in some neighborhoods, such as the last one in which I lived, streets are closed. However, after the first star is seen on Saturday night, the Sabbath has passed, the buses start, and Jerusalemites head to town to meet with friends, go to the movies, or sit in cafés.

On Sunday work starts again, with the city bustling by seven thirty in the morning. Offices open at eight, close at one for lunch, reopen at four and shut down at seven. The weekday world from Sunday through Friday is a hectic one of listening to the news every hour on the hour, of keeping alert for suspicious objects which could be bombs, of worrying about the financial situation of the country and of the family, of arguing about the political situation or prices or services or ideas with anyone or everyone who will argue back.

Such was the situation in Jerusalem when I was there. My two and a half years were spent with Iranians and Israelis, of different socioeconomic classes and educational backgrounds, of various levels of religiosity and contrasting political persuasions, in different neighborhoods and of different ages. At times it was difficult because, as a Jew, I was continuously asked if I would be making *aliya*, immigration, which Israelis and immigrants who chose to do so consider the duty of all Jews. I found myself embroiled in arguments on the political situation, the status of women, the control of the Orthodox on marriage and divorce laws, relations with Arabs, Palestinian rights. I would have to catch myself because, like most Jews and non-Jews, I have my own particular interests concerning Israel. When I would sit back as an anthropologist rather than assuming the role that I was taken for and thus oftentimes acted, that of American Jewish woman, the situation appeared different: Israelis are a product of insecurity, of immigration, the Holocaust, of traditional Eastern European and Middle Eastern values and norms, and their quest for security in the world of war and consequent economic difficulties produces a desire for avoiding ambiguity and for clear-cut answers for their particular lives. Thus, as opposed to the socialists who settled Palestine at the turn of the century and who tried to establish a revolutionary social system without gender role differentiation, where the "bourgeois" values of the women's role being in the house with her family was seen as against the new social order, modern Israelis develop a differentiation of sex roles which produces one of the only measures of security they can attain—they marry young, have children as soon as they can after marriage, buy apartments, and focus, if they can, on furnishing their homes with the most fashionable objects they can afford. Within this quest for security in an insecure environment are people with a wide range of political viewpoints, religious beliefs, and social visions. And I was caught up in this, entangled in the discourse of Israeli life, involved as a Jew and detached as an anthropologist. Disentangled, the discourse in Jerusalem is the tableau, the setting for the Iranians and the Israelis whose interactions this book interprets.

Chapter 1
The Themes

Israeli biomedical practitioners, psychiatrists, psychologists, and social workers express difficulties understanding their Iranian patients. According to the clinicians, Iranians repeatedly utilize the health care services complaining of various aches and pains, sometimes with strange presenting symptomatology. The doctors find nothing wrong pathologically. Some of these patients are unable to function at work or in their familial role, have eating and sleeping difficulties, and do not respond to treatment. The doctors do not know what to do. The clinicians coined a term for the symptoms of the problematic Persian patient: "Parsitis" or "the Persian syndrome".[1] What does "Parsitis" signify? What are these symptoms that Iranians express and why do they generate such malcontentment among the medical personnel that they invented a diagnostic label for it? How do culture and social relations (here, in the form of ethnic encounters in the clinical setting) influence illness behavior, ideas about the body and the self, expression and understanding of symptoms, help seeking, therapeutic relationships, and medical interpretation and diagnosis?

The phenomenon of "Parsitis" is a problem of understanding—or misunderstanding, as it is here—in the clinical setting. The "sickness" label, a gloss for problem patients of Iranian ethnicity, connotes the frustrations that the doctors feel, their lack of success with treatment, the failure of therapy. One primary care practitioner in Jerusalem, an immigrant from Russia, expressed dissatisfaction doctoring Iranians:

> Iranians are shabby. *Primitivim* (primitive) in all kinds of ways. There are no intellectual ones. They have too much of a condition of depression. More than any other ethnic group, they return so many times. They complain of headaches, weakness all over, hands paining and trembling. They exit with many "thank-yous." And they expect medicines, then come in complaining the medicine doesn't work. At one point I became so frustrated with my Persian patients that I felt guilty I was doing something wrong, so I called up Dr. Z. (psychiatrist at the local mental health center) to ask him about it, and he said it's known: Parsitis!

Because the situation is a clinical one, and, as the practioner's stereotypes of Iranians indicate, a social one, the interpretation of "Parsitis" requires an analysis of three themes: the ethnopsychology of Iranians; the social structure and social relationships of Israeli society; and the sociocultural dimension of illness and diagnosis. These three themes are interrelated to argue that medical phenomena (sickness, diagnosis, therapy, medical institutions) are social and cultural products, governed both by patterns of social interaction and social relationships and by patterns of meanings and beliefs that people use to guide their action and behavior. When these social and cultural patterns differ between doctor and patient, an interpretive dilemma can transpire, such as "Parsitis".

Understanding the clinical phenomenon of "Parsitis" requires understanding the different social relations and cultural systems which make up both Iranian ethnopsychology and Israeli society, as the two confront each other as Iranian patient and Israeli practitioner in the clinic. The Israeli practitioner tries rendering the Iranian patient's presenting symptomatology, or illness, into a "disease" that can be made sense of and acted upon (Kleinman, Eisenberg, and Good 1978) but has difficulties figuring out what the problems are (as is apparent in the pseudo-diagnostic label of "Parsitis"). These clinical difficulties are a reflection of social relations and cultural patterns which occur in the macrosocial context of Israeli society. The focus is on cultural influences and social interactions which depict and shape experience, and pattern behavior and knowledge. My intention is to translate the problems that Israeli practitioners have with their Iranian patients in the way that Geertz (1983) defines translation, as "displaying the logic" of a phenomenon.

The logic in the problem of "Parsitis" can be interpreted only by expanding the field of vision out of the clinical setting onto the society in which it exists. The interpersonal encounters which arise in the office behind closed doors, with the different participants framed by their different knowledge worlds, cultural backgrounds, and expectations, can be understood only by looking at the social and cultural situations which mold their interactions. Therefore, translating "Parsitis" requires movement away from clinical reality, those systems, roles, ideas, behaviors, and explanations affiliated with sickness, health, practitioner-patient transactions, and clinical care (Kleinman 1980:38–41) into the society where the clinic exists and the labeling takes place, only later to return to the clinical setting. The intention of these movements, back and forth, out of the clinic and then back in, with Iranians and Israelis, individuals and groups, symptoms and expressions, interpretations and designations, is to shed light on the clinical encounter as a cultural artifact.

Situations of sickness, health-seeking, diagnosis, and healing are influenced by beliefs, behavior, personal experience, and sociocultural form. Such situations revolving around sickness are processual, emerging and changing in time. They are made sense of by cultural meanings and social interactions, and are influenced by such large-scale social factors as social organization, power relationships, economic conditions, political revolution, and migration, and by idiosyncratic events such as industrial accidents, job transfers, family crises, or changes in residency.

The anthropology of sickness—to use a term employed by Young (1982a)—must then look at the situations of sickness as socially, economically, politically, and culturally determined, and as indeterminate (cf. Moore 1975). Sickness and healing are social and cultural processes containing some elements that are fixed and patterned (how to complain about pain; how to treat a cold or headache; how to take a medical history) and others that are temporal, ambiguous, inconsistent, contradictory (a headache that won't go away; patients whose symptoms are without pathological findings; patients who do not comply with physicians' orders). Settings of sickness exhibit pattern and structure as well as indeterminacy and uncontrollability. Interaction in the clinical setting thus takes into consideration the fixed and regular cultural and social elements, and the uncertain and unknown, ambiguous elements which must be interpreted and known in order to be controlled and treated. In the problem of "Parsitis", elements of indeterminacy (such as patients' presentation of undefinable sickness episodes, and the construal of them by biomedical or psychiatric practitioners) are based upon ethnicity, communication differences, culturally determined idioms of distress, culturally patterned ways of emotion expression and somatization, ideology, and social hierarchy. The interpretation of the sickness process is influenced by patterned cultural forms and social interactions as well as by ambiguous and indeterminate transactions that call for meaning by the actors involved in the clinical setting.

Medical interaction and communication are mediated by external social and cultural factors about which the "inter-actors" are ordinarily unaware. These factors, which mark a separation between individuals and groups in cross-cultural situations, are what I call "silent boundaries," the tacit underlying constraints of human relationships that shape our transactions, about which we are almost, but not quite, cognizant. Silent boundaries, like models "of" and models "for" reality (cf. Geertz 1973), delineate and mold experience. They create boundaries, and are boundaries. The silent boundaries in this context are the various social and cultural elements and circumstances which, unbeknown to patient and practitioner, impede successful therapy: communication differences; cultural concepts of emotions, expression, sickness; ethnicity and stereotyping; medical praxis. When doctors and patients come from two different cultures, the silent boundaries are intensified. In the case of Israeli doctors and Iranian patients, social components—revolution, migration, resettlement, financial problems, the discrepancy between an egalitarian ideology and social inequality, unstable economy, social relationships, the biomedical system—are combined with cultural components—Zionist ideology, patterns of communication, familial expectations, health and religious beliefs, the culturally patterned postulates of biomedicine and psychiatry—and form the silent boundaries in the clinical encounter. Blindness to the existence of such silent boundaries creates misunderstandings in the clinical settings when doctors have difficulties diagnosing patients; resulting are problems of power and efficacy for the physicians, dissatisfaction of treatment on the part of the patients, and sometimes, failure of therapy. But the boundaries can be surmounted if people are aware that cultural and social presuppositions mold their assumptions and actions, and are willing to work at understanding one another's meanings and behavior.

The interpretation of what occurs in the microsocial clinical transaction when practitioners label patients therefore involves an investigation of the silent boundaries that influence the people involved in clinical negotiations. This includes the microlevel analysis of what is said and done by doctors *and* patients—their ideas and behavior regarding illness and one another—as well as the macrolevel examination of social and cultural forces which affect both patients and practitioners.[2] Ethnicity, for example, serves as a silent boundary in clinical interaction and negotiation: cultural background and social relationships sway both doctors' and patients' interpretation and understanding of the sickness process and their interactions with the other. Aside from the silent boundary of ethnicity, additional social and cultural forces external to the clinic or the immediate sickness experience must be incorporated in the investigation and analysis of the sickness episode: cultural concepts that mold the understanding, actions, and behavior of doctors, patients, and healthy people in society contribute not only to the social and economic production of sickness but also to the structure of relationships within the clinic. Sickness is not a phenomenon isolated from the greater social and cultural world in which it is experienced.

Accordingly, this ethnography encompasses the cultural and the social, the structural and the processual, the macrocosmic and the microcosmic, to interpret Iranians and Israelis, patients and doctors, illness and diagnosis. Each chapter regards a different aspect of the social and cultural processes that contribute to the problem of "Parsitis". The second chapter places Iranian Jews in the context of Iranian and Israeli history: because Jews have lived in Iran since 700 B.C., they are fully Iranian culturally, communicating, acting, and thinking like other Iranians who come from the same socioeconomic classes they do. Therefore, as Iranians, they communicate to others within the social hierarchy of Iranian society in a way determined by their social status. This subject is approached in the third chapter, whose primary focus is on the expression of dysphoric affects in Iranian society. Such expression is dependent on conceptions of the emotions and the rules about to whom one can show them without jeopardizing either one's social position or the feelings of others. The specific emotion examined in this chapter is called *nārāhati,* a dysphoric affect which means "uncomfortable, ill-at-ease, worried, upset." Nārāhati is defined in its sociocultural and ethnopsychological contexts, illuminating emotional expression as a cultural product which can be manipulated at will, concealed, revealed, or not recognized. The problems of emotional expression in Iranian culture concern issues of social roles, social change, control, powerlessness, concepts of the individual and the family, politeness codes, social hierarchy, and channels of communication. Examined are the different styles of nārāhati expression, from concealment of private emotions to expression of those that others also feel or have felt, or nonverbal expression through acts such as refusing to eat. Because expression of certain negative emotions in Iranian culture is culturally disapproved, people ideally try hiding their nārāhati. The examples of nārāhati-expression take place in Iran, where I knew many distressed people during the months of upheaval, and in Israel.

The fourth chapter moves back to Israel entirely. Here we confront problems of immigration, the ideology of Israel as an immigrant country for Jews, how different communication structures, those of Iran and Israel, signify differences in social structure and hierarchy, and how styles of communication engender social stereotypes about different immigrant groups. The stereotypes influence social interaction and are themes for cultural creations, such as ethnic jokes and a bilingual play. Analyzing these ethnic stereotypes and how they are managed provides a window on the problem of identity for Iranian immigrants in Israel. Finally, the chapter shows that ethnicity in Israel differs as a phenomenon from ethnicity in other countries since the official state ideology demands the development and maintenance of Israeli identity among the populace: yet, although people claim Israeli identity for themselves, they look for ethnic stereotypes in others, thereby maintaining a key social boundary.

The particular problems that Iranian immigrants have adjusting to Israeli society are examined in the fifth chapter: disintegration of traditional familial roles, economic difficulties, loneliness, communicative problems, unfulfilled expectations. People talk about these problems of acculturation while discussing the good and the bad of life in Israel and in Iran. These act as social and cultural stressors that engender nārāhati in some people which may be, unwittingly, expressed through illness.

The sixth chapter discusses somatization—the presentation of personal and social distresses in an idiom of bodily complaints—by focusing on traditional conceptions and constructions of illness in Iranian culture. I examine Ibn Sina's classical theory of humoral medicine, concepts of individual temperament, climatic effects on the body, the maintenance of health by a diet balancing hot and cold foods, and traditional medicines. Cultural definitions of illness categories are explored, such as blood deficiency, weakness, rheumatism, and nerves, as well as supernatural causes of illness, such as the evil eye. Some of these sicknesses are alleviated by traditional ways of healing, such as herbal medicines, talismans, and the prayers of *hakhamim,* or wise men. Also included in this chapter are phrases that use body parts to express emotions. Verbally and behaviorally, the body is used as a metaphor to connote one's feelings.

Most studies on somatization indicate its etiology and effects on patients, such as styles of complaints (Barsky and Klerman 1983), cultural and social influences on symptomatology (Kleinman 1980b, 1982), idioms of distress (Nichter 1981b), or as a way of manifesting depression (Katon et al. 1982). I am unaware of studies showing the effects of patient somatization on physicians who treat somatizing patients. Chapter seven explores this phenomenon. I show how somatizing patients put doctors in an interpretive dilemma regarding diagnosis and a personal dilemma concerning efficacy. Iranian patients are described by Israeli biomedical practitioners as hypochondriacal, difficult, problematic, multi-complainers. This chapter concerns the structure of the Israeli biomedical health care system in which physicians are at a loss when it comes to treating their Iranian patients. Based on interviews with physicians, it is an essay which indicates the double-bind that somatizing patients put practitioners in, rendering them simultaneously powerful and powerless.

In chapter eight I analyze transactions that occur in the psychiatric clinic, to which biomedical practitioners, after they capitulate from inefficacy, send their patients. Here we are concerned about the issues of clinical transaction, misunderstanding, diagnostic labeling, and expectations that practitioners and patients have of one another. In addition, we address the failure of therapy. We see how it is that the silent boundaries—emotions of nārāhati, social stereotypes about Iranians, problems that Iranians have as their expectations and lives change in Israel, bodily complaints—enter into the doctor-patient relationship. The therapists misinterpret and misdiagnose their patients since the categories they use are pertinent to Western culture. Both therapists and patients are frustrated by the clinical encounter, and therapy fails. Thus, "Parsitis" has evolved as a label of vindication for the clinicians with blame on the patients.

The translation of "Parsitis" takes us into the society at large. Its phenomenon is created by social and cultural conditions outside the clinical setting which, when brought inside the clinic walls, assumes a medical guise: because of the practitioners' need for classification of physical and psychiatric symptoms to interpret and label in order to act, the presentation of symptoms which mystify the practitioners must also be labeled. Without the label, there can be no action, as the label presents the practitioner an idea that something can be done. Of course, there are such actions in the medical world for which there are no diagnostic labels, but these come under the rubric of "exploration"—with the answer to be found. So it is that physicians, not knowing what is the matter with the patient, advise tests, x-rays, sometimes surgery, all in the search of a diagnostic label. Naturally, these are all actions, each action with a name, which have as their goal the search for meaning. When that meaning cannot be found, as in the situation of somatizing patients who see biomedical practitioners, both patients and clinicians are dissatisfied, as both want a diagnostic label which signifies the ability to define, control, treat, respond, alleviate the symptoms. Israeli clinicians who label Iranian patients with "Parsitis" attempt to classify, to pretend to know when they know they don't, to not assume responsibility for an illness that is a cultural and social construct, to transfer responsibility for failure to patients, to divorce themselves from the enigma of doctoring. This is shown in chapter nine, where the focus is on culture's influence on psychiatric diagnosis. Why it is that of all somatizing patients in Israeli society Iranians receive a stigmatizing ethnic sickness label concerns the social and cultural position of Iranians outside the clinical setting which is mirrored within the clinic.

In this ethnography of Iranian patients and Israeli practitioners, I show that many problems within the clinic are related to the external social and cultural context of the society in which the patients and practitioners live. Such clinical problems, it must be kept in mind, are common throughout the world, and they are especially magnified in situations where Western biomedical practitioners and psychotherapists confront non-Western patients, whether immigrants, migrant workers, or, most problematic, refugees who had to flee their homelands and their cultures. The purpose of depicting the difficulties and frustrations of the illness experience and its clinical interpretation is to illuminate how we, as healthy or sick individuals, are bound by our own experiences, relationships, and belief systems, as well as by social conditions and cultural influences that are not of our own making, but which have a power that is at times formidable, and often silent.

I consider anthropology an art, the ethnography I take to be an artifact expressing what it is to be human in different guises. Each ethnographic text is an attempt to paint a picture of the human experience. As paintings enable the viewer to sense the visible in a different way, so the ethnographic text permits the reader to understand the variations of the human experience in a different way. As the artist fills in the blank canvas to create background, images, themes, all of which are viewed all at once, I develop, interpret, and analyze the background, images, and themes of Iranian patients and Israeli practitioners whose beliefs and actions exist in the sociocultural system in which I lived, worked, and researched, all of which are to be viewed as a process, and understood at the end. The problem is one of making sense out of the emotion nārāhati and the label "Parsitis" in which, as ethnographer, I am involved in "sorting out the structures of signification" of people locked in a situation of "systematic misunderstanding" (Geertz 1973:9). These structures are the social relations and the cultural forms of Israelis and Iranians which at once are, and create, the silent boundaries that engender misunderstanding. Only by moving in and out of the clinics, visiting people in their homes, interviewing doctors and talking to patients, and understanding what life is like for the different Iranian immigrants and refugees in Jerusalem was I able to interpret, and translate here, "Parsitis." Concerning Iranian patients and Israeli practitioners, my intention is understanding, interpretation, translation, painting another picture of human interaction.

Chapter 2
Undercurrents: Being Jewish and Iranian

"Forget that you are of Persian origin," said Prime Minister David Ben Gurion in 1956 to a group of Iranian immigrants settled in a farming village. "We are all building one homeland and there is no barrier between citizens of various backgrounds."[1]

Ben Gurion voiced the ideology of the founding fathers and mothers of Israel—the ingathering and intermingling of the exiles to create a new Jewish culture in Israel. But their cultural utopianism overlooked the very real and important aspects of cultural baggage the immigrants brought with them. Expectations that the settlers should "forget" their previous heritage and become absorbed into the Europeanized mainstream of the state were pervasive. For the Iranian Jews, as well as for most immigrants, forgetting the past was inconceivable. The culture of origin was measured, valued, defined, elaborated, and treasured in negotiation with the new, unfamiliar, and confusing culture to which they immigrated.

To understand what it means to be Iranian in Israel, it is necessary to examine what it means to be Jewish in Iran and the historical and cultural implications this holds for present-day Iranian Jewish communities as a minority religious group in Iran, and as an ethnic group based on culture of national origin in Israel. In Iran, Jews are one of several religious minority groups influenced by Iran's political, religious, and economic structure.[2] The position of the non-Muslim minorities has depended on both the power struggle between the *ulama* (clergy) and the shah and the political economy (see Fischer 1973). When the secular authorities were more powerful than the clergy, Jews and other religious minorities were politically more secure. At other times, they became prey to the whimsy of the clergy and the masses, who attempted to wrest power from the secular leaders. The instability of their social and political position engendered feelings of insecurity and powerlessness in the religious minorities.

Despite such feelings, Iranian Jews regard themselves as fully Iranian and fully Jewish. Their identity as Iranian Jews is maintained by several factors—religious separation; social segregation; economic integration; political incapacitation; and cultural congruity. These factors will be elaborated in this chapter through accounts of five major periods of Iranian history: rule by pre-Islamic dynasties (700 B.C.—651 A.D.); accommodation to the Islamic conquest (651–1506); the development of Shi'ism as the state religion under the Safavids (1501–1732); modernization and contact with the West under Qajar rule (1794–1924); and life under the Pahlavi regime (1925–79). For nearly twenty-seven hundred years Iranian Jews have maintained commercial links, religious connections (Jews, Muslims, and Christians would procure talismans and amulets from one another's religious leaders), and cultural ties with Iranian non-Jews. These links among the different Iranian peoples fostered the Iranianness of Iranian Jews, in which the "webs of significance" (Geertz 1973:5) that make them inseparable from other Iranians include meaningful cultural motifs: feelings of individual powerlessness within the hierarchy of social relations; humor and feelings of the tragic; appreciation of the Iranian arts of poetry, music, and handicrafts; culturally particular ways of expressing emotions; respect and honor in social relations; preparation of foods; hospitality; etiquette; prominence of the family in social relations and interaction; concepts of illness and health.

The cultural Iranianness of Iranian Jews can be attributed to their lengthy history residing in Iran and going through the religious, political, economic, linguistic, and social changes over the past twenty-seven hundred years, where survival required adaptation to macrosocial and local phenomena. The social, religious, economic, and political events permeated all religious communities, molding each subsector, each area of Iran, into differing but similar interrelated entities of Persian culture, linked by a common economic and political history and language, if not by religion. Consequently, the history of Iranian Jews shows that in spite of the social structural differentiation of Jews in Iranian society, culturally, the Jews of Iran are Iranian.

Jews in Pre-Islamic Iran

It is not known when, precisely, Jews arrived in ancient Persia. Biblical lore provides accounts of Jewish settlement in what is now Iran from the eighth century B.C. in the Second Book of Kings 17:6 "In the ninth year of Hoshea, the king of Assyria took Samaria, and carried Israel away unto Assyria, and placed them in Halah, and in Habor, on the river of Gozan, and in the cities of the Medes." What was Medea is now part of northwestern Iran, its capital city Ecbatana now Hamadan.

After Nebuchadnezzar's conquest of Palestine and destruction of the First Temple in 586 B.C., the Jews went into exile in Babylonia, settling in urban and rural areas of what is present-day Iraq and Iran. Under the rule of Cyrus the

Great (559–530 B.C.), leader of the Iranian Achaemenian Empire, Babylon, parts of North Africa, and most of Asia Minor and Central Asia to the Oxus River came under Persian rule. The biblical prophet Isaiah mentions the conquests of Cyrus, predicting his victory and alleviating the anxiety of the Jews. At the time of Cyrus's conquests of Medea, the Jews were used by the Medes to colonize Rayy, near present-day Tehran. The Achaemenians also relocated their subjects, moving Jews and others to different parts of the empire. Cyrus issued a decree in 537 B.C. permitting the Jews to return to Jerusalem, which was also under Persian control, and to rebuild the Temple. They were to take with them the silver and gold vessels that had been confiscated by the Babylonians. For this decree, which was observed by Darius after Cyrus's death, Cyrus became an honored figure in Jewish history, lauded in Jewish religious texts (the Talmud) and in Judaeo-Persian writings.[3]

The rebuilding of the Temple in Jerusalem was begun in 520 B.C., during the reign of Darius I (522–486 B.C.), and was finished in 445 B.C., during the reign of Artaxerxes I (465–24 B.C.). Although fifteen hundred Jewish families returned to Jerusalem with the prophet Ezra to help rebuild the Temple, the majority of the Babylonian Jews did not return to Palestine. They became, throughout the centuries, part of the fabric of Babylonian life. They were craftsmen, peasants, and merchants, involved in international trade, integrated socioeconomically throughout the Achaemenian empire by their banking and business houses. The Achaemenian empire was tolerant of the Jews as they were of all their subjects, whatever their ethnic, national, or religious variations.

The Jews also had their own institutions, the most notable being the centers of learning. These were the rabbinic academies from which the biblical commentaries of the Talmud—the Mishnah and the Gemara—were composed, codifying laws which stressed ritual and religious, and therefore, social separation of Jew from non-Jew. Jewish belief, ritual, and prayer submitted to Persian influence. Persian religious beliefs of immortality and life after death and the concept of evil in the form of Satan entered Jewish religion and doctrine, later pervading Christianity and Islam.

By the time that the prophet Nehemiah became an adviser to Artaxerxes I (465–24 B.C.), the Jews had secured their positions as loyal subjects of the reigning monarchy and had even devised prayers for "the life of the king, and of his sons," as seen in Ezra 6:10. Jewish involvement in the courts of the kings are also noted in the books of Daniel and Esther. Whether these stories are legendary or factual, they attest to the Jews' position as a minority group negotiating both their religious independence from, and their political allegiance to, the state, themes which have been a continuous part of Jewish history in Iran and elsewhere.

During the Parthian empire (249 B.C.–226 A.D.), wars with Rome persisted for three centuries, Rome trying to expand eastward, Iran westward. Because the Jews opposed the Romans, who were also attempting to take control of Palestine, they enjoyed a favorable status in the Parthian Empire; many were employed as officials in various levels of the Parthian administration, while others fought alongside the Parthian troops in Iran and in Jerusalem against the Romans.

The Parthians "prepared the way for the Sassanians" with economic and social changes (Ghirshman 1978:288). International trade increased with the improvement of roads and the building of caravanserais, and in agriculture small holdings were replaced by large estates in the possession of fuedal lords, leading to new class distinctions. Parthian class differentiation was marked by a split between the rural and urban sectors, as peasants and small farmers became dependent on and oppressed by landed proprietors. A new nobility composed of landed proprietors, courtiers, officials, and families who were not part of the aristocracy arose side by side with urban and rural freemen. Under the Sassanian dynasty (226–651 A.D.) this class structure consisting of four major categories of people under the Shahanshah, the King of Kings—nobels and warriors, priests, scribes and officials, and commoners—became so rigid that mobility was nearly impossible.

At a time when religion was becoming united with political entities (Christianity in Rome and Byzantium and Buddhism in the countries east of Iran), the Sassanians began to establish Zoroastrianism as the state religion of Iran.[4] The result was that at varying periods, when priests became more politically powerful, religious minorities—Jews as well as Christians, Buddhists, Manichaeans, and others—were persecuted. When persecutions were religious, Jews fared no better than others, but when persecutions were political, they were in a better position than the Christians, who were considered sympathetic to Byzantium or Rome.

During the Sassanian empire, Jews and Syrians were involved in international trade from Iran to Turkestan, India, Brittany, and the Black Sea. They were also peasants and townsmen. Like all non-Zoroastrians, the Jews were required to pay a capitation tax, although the Talmud mentions that a Jew could declare himself a Zoroastrian in order not to pay the tax. Little else, however, is known about their economic, social, or religious activities under the Sassanians.

During the Sassian empire, power fluctuated from shahs independent of religious authorities to those influenced by autocratic priests—initiating a pattern of tolerance and persecution vis-à-vis non-Zoroastrian minority groups (a pattern that continued after the Islamic conquest). Tolerence during Sassanian rule was exemplified by exchanges on astrology and medicine between various third-century rabbis and magis recorded in the Talmud. Intolerance emerged during the fourth century with persecutions of Christians when Iran was at war with Rome, and in the fifth century, with persecutions of Jews (including killings and forced conversions) after an alliance was established between secular and religious rulers.

Persecutions of religious minorities were almost nonexistent during the last century of Sassanian rule. The secular leadership, weakened by wars between rival shahs and by wars with Byzantium, was further impaired by the assassination of Khosrow II (591–628) by his Persian generals when he refused to surrender to Byzantium after his capture. His son, Kavad II, ascended the throne but died within six months. He was followed by a series of leaders in rapid succession, including two princesses.

Yazdegard III (632–651) was the last of the Sassanian kings. In 637 the Sassanian army was annihilated by the Arabs. Rustam, the Persian commander, was killed at al-Qadesyah. In 642 the Arabs began their conquest of Iran with a victory at Nahavand. Hamadan fell in 643. Yazdegard fled to Khurasan and was murdered in Merv in 651. With his death, the Sassanian empire collapsed.

Accommodation to the Islamic Conquest

The Islamic conquest of Iran was facilitated by the internal state of the Sassanian government, politically weakened by court intrigues and rivalries and by the social, spiritual, legal, and economic impotence of the majority of the population. The Arab conquerors, making separate treaties with each town or district, found in the Sassanian empire a plan not only for the alliance of religion and state, which is implicit in Islam, but also relatively sophisticated systems of taxation, protocol in court, coinage, and social order, all of which remained (see Frye 1963).

Under Islam the non-Muslim religious groups which had sacred books—the Zoroastrians, Jews, and Christians—became *ahl al-kitāb,* people of the book. They were protected under the sacred laws of the Qoran, as long as these laws were not supplemented by other restrictions, as the case later became. As under the Sassanians, the religious minorities paid special taxes for which they received protection by the government. Their status was known as *dhimmis*, protected people. Dhimmi status was predicated on a contract by which the Islamic community gives hospitality and protection to other "revealed" religions in return for acknowledgment of the rule of Islam.

As before the advent of Islam, the religious minorities were involved in various economic pursuits, and consequently intermingled with other religious and minority groups. Members of the Jewish communities were engaged as artisans, craftsmen, jewelers, silversmiths, shopkeepers, moneylenders, bankers, financial experts, and court bankers for the Buyid, Ghaznavid, and Seljuq sultans. They were also involved in international trade: the first known document in the New Persian language, a mixture of Middle Persian and Arabic elements, is a business letter from the middle of the eighth century written in Hebrew characters.

Religiously, as ahl al-kitāb, Jews, Christians, and Zoroastrians were permitted their freedom to worship. Socially and politically, however, they were restricted by their dhimmi status, separated from the Muslims and from each other. The regulations regarding the dhimmis were codified in the so-called Covenant of Omar, issued by the Caliph Omar b. Abd al-Aziz (717–729). The purpose was to separate Islam and Muslims from other faiths and peoples while instituting it as a state-affiliated religion. At the time when the decrees were issued, Omar ordered a ban on building new houses of worship (synagogues, fire temples, churches), compelled Jews and Christians to wear special articles of clothing (hats, mantles, *zunnār* belt) to distinguish them from Muslims, forbade them to use saddles, prohibited them from employing Muslim servants, and enforced payment of the poll tax. The Covenant of Omar expanded and appeared in a more complete form in the eleventh century.[5] The implementation of the regulations varied according to locality, period of time, and ruler, and depended upon internal conditions of the countries: struggles for power between clergy and secular leaders; conflicts between economic interests; the influence of the dhimmis and their ability to manipulate their positions. The rights guaranteed by the Covenant of Omar included security of life and property (even though harassment and destruction of different religious communities in Iran have occurred at various times due to political, economic, and religious circumstances), freedom of religion, and internal autonomy. In exchange for this protection, the dhimmis were required to pay taxes, and the heads of the religious communities were responsible for tax collection. In the Jewish community this position was that of the exilarch, appointed by the Islamic authorities, following a Sassanian tradition.

By the ninth and tenth centuries, an Iranian reaction to Arab cultural domination arose in the form of the *shu'ubiyya* movement, stimulating a literary response among Persians and other non-Arab Muslims to Arab claims of racial and linguistic supremacy. The movement accentuated the native religious and cultural contributions to Islam and motivated intellectual cooperation between Iranian Muslims and Iranians of other religions. Various Iranian intellectuals, among whom were Hamza al-Isfahani (d. 963), al-Biruni (d. 1048), and the poet Nasir-i Khosrow (d. 1083), studied Hebrew and the Bible with Jewish scholars. This cooperation attests to what Fischel (1949a:822) called "a barometer of the degree of [Jewish] cultural assimilation."[6]

Economic assimilation had laid the groundwork for the kind of "cultural assimilation" Fischel refers to. Jews mixed with others in the course of their work as dyers, tanners, tailors, scholars, scribes, physicians, traders, merchants, bankers, farmers, and fighters. It is no surprise, then, that Jews would communicate with the non-Jewish Persians, and, in times of political and religious tolerance, participate in artistic and intellectual endeavors and in governmental pursuits.

From the development to the denouement of the shu'ubiyya movement, from the ninth to the thirteenth centuries, Iran was ruled by a number of small regional dynasties. Although little is known of the effects of the different dynasties on the religious minorities, one source of information is the journal of Benjamin of Tudela, the noted twelfth-century chronicler and traveler, who wrote about the various Jewish communities of Iran, their populations, and their political status, observing oppression in some places and freedom in others. He wrote about Jewish sovereignty in an area of the Qazvin mountains, where they were governed by their own prince, called Rabbi Joseph Amarkhala Halevy, and he described the intervention of the Seljuq Shah Sanjar (1086–1157) in a dispute among the poor and rich Jewish factions in Susa concerning the coffin of Daniel, both wanting the tomb of Daniel on its side. An agreement was reached whereby every other year Daniel's coffin would be on either side of the river. This lasted until Sanjar Shah saw the coffin being carried from one side to the other (1929:299):

> he crossed the bridge with a very numerous retenu, accompanied by Jews and Mohametans, and inquired into the reason of those proceedings. Upon being told what we have related, he declared it to be derogatory to the honor of Daniel, and commanded that the distance between the two banks should be exactly measured, that Daniel's coffin should be deposited in another coffin, made of glass, and that it should be suspended from the center of the bridge by chains of iron. A place of public worship was erected on the spot, open to everyone who desired to say his prayers, whether he be Jew or Gentile; and the coffin of Daniel is suspended from the bridge unto this very day. The king commanded that, in honor of Daniel, nobody should be allowed to fish in the river one mile on each side of the coffin.

Benjamin's accounts attest to the factionalism among different sections of Jewish communities. In addition, the autonomous Jewish region in the Qazvin mountains occurred at a time when Iran was divided into districts governed by different dynasties: here, then, some Jews also asserted their political independence.

Although there were Jewish office-holders, tax-farmers, bankers, and financial advisers to the viziers of the Seljuq dynasty (1038–1194), their political and economic liberty was curtailed by the vizier Nizam ul-Mulk (d. 1092) who, in helping to consolidate the rule of Malik Shah (d. 1092), denounced the appointment of dhimmis to government service. At that time, susceptible to extortion, torture, and appropriation of their goods by the authorities, many Jewish merchants and their families emigrated to other parts of the Islamic world, to which they were connected by commercial and religious relationships with other Jewish communities.

During the twelfth century, relations between the Persian and Baghdadi Jewish communities were close. Baghdad, seat of the rabbinic academies, was flourishing under the caliphs. The Baghdadi Jewish community collected taxes for the Persian Jews, appointed judges and rabbis to be sent to Persia, established a yeshiva (rabbinical academy) at Hamadan, and conducted correspondence in Persian—all indicative of close social, religious, and educational connections between the two communities.

During the first part of the reign of the non-Muslim Mongol Il-Khanid dynasty (1258–1336) Jewish life in Iran flourished. Hulagu, the Mongol conqueror, abolished the Covenant of Omar, thus eliminating the distinctions between Muslims and dhimmis and granting all religious groups equal status. To consolidate his administrative rule, he utilized minorities who would be loyal to his authority rather than patronizing subjects who supported the local power bases of the Muslim religious authorities and regional secular leaders. Persian Jews thus participated in government service. One Jew, Sa'ad al-Dawla, became influential as head of finances in charge of the revenue and taxation system of Baghdad and Iraq, and later became chief of the entire administration during the reign of the Mongol Il-Khan Arghun (1284–91), a grandson of Hulagu (Fischel 1949a:825). Although law, justice, science, and poetry were fostered under his rule, the fact that he was Jewish raised criticism, which resulted in diatribes, satirical poems, and libels. He was accused of having proposed to Arghun, a non-Muslim, that the Ka'aba be converted into a heathen temple. There were cries of Jewish domination among the Mongols and Muslims, both of whom were dissatisfied with Sa'ad al-Dawla's power. When Arghun became ill, Sa'ad al-Dawla was blamed and executed. This led to a general attack on the Jews of the Il-Khan empire.

Arghun's successor, Gaykhatu (1291–95), ordered an investigation of those guilty of murdering Sa'ad al-Dawla and his supporters. A Jewish physician who converted to Islam at the age of thirty, Rashid ad-Dawla, served Gaykhatu and two succeeding rulers as a financial and political adviser. Ghazan (1295–1304), Gaykhatu's successor, became a Muslim, changed his name to Mahmoud, and forbade Jews and other religious minorities to hold prominent positions in court. The Covenant of Omar was again enacted: churches and synagogues were destroyed, a mosque was built over the Jewish tomb of Ezekiel, and dress codes were issued for Christians and Jews.

Persian culture bloomed under the Mongols with the generation of poetry, the visual arts, handicrafts, and the writing of Persian history. The cultural milieu also inspired the evolution of Persian Jewish literature consisting of biblical and Hebrew nonbiblical translations, transliterations of Persian poetry, and compositions of Iranian-Jewish poetry, all written in the Persian language with Hebrew characters.[7] The usage of Hebrew letters kept the Jewish contribution out the mainstream of Persian literature. In addition, Persian poetry was transliterated into Hebrew characters since few people were literate in the Persian script (Adler 1897:193; Confino 1903:125; Fischel 1949:830–31). The religious minorities were at a greater disadvantage learning to read Persian since learning was through the *madrasseh*, the Islamic religious education system, or perhaps through private tutors. Since most Jewish men were taught Torah, they read and corresponded in the Hebrew script, using Hebrew letters to write Persian words (even today, many Iranian Jewish petty-merchants keep their accounts in Hebrew script as a "secret code" for security's sake).

Little is known about Jewish life and relations with the non-Jewish communities during the Timurid dynasty (1370–1506), the major ruling dynasty between the Il-Khanids and the Safavids. With their access to power, the Safavids (1501–1732) unified Iran into a national state, patronized the arts to a point of creative fruition that has not recurred since, pursued diplomatic and trade relations with Europe, and most importantly, made Shi'ism the state religion with a powerful and influential hierarchy of clergy, setting the basis for Iranian society of modern times.

Shi'ism and Minority Status

The social changes brought about by the establishment of Shi'ism as the state religion affected relations toward minority religious groups. Shi'ism symbolized not only the religious differentiation of Iran from the Sunni Ottoman Empire, but it also represented sociopolitical unity that fostered the social segregation and degradation of both non-Islamic religious groups and other Islamic sects (Sunni and Ismaili). This social differentiation was upheld through the religious idiom of *najes*, ritually unclean or impure. Najes refers to categories of things regarded as religiously defiling—dogs, human excrement, sweat, blood, sperm, corpse, alcoholic drinks. Najes has also been used to characterize non-Muslims as people who are polluting. The humiliations of the Covenant of Omar were thus supplemented with the debasement of najes status. For religious Shi'ites, contact with things najes requires ritual purification, primarily with water.

In daily relations and interactions, najes upheld a de facto segregation and fostered a de jure one as well, regulating social separation between dhimmis and Shi'ites in order to prevent any kind of contact which could ritually contaminate the latter. A new restrictive code known as *Jame'-e 'Abbāsi* combined the Covenant of Omar with principles based upon the najes status of the dhimmis, engendering a series of proscriptions. The concept of najes forbade dhimmis to walk in the rain, as the rain would touch the nonbeliever, then the ground, and pollute the ground; the dhimmi, touching some type of food in a shop, was required to buy what he or she touched, and perhaps the whole lot; dhimmis were required to wear certain clothing, a red or yellow patch, a headcovering unlike that of the Muslims, and Jewish women were restricted to wearing black veils or walk veil-less in the streets to distinguish them from the white-veiled Muslim women. Obviously, these regulations were not enforced everywhere in Iran at all times, since the country is large and customs were often particular to certain provinces. And with the struggles for power between the clergy and secular leaders, Jews as well as other religious minorities often became pawns to be played with, persecuted, or patronized, depending on the situation.

Although Shah 'Abbās I (1587–1629) was considered to have been kind to the Jews, he is also reputed to have ordered the Isfahani Jewish community to convert en masse to Shi'ism between 1619 and 1620 when a former head of the community and convert to Islam wanted to retaliate against the community that deposed him. The shah ordered all Jewish religious books thrown in the Zayandeh River. The effects of these events and others on the Jewish community from a period between 1617 and 1661, during the reigns of three shahs—'Abbās I, Safi I (1629–42), and 'Abbā II (1642–66)—were recorded in the chronicle *Kitāb-i Anusi,* the "Book of Forced Conversion," by Bābāi ibn Lutf.[8]

According to the *Kitāb-i Anusi,* Shah Safi I restored Jewish religious freedom, but under Shah 'Abbās II, instigated by the Grand Vizier Muhammad Beg, Jews and Christians were persecuted and forced to convert to Islam. Publicly, the Jews practiced Shi'ism but privately they observed Judaism. In 1661 they regained their religious freedom, after years of economic and spiritual deprivation as well as physical abuse.

The persecutions during the Safavid era were, according to Moreen (1981:124), religiously, not economically, motivated. Economically, the Jews were petty-merchants and artisans. The lucrative silk trade and money-lending businesses were controlled by the Armenians and Hindus, respectively. Although the Armenians suffered forced conversions, they also were used by Shah 'Abbās I for their artistic and commercial skills. One might add that 'Abbās's pursuit of diplomatic and economic ties with European powers, including expedient relationships with Christian missionaries, gave the Iranian Christians outside support in the face of religious persecutions. But according to the Chronicle of the Carmelites (in Moreen 1981:130–31), conversion for economic incentives occurred: "whoever of a Christian family should turn Muslim should inherit possession of the property of all his relatives, up to the seventh generation. By 1654 it was calculated that in order to escape beggary more than 50,000 Christians were renegades and lost to the Christian faith." Similar prescripts of converts to Islam gaining property inheritance of relatives applied to the Jews as well.

Although Nadir Shah (1736–47) unsuccessfully attempted to replace Shi'ism with Sunni Islam as a state religion, he tolerated different religious groups, undoubtedly for political support. The Jews were better treated politically without fear of harrassment from secular or religious officials. As a non-Shi'ite trading and artisan people, they were politically expedient for the goals of Nadir Shah: in an effort to curb the authority of the clergy in the pilgrimage city of Mashhad and to protect the borders of the east, Nadir Shah settled Jews from Qazvin in Mashhad, where they and other nonbelievers had been previously excluded.

But with the establishment of the Qajar dynasty (1796–1925) and the reaffirmation of Shi'ism as the state religion, the religious minorities again faced legal and political restrictions and the regulations of najes. These restrictions coincided with the weakening of the central government and the political-economic corruption of its officials, Iran's expanding economic ties with Europe (primarily Great Britain and Russia), and the consequent struggle for power between the shah and the *mullas* (clergymen).

Jewish Life in Qajar Iran (1796–1925)

The Qajar dynasty developed political and economic ties with Europe which gave Great Britain and Russia access to resources within Iran and money for the government. This angered not only the clergy, whose socio-political leadership opposed that of the secular authorities, but also merchants, bazaaris, and artisans, whose interests were hurt by the government's economic and political contacts with the West and who frequently allied with the ulamā against the policies of the state. Popular opposition to the secular leaders often took the form of a religious idiom as religious leaders, intent on gaining public support for their position within the ulamā hierarchy as well as against the secular leaders, gathered masses behind them. By focusing on the najes-ness of both foreign investors and religious minority groups (who may or may not have had contact with the foreigners), the clergy appealed to the masses who supported their claims that Western economic influence weakened Iran as an Islamic state. The ulamā were threatened by the government's pursuits of foreign political and economic interests and Western reforms, and because of the weakness of the central government and its provincial leaders, they were unable to control the ulamā. One of the results of this conflict between the ulamā and the secular leaders was an increase in persecution of minority religious groups at the hands of the clergy, and, at other times, by weak political leaders who wanted popular support. In the nineteenth century, the Jews of Iran suffered from religious persecutions as well as from forced conversion, riots, destruction of property, and expulsion from different communities.

By the nineteenth century Iranian Jews had become increasingly urbanized in cities where trade was prominent (Hamadan, Shiraz, Isfahan, Tehran, Kashan),[9] since many were merchants involved in the international marketing of cotton, wool, and silk, and in the local production and trade of other goods. Among the Jews there were artisans, goldsmiths, peddlers, physicians, musicians, jewelers, silverworkers, wine merchants, masons, wholesale dealers, dyers, spinners, and lacemakers. A family's economic situation depended not only on the particular employment of family members, but also on the area or region of the country where they lived. Iran was segmented regionally, ruled by different governors, and swayed by various political and economic influences. For instance, David d'Beth Hillel (in Fischel 1944), writing of his travels in Iran in the 1830s, described the rich Jewish merchants of Hamadan and Senna and the Jewish physicians who were patronized by governors and nobels in Hamadan, whereas Bassett, fifty years later (1887) wrote that many Jews and Armenians of Hamadan were poor, manufactured wine and *arak* (a distilled liquor), and some were traders. He also described the Jews as being physicians and amulet makers. The Armenians, aware of the success of the Jews in the amulet business, started a profitable concern writing amulets for Christians and Muslims. Women were also involved in the family economy. In some cities (Shiraz, Kashan) women worked as spinners, dyers, and carpet weavers in the silk, cotton and wool industries, and in Shiraz Jewish widows sold leeches and administered cupping glasses, and women and girls worked in the bazaars cleaning cotton (Confino 1903).

Despite economic integration, Jewish communities were repeatedly attacked, mostly at the instigation of the clergy with the support of the masses, or at times vice versa. In the first quarter of the nineteenth century, when Iran was pursuing a foreign policy of playing off French, Russian, and British interests in Iran while simultaneously losing territory to Russia, persecutions took place in the northwestern part of the country, where the ulamā opposed Western encroachment and the military reforms of Crown Prince 'Abbās Mirza. The Jewish community of Tabriz was expelled. Blood libels and outbreaks of violence against

Jewish communities occurred in Maragha in 1800 and in Urmia in 1819. One case of blood libel in Urmia in 1826 was described by David d'Beth Hillel, who wrote that the Jews were accused of having murdered a Muslim child to use his blood for Passover, which was then five months away: "Consquently, they rounded up all the Jews and removed them to prison, with the exception of their chief, one Rafael, he being a very old man and much respected by the Mohammedans. His children, however, were taken prisoner. One of the Jews was hewn in two in the gate of the town and the others were beaten nearly to death" (in Fischel 1944:223). The violence was curbed by the intervention of 'Abbās Mirza, who ordered their release from prison and returned the money confiscated from them.

In addition to pillaging religious minorities, the mullas also fomented periodic riots in cities—not aimed at minority groups—at times when they perceived the secular authorities as weak or when there was a change in regime (see Algar 1969, Benjamin 1859). In Shiraz and Isfahan, for instance, outbreaks of rapes, murders, and robberies in 1837–38 were provoked by the clergy against weak provincial secular leaders. Whereas these riots were political in nature, the persecutions of the religious minorities (Zoroastrians, Armenians, and Bahais, like the Jews, received their share of riots against them) took on a religious more than a political or economic idiom, especially when communities were forced to convert to Islam.

Under fear of death there were several cases of Iranian Jewish communities converting en masse to Islam, such as that of Shiraz in the first part of the nineteenth century, where the converts continued to be endogamous and marry other converts (see Benjamin 1859:185–86). Perhaps the most notable of the communities which converted to Islam is that of Mashhad. Jews settled in Mashhad at the invitation of Nadir Shah in the 1730s. In 1839, on the tenth day of Moharram, the day of public mourning for Shi'ites marking the murder of Mohammad's grandson Hossein at the hands of the Sunni Caliph Yazid, a Jewish woman of Mashhad went to a Persian doctor for treatment of a tumor on her hand. She supposedly was told to place her hand in the blood of a freshly killed dog. Rumor started that the Jews insulted the Muslims by killing a dog (a najes animal) on the holiest day and by calling it Hossein. Mobs attacked the Jewish quarter, killing thirty-five people and destroying houses and synagogues. The rest of the Jews were allowed to live only if they converted to Islam, which they did. They were then called *Jedid al-Islam*—"New Muslims."

After the conversion, Torahs were destroyed or taken to the mosque library. On the site of the synagogue a mosque was built. That year some Jedidim (Mashhadi Jews) migrated to Central Asia (Afghanistan, Turkistan, Bokhara, Samarkand, Merv) and India (Bombay and Calcutta). Those who remained in Mashhad instituted practices to preserve their Jewishness while displaying Islam to the outside world. They bought meat from Muslim butchers and gave it to beggars or dogs, eating meat slaughtered by Jewish butchers. They kept their stores open on the Sabbath and Jewish holidays and asked high prices to discourage people from coming, or they placed a little boy in the store to say his father was not there. If people bought anything on the Sabbath, the Jedidim donated the money to the poor or to the secret synagogue. Boys over twelve, who were bar mitzvah age and thus eligible to be members of the congregation, were taught in the cellar of a destroyed synagogue over which a house was built. In the *shahāda*, the Muslim confession of faith, they substituted "Moses" for "Muhammad" as "the prophet of God." Before entering mosques they would say secret prayers. They had a Beit Din (Jewish religious court) to settle their disputes without recourse to a Muslim judge. The Jedidim practiced endogamy by arranging marriages for their children at the age of five or six, and had secret Jewish *ketubot* (marriage contracts) in addition to Islamic ones. Documents were often signed in Hebrew, followed by "Haji" or "Kerbalai," showing they made the pilgrimages. Upon becoming hajis, they obtained permanent positions in the mosque as doorkeepers, lighters of lamps, keepers of the keys to the holy places, and *muezzin* (callers to prayer). Many of those who made the pilgrimage to Mecca went to Jerusalem afterward, and stayed there as Jews, where they established a Jewish-Persian press for their coreligionists in Palestine and Central Asia.

The Jedidim remained secret Jews until the reforms of Reza Shah (1925–1941) which weakened the clergy's political power. They moved to Tehran, where they lived as Jews, and to Milan, London, Tel Aviv, New York, and Paris, where they have been involved in the Persian carpet trade, maintaining economic and social connections with Mashhadi communities in other countries. Even today, some Mashhadi Jews try to arrange marriages for their children with children of other Jedidim, no matter under what nationality (Israeli, Italian, British, Iranian, American) they now live.

During the nineteenth century Iranian Jews also became susceptible to the influences of Christianity and Bahaism. The former offered educational and material help from missionary establishments; the latter offered spiritual, philosophical, and social solace at a time when the Jews were politically powerless and at the mercy of the mulla-shah struggles.

By the second half of the nineteenth century, under the rule of Nasr ed-Din Shah (1848–96), Iran embarked on the path of modernization that increased economic and political ties with the West; it simultaneously suffered military defeat and loss of territory to Russia and Great Britain. Great Britain and Russia became involved in economic and commercial rivalry within Iran. Russia obtained the rights to build a railway and toll road from Russia to Tabriz and to control the Caspian Sea fisheries in exchange for payment to the Shah and a promise of a share in future profits. Great Britain, also with grants to the shah, was awarded a monopoly on building railways, mining and banking industries in Iran, and in 1889 was granted a monopoly on the production, sale, and export of tobacco, which resulted in the Tobacco Rebellion of 1890–91 led by the ulamā. This not only forced the shah to cancel the concessions made to Great Britain, but also launched the beginning of Iran's national foreign debt (see Keddie 1966). The shah's motives in these economic concessions concerned the personal accumulation of revenue as opposed to the potential benefits for Iran as a nation. The mullas had opposed the British tobacco concession as dangerous for Iran politically and economically as well as religiously: because the foreigners were najes, they made tobacco, a popularly used product, najes by their touch.

In spite of the corruption of the monarchy under Nasr ed-Din Shah, political and economic contact with the West modernized Iran through the construction of a telegraph system, building of roads, and establishment of educational institutions. Contacts with European diplomats and missionaries also bettered the situation of the religious minorities during the famine of 1871: Armenians and Jews were aided by British Christian and Jewish societies, respectively. Through European diplomats and missionaries, Iranian Jews established contact with European Jews who, themselves recently emancipated, exerted pressure on the diplomats, who had previously supported Iran's Christian communities, to intervene on behalf of the Iranian Jews.

When Nasr ed-Din Shah went to Europe in 1873, he met with representatives of the Anglo-Jewish Association and the French Alliance Israélite Universelle, who requested improvement in the conditions of Persian Jewry. He promised to rectify the situation and later enacted two laws: in October 1878, care of the Iranian Jewish minority became the responsibility of the prime minister's offices, and in October 1880, the law permitting Jewish converts to Islam to inherit the property of their families who remained Jewish was nullified. Nasr ed-Din Shah also assured Alliance Israélite that they could establish schools in Iran.

Alliance Israélite was founded in France in 1860 as an international Jewish educational and humanitarian organization. Workers for Alliance came to Iran in 1865 to determine the necessity of establishing a school system. The Alliance Israélite developed a Westernized school system in major Iranian cities with Jewish populations, starting in 1898 in Tehran and continuing in other cities: Hamadan 1900; Isfahan 1901; Shiraz 1903; Kermanshah 1904; Sanandaj 1904; Nahavand 1906; Kashan 1911. Children of all religious faiths were permitted to attend the schools, where they were instructed in both Persian and French and were taught subjects of French schools as well as Persian history; only Jewish children studied Jewish history and religion, which formed a minor part of the curriculum.

Along with other nineteenth-century Western travelers in Iran, Alliance workers wrote about the position of Iranian Jews. Alliance reports, as well as missionaries' and diplomats' accounts, document that the Jews were overcrowded in ghettos from which they were forbidden to move (Confino 1903; Bassan 1903; Bassett 1887); that they were humiliated in the streets by passers-by who would throw stones or dirt at them (Benjamin 1859); that Jews were often victims of entertainment at the whim of Muslims who would, for instance, dunk them in tanks of water in front of crowds (Sykes 1910); that they formed a dispised but patronized class of musicians, singers, and dancers (music being "anti-Islamic" and often off-limits for Muslims to engage in professionally) (Browne 1893; Confino 1903; Sykes 1910); that they were sometimes murdered during Ashura, the tenth day of Moharram, if they were caught walking in the streets (Benjamin 1859); that they were poor and uneducated, with a rudimentary reading knowledge of Hebrew, if anything (Benjamin 1859; Bassett 1887; Adler 1897; Bassan 1903; Confino 1903; Sykes 1910); and that those who had money feared showing their wealth because of confiscation by secular or religious authorities (Tavernier 1684; Benjamin 1859; Bassett 1887). In addition, they were required to abide by the humiliating regulations of the Covenant of Omar and the *Jame'-e 'Abbāsi*.

The situation of the Jews varied in the different cities of Iran, as the cities were separated by wide distances from one another and were influenced by different historic, economic, and religious conditions. The Jews who migrated from the provinces to Tehran at the end of the eighteenth century, when it became the capital of the Qajar dynasty, fared better than those in the provinces since they were under the protection of the central government.

Confined to ghettos in most cities, Jews lived in crowded, impoverished, and dirty conditions. Kashan was the exception, as it was, during the reign of Nadir Shah in the eighteenth century, the intellectual center of Persian Jewry, and from the reign of Muhammad Shah (1834–48), the center of the silk and wool industries, in which the Jews participated. In Kashan the Jews had the respect of the Muslim clergy and population (*Bulletin d'Alliance Israélite* 1907:72–73). Shirazi Jews, on the other hand, lived in an unhealthy and dirty environment: one thousand families were confined to a ghetto of 220 houses large enough for 150 families; the streets, which were one meter wide, were laden with rubbish and refuse, and the inhabitants suffered from epidemics of such diseases as typhoid, smallpox, and diphtheria (Confino 1903:124). The Jewish community of Borujerd, however, lived in an overcrowded ghetto where the streets were not dirty, and where trenches of potable water went to each house; there were well-to-do people as well as poor ones, but all were subject to the degrading social regulations of dhimmi status, and fearing attacks from Muslims, they thus observed their religious festivals with no overt celebration (Bassan 1903:130–31).

The relationship between the Muslim clergy and the population and the Jews with the political leaders and the Jews also varied from city to city. In the village of Zargun, north of Shiraz, for instance, there were fifty Jewish families, most men being peddlers. Their religious leader was appointed by the governor of Shiraz, and relations between the Muslims and Jews of the town were good (Confino 1903:118). By contrast, the Jews of Shiraz, wrote the author (pp. 125–26), were often humilated, yet took no recourse to complain to the political authorities: one mulla shaved the Jewish men's sidewhiskers and part of their chins and made them wear dunce caps; Muslims borrowed money from Jews and "forgot" to repay; others entered Jewish homes, drank their wines and liquors and left with a household object or piece of furniture. If the Jews did complain to the authorities in Tehran, there was usually no response. But if the clergy were involved in inciting riots against the Jews, the response was often favorable. An incident occurred in Borujerd where a Muslim school was located near the Jewish quarter. The clergy, who incited riots against the Jews, lived in luxury and exploited the ignorance of the masses (Bassan 1903:130). Fifteen years before the author's visit, in 1888, a synagogue was destroyed. The community complained to the governor of Isfahan, who was also the shah's brother. He ordered it rebuilt and fined the Muslim population.

The situation of the Jews was thus one of insecurity, instability, and relative powerlessness on the social level, where they lived in fear of persecutions from the Muslim majority. They petitioned to secular authorities when riots broke out against them by the religious-led masses, and yet were able to utilize the system of sanctuary, *bast*, at the hands of the clergy when fearing retribution from individuals. Benjamin (1859:213) writes that Jews' positions as physicians and tradesmen earned them recognition from the majority population, who, nevertheless, also persecuted them: "Their integrity in trade is recognized by the Persians to such a degree that a Jew, who fails, finds refuge with the Achund [mulla] against all prosecutions, and thus gains time to settle with his creditors." In addition to their appealing to different secular and sometimes religious authorities to come to their aid, the Jews solicited the aid of European diplomats and missionaries as well as members of the Anglo-Jewish Association and Alliance Israélite. As European outsiders, Alliance workers met with different local political and religious leaders negotiating on behalf of the Jews. Bassan described one such incident that occurred in Kermanshah (1903:130):

> A Muslim came to buy some gunpowder in the store of a Jewish merchant. He was just seated when a dervish approached the client to light his pipe. The charcoal fell, the gunpowder took fire. Three persons were badly burned and one died yesterday. This

> was an incident which, in other circumstances, would have been the cause of a great danger for the community. The rumor had gone through the entire city that a Jew had killed three Muslims. A mob gathered around the store of our coreligionist. . . . They went to the house of Imam Jomeh to demand the death of a Jew. The *mujtahid* promised severe punishment. That evening I was invited to the house of Son Altesse Ferman-Ferma, when a letter arrived from Imam Jomeh demanding the punishment of the Jewish merchant. Son Altesse, the prince Ferman-Ferma, asked me if I know Persian and when I said yes he gave me the letter. The accident was fabricated; I explained how this fact was produced in reality and the governor convinced himself that our coreligionist was not to be blamed. Ferman-Ferma told me that another governor in his place would have put around ten notables of the community in jail and would not release them without having inflicted a fine on them. He promised me not to impose any fine on the gunpowder merchant but that he would leave him in prison for a few days to appease the excitement. He kept his word.

By the late nineteenth and early twentieth centuries, contact with European Jews and new educational and economic opportunities improved the socio-economic conditions of Iranian Jewry. Jews educated by Alliance were employed by the newly introduced foreign and domestic firms, such as pharmacies, the Persian and Belgian printing presses, the tramway administration, the telegraph offices, and the customs workshop of Singer sewing machines. Both the affiliation with Europeans and Western education enabled them to participate in the industrializing Iranian economy and to develop closer ties with world Jewry.

However, people's present-day memories of that period focus on the pillaging and plundering of their neighborhoods and the physical dangers they often endured. Riots against Jews occurred in various cities (Borujerd, 1888; Isfahan, 1898; Hamadan, 1892; Tehran, 1901; Shiraz, 1905–07; Jahrom, 1907; Lar, 1907; Hamadan, 1908–09; Darab, 1909; Seneh, 1910; Shiraz, 1910; Tehran, 1922).[10] The riots against Jews and other minorities were carried out as protests against non-Islamic people who were najes, who were not obeying the laws requiring minorities to be submissive to Muslims, or, less frequently, who were allies of the foreign governments that economically dominated Iran. No matter the rational for the riots, the idiom was religious, and the fight was one between the xenophobic and zealous clergy and the weak and often corrupt secular leaders.[11] The riot in Jahrom, for instance, was opposed by the governor who wanted to protect all the subjects of the shah, but when the Jews were blocked in their quarter and one was killed, the governor was powerless to do anything; he ordered the guilty punished, but blamed intrigues and plots among the civil servants as thwarting his attentions (*Bulletin d'Alliance Israélite* 1907).

The Iranian Constitutional Revolution of 1906 brought, in law if not in practice, an end to discriminatory measures against dhimmis, enabling each community of dhimmis to have one representative in the parliament and to have equal rights in terms of the law. But to please the clergy, certain articles were added that did not give dhimmis equal status before the law, such as article 58, which forbids dhimmis from becoming judges or ministers. Although the constitution was never really adhered to, the dhimmis' representation in parliament was an improvement over previous legal conditions, even though voting in elections was restricted to their own representative. Other positions in the government were closed to them.

The Jews saw the Constitutional Revolution as a step toward their civil and legal emancipation, and they used the opportunity of electing a representative to communicate with one another politically for the first time. Previously, most contacts among Jews of different cities were primarily commercial. The new contacts facilitated the organization of intellectual Jews, who began publishing Persian Jewish journals and newspapers in the Persian language with Hebrew characters.[12] After the Balfour Declaration in 1917, which provoked a renaissance of interest in Jewish history and the Hebrew language, Iranian Jews organized national Zionist movements, publications of Hebrew textbooks and, later, the development of Iranian Jewish schools different from the Western-oriented Alliance system. Although Iranian Jews were obliged to terminate their Zionist activities during the Pahlavi dynasty, when all organized political activity was prohibited, they continued to improve their social, economic, and political situation and to participate in various aspects of the society that had previously been off-limits to them.

Under the Pahlavi Regime (1925–79)

For the Iranian Jews, Reza Shah's capture of the throne in 1925 was the beginning of the end of the humiliating situation under which they had lived for hundreds of years. The *jeziyeh* (capitation) tax was eliminated, as were dress codes, housing restrictions, and other restraints that separated dhimmis from Shi'ites socially and economically, such as the prohibition against hiring Muslim workers and the enforcement of najes behavior codes in public (usually governmental) places. Jewish children were, for the first time, permitted to attend state schools and universities. The objectives of Reza Shah were to consolidate his power by diminishing the power of the clergy and to modernize Iran rapidly. To do this he needed the support of, and thus supported, the non-Shi'ite religious groups in the society.[13] Muhammad Reza Shah (1941–79) continued his father's policies concerning the religious minorities.

It was during the Pahlavi dynasty that the Iranian Jewish community was able to participate in Iranian social, cultural, and national life as full Iranian citizens. Traditionally, their economic position in Iranian society—as traders, jewelers, physicians, craftsmen—had always brought them into contact with various classes, religious groups, and ethnic groups. Since the 1960s Iranian Jews who studied at national and foreign universities entered the newly opened fields of engineering, economics, social work, medicine, architecture, and education, all critical occupations for a modernizing society. Some Jews also became wealthy businessmen, entrepreneurs, importers, and storeowners, as well as professionals. After World War II they were no longer restricted to residency in the Jewish ghetto, the *mahalleh,* and whoever could afford to build or buy a house in a newer neighborhood did so.

As twentieth-century Iran encountered industrialization, economic development, civil and legal reforms for minorities and women, educational expansion, Westernization and, ultimately, the Islamic Revolution, its Jewish citizens experienced a resurgence of national pride, but mellowed with ethnic concern. Although the religious minorities were supported by the state before the Revolution, contacts with individual Muslims often hinged on the notion of najes, and confrontations with anti-Jewishness were common: many of the more traditional Muslims refused to serve Jews tea since the glass would become najes and would have to be ritually purified (washed seven times) or thrown out; Jewish children were often taunted by classmates who told them their touch was najes; Jews were frequently derided by the derogatory term *Johood;* occasional riots broke out during the Iran-Israel soccer matches of the Asian games in the late 1960s; the clergy called for a boycott of Jewish-owned stores after the Six Day War and were instrumental in prohibiting the sale of bread to Jews in some cities until the government intervened. Modern anti-Jewishness, derived partly from the historical and religious status of Jews in Shi'ite Iran, was exacerbated with anti-Zionism: the Jews were seen, by the masses, as Iranian citizens but ritually unclean and politically untrustworthy. Thus, Jewish negotiation of anti-Jewishness took on a new dimension with the birth of Israel. Although Iran had unofficial commercial, political, and military relationships with Israel, the majority of the population, spurred on by the ulamā, were against these policies. Thus, any situation of conflict between Israel and the Arab countries engenders apprehension and anxiety among Iranian Jews regarding the possibility of riots breaking out against them.

The fear of physical and moral persecution is a very real fear among Persian Jews (as it is among Bahais, Zoroastrians, and Christians in Iran, as well as among some ethnic and tribal groups—such as the Baluchis, Kurds, and Turkomans). The means of living with it for centuries consisted of keeping a low profile in public. In addition, to ensure security in a social situation which was insecure, as minorities they informally appealed for support to various political, and sometimes, religious leaders, supporting the shahs, and now, Khomeini.

The fears of persecution were intensified during the upheavals of the Islamic

Revolution and its aftermath. The Jewish communities felt endangered regarding the demise of secular authorities as the religious forces began to usurp power, since most riots against them as a group were instigated by or supported by the clergy. Because the Iranian Jews of the twentieth century have participated in the social and economic mainstream of Iranian society with the support of the government and of the secular educated classes, and because the Jews feel *culturally* Iranian, they wanted to remain in Iran, as Jews. They thus announced their allegiance to Iran as Iranian citizens and affirmed their support of Khomeini, as well as claiming severance of ties with Israel.

The history of Iranian Jews indicates two major themes: social insecurity and cultural perseverance. The insecurity that minorities suffered in Iran due to their submission to the domination of the Shi'ite majority was time and again intensified by religious riots. This is not to say, however, that only religious minorities experienced social insecurity, as insecurity is a theme which exists throughout Iranian culture (elaborated in chapter three). The insecurity minorities have experienced historically concerns the powerlessness and instability of living in a situation where the clergy and the secular leaders were at odds with one another, and the minorities were the people played with in their struggles for power. The riots, coupled with the debasing religiously inspired Covenant of Omar, put all religious minorities, not just Jews, in humiliating positions. The alleviation of their abject status by the Pahlavi dynasty only further elicited anti-Jewish sentiment when Israel came into existence. Some Jews coped with this new anti-Jewishness by moving to Israel, whereas others, less influenced by the occasional anti-Jewish slurs and demonstrations, remained in Iran as full-fledged Iranians.

Cultural Congruity

Despite the social structural separation of the different minority groups (religious as well as tribal) in Iran, Jews have always been involved in the aesthetic and cultural aspects of Iranian society: as musicians, singers, and dancers, they were entertainers for the common people as well as for the elite; as craftsmen, they made objects which adorn peoples' homes; as Persian-speakers (as well as speakers of local Judaeo-Persian dialects which vary from city to city), they wrote and recited poetry; some became involved in Sufi movements; others who were religious were patronized by Muslims for their knowledge and powers, such as the amulet makers; as physicians, they were supported by rich and poor, shahs and commoners. They cook Persian food and observe the hot/cold dietary regulations (see chapter six).[14] Most Iranian Jews have Iranian first and last names, as an emblem of their Iranian citizenship, making them indistinguishable from other Iranians. Like the Muslims, Jewish parents arranged marriages for their children. In the nineteenth century girls were six to nine years old, boys sixteen to eighteen (Confino 1903), whereas in the late twentieth century, some girls still marry at thirteen or fourteen to men ten or twenty years their senior, while others marry in their twenties to men of their own choosing.

Ritual, religious, and communal life within the Iranian Jewish communities has been greatly influenced by the non-Jewish world around them and by reactions to persecutions. The reaction to persecutions engendered the development of rituals commemorating the sense of the tragic, which is so much a part of Shi'ite ritual regarding Moharram and the reading of the death of Hussein. One such Jewish ritual is the celebration of Rosh Hashana, the Jewish New Year, at a meal with several ritual foods, all of which are preceded by a prayer pertaining to the food and to the lives of the people. In this Sephardic rite, which is followed by Jews of Spanish and Middle Eastern origin, several of the foods have prayers which are more or less apparent (one eats lungs so that one's sins may be as light as a lung), whereas others are more abstract.[15] Dates are eaten, not for the connotation of something sweet, but so that God will do away with his enemies: the letters of the Hebrew word for date, *tamar*, are related to the root of the Hebrew verb, "to end, to be finished," *tam*, in the prayer for getting rid of the enemies. Another prayer and food against enemies is the scallion, which is bitten in the middle and both halves are thrown behind the shoulders, so that "God would destroy his enemies in the way we destroy the scallion." The scallion in the prayer symbolizes the root of the Hebrew verb *karat*, meaning "to cut off, fell, destroy," because of the similar-sounding Aramaic word for "leek green," *karti*. The scallion also happens to be used in the Iranian Passover meal. Iranian Jews hit one another with the scallion during the part of the Passover ritual meal when the song, "Dayenu," commemorating God's "gifts" to the Jewish people, is read or sung. Instead of interpreting the song to mean that the Jewish people would have been satisfied with *one* of God's "gifts"—such as freedom from slavery, the Ten Commandments, or the Holy Land—Iranians interpret the song to mean the end of slavery. With the Hebrew word *dayenu* (translated as "it would have been enough" in English, and, in Persian, *kāfist*, "it is enough," or *barāyi mārā kāfi bud*, "it was enough for us"), people go around the table swatting each other in jest with scallions or leeks, representing the whips of slavery. According to several of my informants, this is a ceremonial way to legitimately express resentment to someone in the family by hitting that person over and over with the scallion "whips."

Iranian Jews share other religious similarities with the Muslim majority: like their Muslim neighbors, Jews engage in religious pilgrimages to shrines (of Mordechai and Esther in Hamadan, of Serah bat Asher, a legendary heroine, in

Isfahan); sacrifice animals to celebrate a happy occasion or in commemoration of a vow; observe the Iranian New Year, No Ruz; and some Jews I knew in Iran consider religious status to be patrilineally descended, in spite of Judaic laws deeming religion matrilineally descended.

Within the Jewish communities an informal type of philanthropy has existed to care for the poor of the community who are supported, not by organized charity and donations (except for food given at ritual commemorations or celebrations, such as ritual sacrifices before Yom Kippur), but by being hired to perform certain religious functions, such as taking care of the synagogue. One of the most prominent of these, in Shiraz, is hiring poor Jews who can read Hebrew or poor mullas (Jews use this term for their religious leaders) to read the Torah in the home of a family in which a member recently died. Some wealthier families hire several men to read the Torah every day for the first year after a person's death. Once I saw eleven men from the Shirazi mahalleh (ghetto) sitting in a room of a wealthy family's house, reading from the Torah. And at each anniversary of the death, at the yearly commemoration, the *sāl*, poor mullas are hired to read the Torah.[16] Since each community always has a family in which a member died during the year, these mullas usually have a steady job.

The Jewish communities were not only socially separated from and culturally similar to the Muslims and other minorities, but they were, within the communities, socially stratified. Benjamin of Tudela wrote about the split between the rich and the poor in Susa during the twelfth century; the Alliance report of 1903 relates a split within the Shirazi community around five hundred years ago and Loeb (1977) reports of socioeconomic class differences among Shirazi Jews in the late 1960s; Fischer (1973) mentions several divisions among the Yazdi community. During my stay in Shiraz (1974–75, 1978–79), the Jewish community, in spite of its sizable middle class, was obviously divided between the rich and the poor, from such extremes as a wealthy endogamous and politically influential family to the poor hawkers of second-hand clothes. The only Jewish school in Shiraz was populated with poor students; those who could afford it sent their children to Muslim schools since the Jewish school had a reputation of teachers hitting pupils. In Tehran, the Jews are separated into rich and poor, educated and noneducated, religious and secular, Iranian and Iraqi, and among Iranians, according to the towns or cities from which they migrated.

In conclusion, Jews in Iran perceive themselves as Iranians and as Jews. The two identities do not necessitate ambivalence nor ambiguity, except, perhaps, in the eyes of the Muslim majority who view religious minorities as najes and as socially subservient and politically suspect. The fact that the Jews are culturally Iranian is an obvious outgrowth of twenty-seven hundred years living in one country. However, because of the insecurity they experienced as a minority religious group in Iran, or because of their religious or Zionist aspirations, many Iranian Jews moved to Israel to avoid the degrading dhimmi status and riots aimed against them.

Immigration to Israel

Until the nineteenth century, contact between Iranian Jews and Palestine was primarily through pilgrimage by Iranians to Jerusalem or visits to Persian communities by Palestinian rabbis. But events of the nineteenth century helped launch immigration to Palestine: anti-Jewish riots; contact with Europeans; Western education at the hands of Alliance Israélite; forced conversion to Islam; voluntary conversion to Christianity and Bahaism. The first en masse immigration occurred in 1858, the second in 1884, two years after the first group of Russian Jews settled in Palestine as Zionists. Another large group of immigrants arrived in Jerusalem from Shiraz in 1891.

By the end of the nineteenth century Jerusalem had become a cultural as well as a spiritual center for Iranian Jews. The cultural activity took place in the Bukharian quarter of the city, a neighborhood built by the Persian-speaking Jews of Bukhara outside the walls of the Old City in the late 1880s, when overcrowding within the Old City's walls permitted no more inhabitants. The Bukharians established printing presses for Judaeo-Persian literature, religious books, poetry, songs and stories, and for translations of secular works, such as *The Arabian Nights* and Shakespeare's *Comedy of Errors* (Fischel 1949a:847). The Iranians who immigrated from different cities built synagogues for people of their towns, and organized burial societies to perform the required death rituals as well as to provide aid for poverty-stricken families.

Upon arrival in Jerusalem at the turn of the century, the Persian immigrants settled where family or friends had settled. Neighborhoods developed that were Persian, and that were regionally Persian: Mashhadi and Hamadani Jews settled in the Bukharian quarter; Shirazis in Nakhlaot, near Makhaneh Yehuda, an area once of fields and farms which is now an overcrowded working-class residential quarter that houses the largest open market in Jerusalem. Nakhlaot is still recognized by Iranians as a Shirazi neighborhood.

Nehemiah, originally from Shiraz, is an owner of a *makolet* (a small, usually corner grocery store) in Nakhlaot. His house is near his store, on a street too narrow for cars to pass. The streets are lined with walls of houses upon which, once entering, the world of Iran is in view: a *hayāt* (courtyard), with trees, roses, herbs, a fountain, surrounded by rooms of the house, each with an entrance onto the hayāt.

Nehemiah, now over seventy years old, left Iran for Jerusalem around 1920 with a number of Iranian families from Shiraz, Bojnurd, and some other towns:

> There were around five families and forty people. We left because of love for Jerusalem. Someone just had to mention the name of Jerusalem and we honored the city and loved the city so much that we would bow down.
>
> We were on the road to Jerusalem seven years. It was the time of the Mandate and the British wouldn't give us visas. So at several places we stopped and waited. My father was a *lehāf-duz* (quilt-maker) so he was able to work and support his family. Among the places we stayed were Bushire [a port on the Persian Gulf] for a year and Basra [Iraq] for two years and Beirut. At Beirut we had relatives who told us they would try to get us to Jerusalem—that we would have to pay an Arab driver to get us across the border. The cousin in Beirut fixed the passports. Before, there was a committee of Jews in each city to get passports and visas and it was impossible. But in Beirut it was arranged. We gave money to the Arab driver to get to Jerusalem, that we would pay him when we arrive in Jerusalem. The driver told us at the border we should not speak Arabic, no language, that he will do all the talking for us. At the border the British police asked for our passports and we spoke only Farsi and didn't know what he was saying, and the driver did all the negotiations for him, and we were permitted to go to Jerusalem. There we gave money to the driver.
>
> In Jerusalem, we got off at Makhaneh Yehuda, at an address we had—my grandfather and an uncle, who was single, who left for Jerusalem ten years before we did. We stayed with them when we arrived. We had no money, no work, no help from the government the way people get help now. There were some people from Shiraz in the neighborhood besides my uncle and grandfather.
>
> We rented a room. There was nothing there in the area. Makhaneh Yehuda was fields of Arab peasants. It was slowly built up. There was no water, only rain water collected in reservoirs under the houses. The food we bought from the Arabs in the Old City. One year, or for a few years, there was no water, and we bought water, eighteen kilos at a time, from Arabs. But we didn't know if it was dirty, so we used it for cleaning. And to clean the water to use it again, we put ashes in it, which filtered the dirt to the bottom, and we used the water the following week, on Friday only to clean the floors [for the Sabbath].
>
> The neighbors in the Nakhlaot area were Persian, Kurdish, Yemenite—each with their own section in the neighborhood. Among the Persians there weren't only Shirazis, but also Tehranis, Isfahanis, Bojnurdis, and Hamadanis.
>
> There were no problems with the Arabs. Everyone visited each other, respected each other. We were all friends. In the Old City there was a building in which twenty families lived—Jews, Christians, Muslims—they all helped each other and the relationships were good. It was only when England came in did they put in the separation between the peoples. They caused the destruction. After Hebron [in Hebron there was a massacre of the Jewish community in 1929 in which over 130 people were killed by Arab residents] people didn't see each other any more. Before that, children would

> invite each other over. When my father and I used to go to the Arab villages to sell quilts, they would honor us so much. They would give us their beds to sleep on and they would sleep on the floor. They would give us all the foods permitted for us to eat—yogurt, cheese, bread, olives, fruit.

Nehemiah's family fit into similar socioeconomic patterns and activities in Palestine that they had had in Iran. His father was a craftsman and peddled his wares to surrounding villages, as he had done in Shiraz. Like most of the Iranians, and for that matter, Jewish communities from other Middle Eastern countries, they came to Palestine for reasons religious in nature, motivated by social and spiritual redemption—unlike the majority of the Western immigrants who were motivated by Zionist ideology to form a new society with new economic and social organizations.

Born out of the reaction to a series of pogroms in Russia in 1880–81, Zionism was a European-originated national liberation movement of the Jewish people. It was based upon the action-oriented ideology of such activists as Leo Pinsker (1821–91) and Theodore Herzl (1860–1904). The First Zionist Congress, organized by Herzl, was held in Basel, Switzerland, in 1897. Its goal was to create a new Jewish identity in a new state, free from the insecurity perpetuated by the persecutions of the Diaspora. This was to be accomplished by manual labor and cooperation through *geulat ha-aretz*, redemption of the land, and *kibbush ha-adama*, conquest of the soil. The socialist aspect of the ideology stressed development of a society based upon work, socialism, collective identity, belonging to organizations of peers (such as youth movements), labor organizations, and the pioneer image of the *kibbutznik*, the collective farm worker, consisting of self-reliance, self-sacrifice, self-defense, agricultural labor, and equality between male and female, old and young. Hebrew was revived as a unifying language. Immigration (*aliya* in Hebrew, also meaning "ascent", as "going up to a higher plain when immigrating to Israel"; immigration to other countries is *hagirah*) was emphasized as the only way to accomplish the Zionist goals of creating a Jewish homeland.

The European pre-state mass immigration was categorized into five *aliyot* (immigrations), each with its own particular image—pioneering, socialist and single, middle-class, family, refugee. The differences between immigrants in the Yishuv, the pre-state social and political organization, were based upon whether or not they had the "pioneering spirit." This "pioneering spirit" was catalyzed by the influx of Russian socialist immigrants of the second aliya (1904–14) who, having struggled for the Russian socialist October Revolution of 1905 and suffered the aftermath of pogroms, laid down the socialist foundations of the state, and, with Polish and Rumanian *halutzim* (pioneers), built up the Yishuv.

During the period of the British Mandate, from 1919–1948, there were 487,000 immigrants, of which 87 percent were European, 10 percent Asian (Middle Eastern, Central Asian), and 3 percent North and South American, North African, and Oceanian (Matras 1965:30). After Israel became a state and instituted the Law of Return granting all Jews the right to immigrate to Israel, its population changed radically. From 1948 to 1951, Israel received 15,000 Jews monthly, 687,000 in a four-year period; many of these were European refugees from World War II; others were Middle Eastern Jews brought to Israel by the state, such as "Operation Magic Carpet" which transported 40,000 Yemeni Jews to Israel, and "Operation Ezra and Nehemiah" (recalling the prophets of Babylonia) which brought in 124,000 Iraqis and 27,000 Iranians (Matras 1965:33–35). With mass immigration, *kibbutz galuyot,* the "ingathering of the exiles," along with *mizug hagaluyot,* the "mixing of the exiles," became the backbone of the state ideology.

The immigrations of the 1950s transformed the character of the Jewish population of Israel into a Western minority who were the political and economic elite, and a non-Western majority who were less educated in Western culture and more religious than the Western Jews, had large families, and lacked the socialist ideology of the Western immigrants. In addition, many of the non-Western immigrants immigrated to Israel as a community and wanted to settle together. The bureaucracy built to cope with the influx of immigrants took care of housing, food, health care, and education, placing people in temporary immigrant camps, *kibbutzim* (collective farms), *moshavim* (collective settlements of individually or family owned farms), development towns, and urban neighborhoods.[17] Although numerous Iranian families were settled on moshavim, most moved from the farms to the cities which already housed substantial Iranian settlements.

Most of the Iranian Jews in Palestine, like other Middle Eastern Jewish communities, had little direct, influential, or participatory relationships with the institutions and leadership of the pre-state social and political organization, the Yishuv, which was composed of and controlled by European Jews who immigrated as a result of the Zionist movement. The Middle Eastern immigrants to Palestine did not arrive equipped with an ideology to remold Jewish life and to construct a new society. The European Jews did.

The Zionist movement did not reach Iran until after the signing of the Balfour Declaration in 1917. According to Netzer (1980:228), "Iranian Jews approached [Zionism] from the religious source. They did not see Herzl as the founder of a modern nationalist movement, but as a contemporary prophet, moved by supernatural powers. When the mandate for Palestine was given to Britain, emissaries to Iran were asked if Herbert Samuel was king of the Jews.

For centuries the Jews of Persia had no part in determining historic processes and, more recently, they had no opportunity to develop party or political consciousness." Consequently, for Iranian Jews, immigration to Palestine took the form of a spiritual redemption movement from their degrading life in Iran.[18] Iranians who immigrated to Palestine came from Hamadan, Mashhad, Shiraz, Yazd, Isfahan, Kashan, and Tehran, and settled primarily in Jerusalem and secondarily in the other pilgrimage cities of Tiberias, Safad, Hebron, Jaffa. By 1907 there were 950 Iranians in Jerusalem, and by the mid-1920s, 7,275 Iranians had arrived in Palestine (Netzer 1979:25). By 1981 Iranians numbered 114,500 out of a Jewish population of 3,282,700 (*Stastical Abstracts of Israel* 1981:58). Of these, 52,000 were born in Iran.[19] The rest were born in Israel to Iranian parents.

We can divide the Iranian population of Israel into four immigrant categories, each from a different period (before 1948; 1948–67; 1967–77; 1978 on), each with its own characteristics, including reasons for immigration and educational-work background, which influence integration into the Israeli socioeconomic system. Those who came before 1948 were attracted to Palestine by religious ideology and by fear of anti-Jewish violence in Iran. The men were merchants and peddlers in Iran and many became merchants and peddlers in Israel, such as Nehemiah's father, whereas others became skilled laborers, most notably quarry workers, cutting stones for houses in Jerusalem. Although many Jews of the lower socioeconomic classes in Iran immigrated to Israel between 1948 and 1967 to improve their standard of living, others were store-owners, traders, and craftsmen who wanted to live in a Jewish state to escape the prejudices which made life difficult for them in Iran. Some were illiterate. Others were educated in the Persian (Islamic secular or Jewish) school system, where Persian history and literature as well as arithmetic and basic sciences formed the foundation of formal schooling. Some studied at the Alliance Israélite schools, receiving a more Western education, whereas others attended trade schools, such as those sponsored by ORT.[20] The men of this immigrant group often received employment from state bureaucrats. They worked as skilled or semi-skilled laborers, or if continuing their studies in Israel, became professionals, clerks, technicians, or bureaucrats. Some women also worked as skilled or unskilled laborers, as assistants in the family business or as *metapelets*, women who have private daycare in their homes. This was something new for Iranian Jewish women, since in Iran they worked only at home with childraising and housework: the economic situation was difficult in Israel and many families needed the extra income brought in by a working woman.

Another immigrant group came between 1967 and 1977, after the Six Day War and before the Islamic Revolution. Unlike the immigrants before them, they were essentially better-educated, middle-class Iranians who were able to take advantage of the economic, social, and educational opportunities available to them as a result of the oil-boom economy and the shah's modernization policy. Many of these immigrants had owned elegant clothing boutiques in the newer commercial areas far from the bazaar. Others, both men and women, were educated in professional schools and universities, and worked as engineers, teachers, economists, doctors, social workers, travel agents, electricians, and secretaries. In other words, they were participating in the social and economic mainstream of modernizing Iranian society. Those who came to Israel were motivated more by Zionist than religious ideals of living in a Jewish state. Upon immigration to Israel, some opened clothing boutiques similar to the types they had in Iran, whereas others were employed in various professions, and many younger immigrants attended the universities.

In contradistinction to the three previous voluntary immigrant populations were the refugees who came between 1978 and 1979 as a result of the Islamic Revolution. Some wanted to remain in Israel; others hoped to return to Iran or move to the United States. These immigrants had been economically well-off in Iran, professionals, factory owners, import-export merchants, antique dealers. They were well-educated in the Iranian school system, Alliance Israélite, or in the Western school systems in Iran, such as the American School and Community School in Tehran. Some were professionals: physicians, engineers, pharmacists, executive secretaries, or dentists. Young women who were not mothers worked outside the home. Many had traveled to Europe and had been in Israel before the Revolution to visit relatives. In Israel some began to wait out the Islamic Revolution—primarily the older generation—whereas others, mostly the young, studied Hebrew and entered the university, professional training programs, or the job market. Some, as had other immigrants before them, opened clothing stores, falafel stands, appliance shops, and a few started businesses catering to the new influx of a more cosmopolitan Iranian immigration, such as Persian restaurants and an Iranian nightclub.

Unlike immigrants from other Middle Eastern countries, Iranians, until the Revolution, had close contact with their country of origin. Some would return periodically for visits. Others were hosts for family who came to tour Israel. Ties with the Jewish community in Iran and with Iranian culture as a whole were maintained through economic, social, and political connections: Iranian merchants in Israel sold Iranian goods picked up on business trips; Iranians in Israel collected and sent money for natural disasters in Iran, such as earthquakes; Israel had informal diplomatic and economic relations with Iran. Finally, many Iranians who found life not to their liking in Israel returned to live in Iran.

The Iranian community in Israel is primarily a middle-class one composed of workers, merchants, and professionals (the latter, however, are few). For years, the community had been split along lines of cities of origin from which they based their identity vis-à-vis each other. *Landsmanschaft* units in which people from different cities (Shiraz, Mashhad, Isfahan, Yazd, Hamadan) built their own synagogues and had their own welfare organizations took care of ritual and synagogue matters. In addition, there were several immigrant and cultural organizations, some affiliated with national immigrant organizations of other countries, but all were marred by relations of political conflict. The Iranian community as a whole in Israel had no leadership. They were separated by self-imposed identity criteria of city of origin, class, education, religiosity (observant or secular), political persuasion (Labor or Likud, and so forth). The community, unlike other immigrant groups, provided no Persian language newspaper for the Jews of Persian origin (although in the 1950s there were a few Persian newspapers affiliated with some of the political parties), nor did they, like the Yemenis or Moroccans, popularize the music, food, and poetry of their native culture within Israel, saying that non-Iranians would not appreciate these elements of Iranian culture.

It was only during the upheavals of the Islamic Revolution and its potential threat that the Iranian community was able to organize on a national level. With the help of Moshe Katz, a young member of the Knesset (parliament) who was born in Yazd, all the factious organizations were grouped under an umbrella organization whose functions included helping refugees from the Revolution by changing customs laws to allow Iranians to bring in carpets and electrical appliances without taxes, placing Persian translators in offices that have contacts with immigrants, and getting immigrants jobs in banks, schools, and government offices. They sought to raise the image of Iranians in Israel, too long characterized as stingy and suspicious (see chapter four), through programs on television and radio and by public lectures. This was also abetted by a group of Iranian intellectuals and academics who have been compiling folklore and history of Iranian Jews with the intent to establish an Iranian cultural center and library.

The impact of the Islamic Revolution in Iran on Iranian Jews in Israel was a sudden upsurge in ethnic pride, a reawakening of positive self-evaluation in light of negative stereotypes, and an interest in Iranian heritage from some Israeli-born children of Iranian parentage. The influx of a new group of immigrants, wealthier, better educated and more cosmopolitan than previous Iranian immigrants, had a positive effect on the Iranian community. The Iranianness of their heritage was being expressed publicly and affirmatively. Iranian restaurants appeared; an Iranian nightclub opened in Tel Aviv; the immigrant association held evenings of Iranian music and poetry (albeit for Iranians only); university students organized evenings of poetry readings; conferences were given at different universities throughout the country on Iranian Jewish history; the radio station increased its Persian-language broadcast from twenty minutes to fifty-five minutes per day; cultural programs of Persian music and plays, presented in Jerusalem two or three times a year, were put on every two months and were presented in theaters around the country for Iranian audiences.

For the non-Iranian Israelis, as well as for the Iranian-Israelis, the lack of a mass exodus of the Iranian Jews from what they thought would be a holocaust at the hands of Muslim fanatics was inconceivable. Emotional comparisons were made between the Islamic Revolution, its sociopolitical disorder, and the Nazi regime. They feared that the Jewish community in Iran would be annihilated. The fact that most Jews chose to stay in Iran was seen by the Israelis (Iranian and non-Iranian) as indicative of their overconcern for wealth and the fancy lifestyle they managed to acquire during the years of economic prosperity in Iran. However, for those Jews who chose to remain in Iran, their decision was based on their identities as Iranians, since they feel more comfortable living in Iran than in Israel. In spite of the social and religious discrimination against them in Iran, Iranian Jews have always considered themselves both Iranians and Jews, and this is brought to the fore in Israel, where their cultural identity as Iranians influences their integration into the society and interaction with others.

Chapter 3
Emotional Nārāhati

In Shiraz early in the fall of 1978, when Iran was undergoing the traumatic transformations of the Revolution, I received a letter from my parents saying that they would accept a young Iranian friend of mine, Nasreen Yaghoobi, to live with them for a year in order to complete high school in the United States, after which she would join her older brothers who were living in California. That fall was filled with tension and turmoil. There were protest marches against the shah's regime, killings of the protestors by the shah's army, and public mourning ceremonies for those killed alternating with more protest marches and more killings. Businesses were on strike, the bazaars were closed, schools were shut down, and rumors of what happened and what would happen were everywhere (Pliskin 1980).

Such was the situation when I received another letter from my parents, sent to me at the Yaghoobi's house. As usual, I read the letter while Nasreen sat nearby waiting to hear news from my family. This letter, however, had put me in a predicament: my parents wrote that they had second thoughts about taking Nasreen; they were feeling too old to be tied down with the responsibility of caring for a teenager from such a foreign culture. I had been in Iran long enough to know that communication of negative information is a delicate procedure. This was negative information concerning the Yaghoobi family, myself, and my parents, and I was in a dilemma as to how to present it. What followed was a series of verbal and nonverbal messages which were communicated, interpreted, and misunderstood by the Yaghoobi family and myself, creating a complex emotional situation that was alleviated later on only by the mediation of Nasreen's older sister, Nadia, a graduate of an American university who was at work when I received my letter.

Mrs. Yaghoobi asked me what my mother had written. I replied that she is *nārāhat* [here meaning "upset"] and misses me. She asked if my mother was crying. I said yes, although I don't know why I did. Then I told Mrs. Yaghoobi that I would tell Nadia everything my mother wrote, since she could better explain the situation. After a few minutes of small talk, I left to talk about my predicament to Jim, an American who was renting an apartment at the other end of the Yaghoobi's hayāt (courtyard).

As I was leaving their compound, Nasreen and her mother called out that I should come back for lunch because Nadia would be there. When I returned an hour later, Nadia was still at work. Nasreen asked me to stay, saying that Nadia would be home soon. Telling her I wasn't hungry, I declined the invitation since I had eaten a late breakfast and I also wanted to do some errands. Mrs. Yaghoobi was standing outside by the kitchen door. Nasreen, insisting I stay because her mother was very nārāhat from my letter, mentioned her mother would be very nārāhat if Nadia didn't come home for lunch. But, I said, she just told me that Nadia was coming. Well, maybe she wasn't. So I asked Nasreen to tell Nadia to come see me when she had time, and, declaring that her mother had nothing to be nārāhat about, I said good-bye to everyone and left.

Around seven that evening Jim came over to inform me that Nasreen and Mrs. Yaghoobi cried all afternoon. Nasreen implied to Jim that I was not disclosing the truth concerning the letter. They had assumed that my letter contained bad news about the health of one of their sons in the United States, and that I was being very Persian and didn't want to tell them.

This incident illustrates several problems I encountered in attempting to understand and manage Persian communication codes. One problem was that I had known about the noncommunication of negative information in Persian culture. Attempting to avoid communicating what I perceived to be negative information—and I was totally inept at this—I gave conflicting messages. By saying on the one hand that my mother was nārāhat, and on the other, that I would explain the situation in depth to Nadia, I had inadvertently created a distressing situation for the Yaghoobis. Another problem was using the word nārāhat. I had heard it employed numerous times in reference to people being upset about one thing or another, and Nasreen had used it to refer to her mother's being upset about my letter. What added to the confusion were the other messages I had presented. I said I wasn't hungry, I avoided discussing the letter, and I returned to my apartment. Only later, when researching nārāhati, did I realize that avoidance of food and of social interaction is indicative of profound nārāhati, or dejection.

My interaction with the Yaghoobis, resolved later with the mediation of Nadia, was based on my early and inadequate notions of the cultural communication of negative information and the meaning of nārāhati. I was ignorant of the proper signals in the Iranian context concerning such issues, and I was presenting the wrong signals to my friends. I had interpreted the transaction as an American, while they interpreted my statements and behavior as Iranians.

The result of this awkward exchange was their fear for a relative far away—their feeling extremely nārāhat—and my discomfort and embarrassment about what had occurred. It was then that I realized that nārāhati means more than simply being upset and that the noncommunication of negative information has much to do with nārāhati.[1]

Defining Nārāhati

Nārāhati, explained an Iranian physician in Jerusalem, is "when you are not comfortable. It may be because you see someone you don't want to see, which will make you nārāhat. You can sit on an uncomfortable chair which will make you nārāhat. . . . If he's Persian, you won't understand he's nārāhat. He won't tell you, unless he is at the top of his nārāhati, and has passed all the borders and you can't get him back. The moment you see someone is nārāhat, making them go back is difficult. It is a time when they can't stand it any more. . . . [I know someone is nārāhat] from the face without speaking. The smile isn't a smile. The eyes aren't smiling."

Nārāhati (a noun; the adjective is nārāhat) is a general term used to express undifferentiated unpleasant emotional and physical feelings in Iranian culture. It is not entirely translatable into other languages. The dictionary translation is "uncomfortable, uneasy, inclined to make trouble or mischief" (Haim 1958:739). It is the opposite of *rāhat,* which means "comfortable, quiet, ease, convenient, in easy circumstances, feeling at home" (Haim 1958:330). But nārāhati is used to denote a wide range of negative emotions, some of which were explained to me by Iranians in Israel as depressed, inconvenienced, nervous, anxious, troubled, uneasy, worried, upset, disappointed, bothered, not tranquil, being in a bad mood, not feeling well, restless.[2] Although many of these words exist and are used in the literary language (*ketābi*), nārāhati is employed in ordinary conversation to express and describe a variety of negative feelings. What causes nārāhati and how it is expressed vary from situation to situation, from person to person, from family to family.

Nārāhati is as an emotion which is not only context-dependent but also culture-dependent, related to notions of private and public, inner and outer, and the individual and others as conceptualized and practiced in Iranian culture, social structure, and communication patterns. It is a culturally delimited emotion with social, psychological, and physical repercussions, reflective of personal sensitivity and related to feelings of individual powerlessness. Interpreting the meaning of nārāhati thus requires an analysis of the hierarchical nature of Iranian society and the contradictory conceptions of the individual within the hierarchy as externally shrewd and internally sensitive. Understanding nārāhati is essential to the understanding of Iranian culture, and to the understanding of emotions in general.

Emotions and Culture

Understanding emotions is not simply a problem of language, nor is it a question of universality, culturally veneered biological innateness, or individual inner states.[3] Rather, emotions must be understood as individual communicative reactions to the social and cultural milieu, with meanings other than simply recognition or expression of feelings. Social practices, personality traits, values, beliefs, and social organization influence emotion expression and the meaning of emotions, even though many emotions may not be expressed verbally or nonverbally.

Human emotions are cultural products. Culture and perceived patterns of social relationships determine people's ideas of emotions, what we will react to emotionally, which emotions should be invoked, and how and to whom our emotions will be expressed. Although superficially people may express what seems to be a universal emotion, emotion experience, expression, and meaning are uninterpretable unless they are understood in cultural and individual contexts, since emotion expression and cognition reflect, and are reflected by, the concept of the person within society and social relations. Accordingly, one must not lose sight of the fact that the meaning of experiences which induce emotions varies from person to person as well as from culture to culture, in that people value, apperceive, and endure situations differently. One has only to read the bewildered and somewhat horrified Dane's account (in Geertz 1983:37–39) of three concubines of a dead rajah in Bali jumping into a funeral pyre to understand this point: he is puzzled and disgusted that neither the Balinese concubines nor the thousands of people watching the spectacle show any emotion of sadness, fear, distress, or unhappiness, but, instead, react with the festivity that the situation calls for culturally. The reactions of the Danish observer, socialized in a culture where death calls for sadness and sobriety, and where self-immolation is culturally unknown, differ from those of the Balinese concerning the funeral ritual.

A proper study of emotions should include references to a people's ethnopsychology, the different cultural understandings of the individual in a system of social relationships. Ethnopsychology also concerns people's ideas about human nature, and about emotions as revealing human nature and social relations.[4] In addition, many of our theories about emotions and the individual person expressing them (or "the self" as it is often referred to) are derived from Western ethnopsychology, which views emotion as an internal, personal, sometimes private experience located *within* the individual, a feeling that may or may not be expressed. According to contemporary Western ethnopsychology, which is based upon a tradition of scientific empiricism, emotions may be physiologically measured and tabulated, and expressed emotions may be identifiable and quantifiable. However, such studies, often done as experiments in university psychology laboratories with undergraduates as subjects, tell nothing about the meaning and values the emotions have for those people feeling or expressing them, let alone how people would react emotionally in real life situations. Moreover, sometimes our own Western ethnospychology becomes so much a part of our seeing the world that we take for granted our concepts of individuals and emotions as being part of human nature (see Lutz 1985).

In Western ethnopsychology, the emotions are posited as having an individual component, as internal feelings and characteristics concerning the self as a voluntary agent in society. Much of Western ethnopsychology divorces the individual expressing emotion from the social contexts in which the emotions were expressed, and from the cultural influences on the individual expressing or hiding his or her feelings. On the other hand, many non-Western ethnopsychologies concern the social components of emotions, derived from external causes, pertaining to feelings regarding the self and other where the self is socially determined (Heelas 1981; Shweder and Bourne 1982). Thus, Western conceptions of emotions as universal, as centered within the individual, and as primarily psychobiological experiences that are culturally labeled need an anthropological view of emotions which regards emotions as culturally induced individual responses or valuations to social or personal situations, in which the emotion communicates the interface between personal and social experience.[5]

Although some anthropologists consider emotions to be psychobiological phenomena cast by culture into particular hues,[6] individuals may not react biologically to sociocultural stimuli. For example, there are emotions, such as sadness and anger, which one cognitively knows and senses, but may not feel or express physically. In addition, such affects as depression, sadness, and anger are often dissimulated in specific social situations in the West, as is nārāhati in Iranian culture, via impression management; it has not been determined whether there are physiological correlates to these cognitively masked emotions. Although there are some emotions which seem to be universal according to cross-cultural psychology research, it is the different meanings of emotions for the people who express them that is of interest to anthropologists. Anger, for instance, is viewed in the United States as personal catharsis, as expelling emotions from the self which could be dangerous if kept within, whereas in Iran, the outward expression of anger is considered a social, personal, and physiological danger, and it is deemed best not to express it. These examples indicate that differences in emotion expression and in the meaning of emotion can be fully comprehended only when one understands the ethnopsychology of a people. With this in mind, we must first understand Iranian ethnopsychology in order to understand nārāhati as a particular Iranian emotion.

Social Hierarchy and Communication in Iran

Iranians have been puzzling to the outside Western observer trying to make sense out of their actions, beliefs, society. I quote here one Englishman's appraisal of hierarchical relationships in Iranian society in the early part of the nineteenth century:

> The Persians are very abject; they take hold of the hem of your garment, and entreat permission to kiss the dust off your feet. Their civilities are overwhelming, their language fascinating; for who is there that does not like to be told, "My eyes are enlightened by seeing you"? But their creed is that of Saadi: "Truth is an excellent thing when it suits our purpose, but very inconvenient when otherwise." Slavery is their atmosphere; they despise all other government. I can easily understand this, since every class exercises the same despotism to their dependents. Had the Shah been in the village, the Kahn would have been prostrating himself, and playing the same part as the Ketkodeh [headman] was now performing towards *him;* and when he quits the Khan's presence, he acts the despot to those below him, and so the comedy goes on from one class to another, each content to become the slave, that he may in his turn play the monarch. (Fowler 1841:177–78).

Fowler describes a society based on relationships of hierarchy that are mediated by prescribed forms of communication in social situations in which persons of different statuses interact. The patterns of hierarchy and communication codes which exist in Iran are mutually constituted, reinforcing one another as well as reinforcing cultural ideas of individual persons who, singly and in groups, make up the society. We will see how hierarchy, communication codes, and the cultural characterization of the individual and emotions are supported by a system of social relationships which is molded and maintained by cultural values.

In general, Iranian society is similar to other Middle Eastern societies in the areas of social relationships and behavior (the values and beliefs of Islam aside), systems of hierarchy, social mobility, the bazaar economy, and arid land agriculture and its ensuing social relations. Iranian society, like Morocco (Eickelman 1976; Rosen 1979) and Lebanon (Gilsenan 1976), is both hierarchical and socially mobile, with social interaction influenced by economic class and personal-familial status. In Iran there exists a kind of unconventional social mobility enabling a clever person to raise his or her status by manipulating self and other within the context of social interaction. One of the best-known examples in recent history of someone who accomplished such a feat was the semi-illiterate peasant who became Reza Shah. The combination of hierarchy and social mobility engenders the development of a series of dyadic relationships or patron-client relationships of obligation and servitude to raise or guard one's status. Conversely, one could fall out of favor with a powerful other and then lose one's higher status position altogether. These factors create a situation in which people are often distrustful of others, suspicious, and guarded in their behavior. One must take care to protect oneself and one's family in social situations where potentially powerful others could create contexts of domination and subordination. So it is that Fowler writes of the behavior of the shah, khan, and ketkodeh.

Western writers have observed similar behavioral styles among other Middle Eastern peoples, such as Gilsenan's (1976) study of the lie (*kizb*) among young male Lebanese villagers: he shows the connection between lies, dominance, and control where there is an uncertainty in communication, whereby the manipulation of meaning by the liar enables the constitution of the self. In a similar context, Eickelman (1976) writes of obligation in asymmetrical relationships between people in Morocco, where those who are unable to reciprocate a service rendered become clients in relationship to those who performed the service. This creates a situation in which the individual tries to juggle relationships of obligation to others while simultaneously trying to maintain relationships of obligation over others. The situation is reminiscent of the one Fowler depicted.

The asymmetrical interpersonal relationships of societies such as Iran (and Morocco and Lebanon) that are both hierarchical and socially mobile foster people's development of personal contacts in order to attain their goals. Naturally, however, a person's ability to develop such personal contacts depends upon background, time, gender, location, and other social, cultural, and environmental circumstances.[7] Such asymmetrical interpersonal relationships are further reinforced by what Geertz (1979) calls "imperfect communication"—the communication of the Middle Eastern bazaar. Bazaar communication is highly valued, but accurate information about the quality of products and their worth is rare. People who work in the bazaar, merchants, and those who sell to merchants manipulate people according to what they want others to know or not to know about what is being sold. "The search for information one lacks," Geertz writes (1979:125), "and the protection of information one has is the name of the game" where "the only thing that can really hurt you in the bazaar is what you don't know . . . and someone else does." (1979:216).

Similar information control reverberates into social relationships in which people regulate information about the self that is given to others. This control is a form of self-protection in a situation of uncertainty created by a world where appearance and reality do not necessarily mesh. Appearance and reality invariably differ when cultures have highly developed communication codes protecting the social transactions of the individual in individuated, hierarchical societies. Such communicative protection is necessary when others are not whom they seem to be, are of different statuses, and, in situations of social mobility and hierarchy, when peoples' statuses may change from high to low and vice versa, with the possible entanglements of obligations to and subservience from others. The private self is thus protected from others by information control. Inner feelings and ideas are often concealed from unknown outsiders to maintain the boundaries of interpersonal relationships.

While Iran is similar to other Middle Eastern societies in these ways, it is distinctive not only in Shi'ite Islam, but also in its communication codes and its concepts of individual sensitivity and cleverness. These are the concepts we must understand in order to understand how nārāhati fits into and illuminates Iranian culture. In Iran, the boundaries of interpersonal relationships are culturally buttressed through verbal, nonverbal, and environmental mechanisms to manage personal and familial privacy. Houses are separated from one another and from the street by high walls which assure familial privacy. Within the walls of the housing compound are, in traditional families, the *birun*, the outer quarters, the public arena for the men to be with their associates, set off from the *anderun*, the inner quarters where the women carry on their daily activities. In less traditional families (these were the families that I knew), the public sector of the house, where the family entertains non-intimates, whether more distant family, friends or acquaintances, is the salon, often decorated with costlier carpets and fancier furniture than the rest of the rooms used daily by the family. Within the walls of the compound, which includes the house as well as a courtyard and perhaps a fountain and garden, family members dress informally: often men return home from the world outside to rest in pajamas. Once outside the walls and into the public sphere, dress becomes formal: traditional women wear *chādor*s insuring female privacy and family honor; more modern women dress in more formal Western dress in public (now, however, with long kerchiefs covering their hair to abide by the injunctions of the Islamic Revolution), whereas at home they might wear older, worn, more comfortable clothes or jeans and T-shirts. Men replace their pajamas with suits or pants and shirts (sometimes putting these on top of the pajamas for quick removal once home) for the public arena.

The public arena of a social world that is hierarchical and somewhat dangerous and unpredictable due to the social circumstances which generate domination, control, subservience, and "imperfect communication," contrasts with the more intimate world of family, separated and signified by the high walls surrounding houses. In the world outside the house, individuals maintain personal boundaries in social interaction through the formalized verbal and nonverbal transactions of ritual courtesy known as *ta'ārof*.

Ta'ārof molds interactions between people of differing statuses and relationships, where social interaction is delineated into relationships with intimates and non-intimates, and these two groupings are further divided into relations with persons of equal or unequal status.[8] Communication in Iran (as in many societies) proceeds vertically in relations with non-intimates and horizontally in relations with intimates. However, in Iran, the differences in the kinds of relations one has are portrayed and enacted in differential communication patterns. Concerning non-intimates, one maintains one's distance through ta'ārof, in which varying verb forms, titles of address to others, referral to self, and forms of hospitality, ceremony, politesse, and etiquette indicate status differences and social distance. With intimates, such formalities are dropped.

Ta'ārof regarding verb forms concerns distance and respect to those of high status. For instance, the verb "to come" (*āmadan*) is changed when speaking to one of much higher status than oneself to the compound verb from which means, literally, "to bring your honor" (*tashrif āvardan*), and becomes, in reference to the self in the context of talking to one of high status, literally, "to make a pilgrimage," "to arrive in service," or, in the context of ta'ārof, "to meet" (*ziārat kardan*). The ta'ārof of hospitality concerns ritualized behavior of host and guest, such as the host presenting guests with plates of fruits, often peeling the fruits for the guests. Guests ritually refuse the food several times while the host ritually presents the offerings until the guests take something. Other forms of ta'ārof consist of seating the high-status guest at the head of the room; jockeying for positions of status, especially lower status, in leaving a room in which the high-status person leaves the door first; asking a long series of questions about various members of a person's family when meeting a person in the street or when talking on the telephone before proceeding to transact business; seeing someone in the street and inviting him or her to one's house for tea, both knowing full well that the invitation is simply a formality; making offers to people which they have to refuse, such as telling someone who admires an article of clothing that she can take it as a present (*pishkesh*). By making the offer and by refusing the offer, people enter into a relationship in which one person ritually displays vulnerability which the other knows not to accept (see Bateson 1979).

Ta'ārof connotes strategic interaction according to status differences. Iranians must know how to function at various levels in different situations where social obligations are in a state of flux, especially if there is the possibility that the relative status of others may shift. Ta'ārof then structures interaction through maintaining social distance by using stylistic variations in language to manipulate oneself within the status hierarchy of interaction. Because of the hierarchical social organization in Iranian society, people are continuously having to change their speech and behavior patterns concerning others; in one situation one may be of a higher status than another, and yet in a different situation one may be of a lower status, and one must communicate accordingly. This difference in status regarding interaction between nonequals and non-intimates involves what Beeman (1976a:307) describes as the ethic of noblesse oblige on the part of the higher-status persons, by which they confer favors and rewards and give orders to lower-status persons, whereas relationships from low to high status involve "rendering service, paying tribute, and making petitions" within an ethic of duty. This establishes an asymmetrical relationship that requires the overdetermined and restricted expression of ta'ārof. The ritual politeness code of ta'ārof thus both delineates and is generated by the boundaries between people of different statuses.

When the status of another is not known, writes Beeman (1976a), the optimum strategy is to choose lower status for oneself by raising the status of the person to whom one is speaking while simultaneously lowering one's own status, invoking noblesse oblige in the other and giving oneself more options in the inferior, and thus vulnerable, position. The ethic holds that exposed vulnerability to a person of higher status, especially one controlling certain resources, would not be exploited. Thus, an Iranian immigrant I knew in Jerusalem broke down in tears in an employment office in Israel while petitioning for a change in jobs. In Iran, such a petition might have been granted. In Israel, however, this action was considered inappropriate and a sign of emotional instability, and his petition was not granted.

Unlike interactions with non-intimates, which are marked by separation and distance and mediated through the ceremonial decorum of ta'ārof, interactions with intimates are distinguished by the absence of ta'ārof. With non-intimates, one who speaks freely, saying what one wishes, is considered brash and audacious—*por-rou'i*—"full-face." In relations with intimates, such expression is not restricted. Although communication codes of ta'ārof are determined by intimate and non-intimate relationships, ta'ārof becomes ambiguous when statuses and relationships are in the flux of change from non-intimate to intimate. In this situation, ta'ārof can be verbally denied. For instance, an invitation for tea may be proceeded and followed by the qualifier, "This is not a ta'ārof."

Intimates, those with whom one does not ta'ārof, may be status equals, such as siblings, cousins, classmates, friends, or nonequals, such as parents, children, grandparents. Intimates are those with whom one has a mutual relationship of moral, personal, and social responsibility, involving commitment, loyalty, and respect. This is in opposition to non-intimates to whom one does show respect through ta'ārof, but for whom mutual responsibility, commitment, and loyalty are lacking.

Respect (*ehterām*), a vital ingredient for social interaction in Iran, resonates with several connotations. Respect is an important component of ta'ārof, concerning proper behavior toward another person, especially one of a higher status than one's own. Respect also signifies care and regard for other people as autonomous individuals and as members of groups (familial, political, economic, religious, educational) within the social system. In addition, respect suggests separation between self and others, implying social boundaries which are conveyed by different communication codes.

In relations between intimates, respect reflects familial hierarchy by obeisance to those of higher status. Within the family, the father, as the oldest male whose dealings with the world of non-intimates support the family, is regarded as the person of highest status. Generally, it is more common for his children, and sometimes his wife, to call him *āghā*, a title of Turkish origin meaning "gentleman" or "sir," than to call him by his name or the Persian word for addressing one's father, *bābā* (although there is the tendency for the modern educated Iranian fathers to have their children call them *bābā*). Even though familial interactions and situations vary, frequently the father's decisions concerning family matters are carried out by his wife and children with little or no objection. A less distant, more informal relationship exists between children and their mother, whom they refer to as *māmān*, the Persian word of French origin to address one's mother. Her husband as well as her children may refer to her as *khānum*, meaning "lady," "wife," or "Mrs.," but more often her husband addresses her by her first name. Ideally, younger siblings show respect for the judgment of older siblings, sisters frequently deferring to the opinions of brothers. Consequently, within the circle of familial intimates, the hierarchy of status differences is delineated along lines of age and gender, marked by attitudes of respect, reliance, responsibility, and feelings of close interpersonal bonds. This is in opposition to relationships in the world of non-intimates which, although marked by—or masked by—respect for others, is depicted by formalized patterns of ta'ārof, separation, and distance, culminating in feelings of insecurity concerning the motivations, actions, and beliefs of others.

The Individual: Sensitive and Clever

The themes of insecurity, distrust, and deception play a major role in the writings of Westerners and Iranians concerning the so-called Iranian character.[9] Beeman (1976b) relates these traits to a hierarchical communication structure in which one often never knows the actions and motives of others, since these may be concealed. Individuals moving within the social hierarchy manipulate their own messages to gain advantage while interpreting the verbal and nonverbal messages of others who may be operating in the same manner. This creates a situation of insecurity, mistrust, and suspicion of others whose messages might not be what they seem.

Beeman's interactionist view of interpersonal communication explains certain Iranian character traits. Some of these character traits help constitute the nature of Iranian communication while simultaneously being reinforced by it. To carry this further, it is my contention that the qualities of insecurity, distrust, and deception found in the "Iranian character" involve feelings of powerlessness resulting from the ongoing dialectic between, on the one hand, hierarchy, mobility, and distance on the social structural level, and on the other hand, cultural conceptions of the character of the individual in the social sphere as externally clever and internally sensitive.

These conceptions of the individual character are an elaboration on, and contrast with, those of Bateson et al. (1977), who utilize a Sufi abstraction about the internal purity and goodness of the individual, *safā-yi bātin,* which must be protected or concealed from the evil corrupting society or social life. Bateson et al. differentiate the stereotypic characteristics of Iranians as shrewd, manipulative, and distrustful from the internal purity, kindness, and generosity of the person. Iranian culture values character traits in which the internal nature of the individual is reflected in his or her external appearance and actions, rather than concealed in front of others. According to Bateson et al., two character types meet these criteria: the *luti,* who believes in ta'ārof literally and acts accordingly, meaning his ta'ārofs and capitalizing on those of others, and the *darvish,* who ignores ta'ārof altogether. The characters chosen are male stereotypes: the totally accepting insider (the luti) and the rejecting outsider (the darvish).

While Bateson et al. were concerned with portraying positive, rather than negative, features of the "Iranian national character," their analysis reflects the conversations of a group of middle-class, mostly male, Muslim Tehrani intellectuals who formed the basis of their study. But how widespread are these Sufi values of safā-yi bātin? Certainly, the literate familiar with Persian Sufi poets—as were the professionals who were part of their group analyzing Iranian character traits—are familiar with these concepts, as are certain religious people. By contrast, the people whom I met and spoke with, when asked, had not heard of safā-yi bātin and do not admit to focusing on an inner purity corruptible by evil society. Rather, their daily discourse assumes a different guise, that of individuals being sensitive, of having to show respect to others because of both the sensitivity of others and the hierarchy of relations, of being in a continuous state of awareness of relationships of people more and less powerful than oneself. Bateson et al. look at Sufi concepts of character traits, but not at everyday conversations of average Iranians in transactions with one another or at the structure of society and communication which influence the luti, the darvish, the Sufi, and others in the society to behave the ways they do. On the other hand, by studying popular discourse, Beeman (1976b) looks at how communication and hierarchy engender the negative character traits associated with Iranians. Nevertheless, the question remains, how do communication *and* character traits, those psychological predispositions and values of people in a culture, influence one another in Iranian society?

The difference between one's external appearance and behavior and one's internal essence and feelings is a pervasive motif in Iranian culture. Because of the social hierarchy and the ritual language of ta'ārof, one's actual beliefs and feelings are often not revealed in transactions with non-intimates. What this connotes is an external world which is threatening and suspect, an arena of known and unknown social relationships: the individual must guard against the potential power of others, against relationships of obligation and subservience which might not be to one's advantage, against the possibility that others are carefully concealing their intentions and raising their statuses through proper manipulation of self and others. The world then becomes one in which no one really knows the intentions of the other.

In social interaction, especially with non-intimates, and sometimes with intimate status unequals, each person thus opts for the best of all possible worlds, and does so with an element of *zerangi*, cleverness (see Beeman 1976b). A zerang person is one who successfully conceals his or her motives in order to accomplish certain goals. A clever, wily, manipulative person, one who is zerang, can shrewdly utilize the formal ta'ārof system to his or her own advantage in numerous ways: for instance, lowering one's own status in front of a non-intimate in order to gain some advantage, such as a loan, or representing oneself to non-intimates in a way that hides one's true position in order to protect oneself and to better steer oneself and manipulate others within the social hierarchy. The wealthy bazaar merchant who wears tattered clothing in his shop comes to mind. On the one hand, such appearance connotes disdain for the material world. On the other hand, a wealthy person is suspect: how did he get his wealth, does his wealth give him power and social connections and the kinds of sociopolitical protection garnered by the few (with its counterpart, corruption), and will he accept granting favors to those less fortunate than himself? The ragged, stubbly-bearded store-owner looks so vulnerable and poor—like the men who clean the gutters of the streets in Iranian cities—that one simultaneously pities him and knows that, as a *bāzaari*, capital lurks behind his personal appearance.

Being zerang connotes being in control of oneself and of others. This is valued in interpersonal transactions since the clever, shrewd person is able to utilize social connections for self and familial aggrandizement. In addition, zerangi can also influence transactions with intimates. For example, one young mother suffering from post-partum depression was feeding her infant while her three-year-old son was playing with a sharp knife. Because of her delayed reactions and the danger posed by such a sharp tool, I asked if I could put the knife on top of the refrigerator. Less than five minutes later, he was back in the living room with the knife, having pushed a chair to the counter to climb on to reach the top of the refrigerator. His mother smiled and said, "He is zerang." Although zerangi in this sense connotes cleverness and shrewdness, it also is valued as an element of power, sometimes encouraged for the traits of strength, the ability to get something done, to act effectively. This element of zerangi in her son did not unnerve the mother. Rather, she and her husband appeared to encourage such behavior by lack of negative reinforcement, neither talking to the child about the dangers of the knife nor taking the knife away.

In addition to being an element of interpersonal transactions, zerangi connotes the concept of cleverness as intelligence as well as social discernment of the behavior and actions of others. Zerangi signifies the individual being a voluntary agent within a system of social relations. Although Iranians are not always involved in zerangi behavior with non-intimates, certain stiuations of competition and/or protection warrant its use, such as bureaucratic settings when people vie against others within a defined hierarchy, and economic transactions when buyers and sellers pursue profits. In a world of non-intimates where one must continually be aware of the statuses of others in order to act appropriately, to maintain the public honor (*āberu*) and respectability of oneself and family, and to conceal one's intentions from others for fear of being undermined, whether by their power and connections or by the evil eye (see chapter six), the element of zerangi enables people to operate in the sociocultural milieu. In addition, zerangi behavior arises in the more intimate family and friendship contexts when members want to protect the physical and emotional well-being of others.

The obverse of zerangi is mistrust (Beeman 1976b): one is never quite sure what others mean, especially regarding transactions with non-intimates, and, as we will see further on concerning nārāhati, with intimates also. Because Iranian society abounds in communicative discrepancies between intimates and non-intimates, between people of equal status and those of unequal status, between private circumstances and public appearance, between internal state and outer action, the message is that one's external appearance and behavior are not necessarily indicative of one's actual condition. Consequently, messages, both verbal and nonverbal, are often considered to have some underlying meaning. Peoples' actions and speech are commonly being interpreted from outer mask to inner essence. This is depicted in the writing of Lady Sheil, wife of the British ambassador to Persia from 1849 to 1853, who, not comprehending the hierarchical relations in Iranian society, was unable to understand Persian communication patterns:

> These Persians are very strange people; they are ever on the watch to discover each other's intrigues, falsehoods, and finesses. A movement of the finger, a turn of the eye, is not left unnoticed, and receives an interpretation. Yet each man invariably thinks that his own plots and intrigues are the acme of human ingenuity, wholly unfathomable by the rest of mankind. How often have I heard the Persian secretaries of the Mission preparing little paltry schemes, which the dullest understanding could unravel, for arranging insignificant matters in which all that was necessary was to tell the truth, and all the time thinking they were performing the cleverist and most impenetrable feats of diplomacy. (1856:247)

And in the same vein, the eminent Iranian writer, Sadeq Hedāyat, criticizing his own society in his novel *Hāji Āghā,* describes the character Hāji Āghā:

> Outwardly, he assumed many guises, often speaking in completely contradictory terms—and all, as he himself said, so that he "might not one day want for bread"; for Hāji was convinced that life consisted of trickery, lies, deception, fraud, and swindling. His society, after all, was based on such principles: whoever could best swindle and deceive would best serve his own interests. He conceived himself like others, to be a sinner, and was not particular what means he employed to extricate from other people's intrigues and stratagems and trickeries. He thought of the tongue as a mere lump of meat that could be twisted this way and that. Thus, fixing deals, sleight of hand, spying, flattery, and general deception had all become part of his very nature. The age looked favorably on such attitudes, so he (as one of the outstanding men of that age) was not prepared to be swindled himself in the thieve's kitchen of life. (1979:45–46)

What has been delineated so far is interaction primarily with non-intimates, with people with whom one must ta'ārof, with people bound by separations of status, age, religion, wealth, gender, and power. Power—and control—are significant for self-management within the hierarchy of relations. On the one hand, the possibility of attaining some sort of power via personal zerangi is positive because of the network of personal relations and consequent possibilities of influence one acquires. On the other hand, power is highly distrusted, and those who attain it are therefore suspect. The problem then becomes attaining power but pretending not to have it—a rather clever move on the part of those individuals within the system, such as Hāji Āghā, who play a game of zerangi, ta'ārof, and concealment in the outer public realm.

Zerangi as a character trait thus concerns positive and negative personal qualities which enable one to interact within a complex hierarchical system. The counterpart to the active, manipulative zerang person is the characteristic of sensitivity (*hassāsiyat*). Sensitivity is deemed an inherent trait of people, a characteristic which must be concealed in social interaction to protect the (sensitive) individuals from the actions of others who might take advantage of them. In this respect, ta'ārof protects the sensitivity of self and other in interactions by creating a semblance of niceties and balance, a smoothness of relations.

Although some people are more zerang than others, and some people might not be zerang at all, nearly everyone is sensitive and some people are more sensitive than others.[10] And while zerangi is an external part of one's character, connoting action, power, strength, and control, sensitivity is the internal essence of an individual. Indeed, as a positive character trait, sensitivity is spoken about by the average Iranian more often than the Sufi concept of safā-yi bātin. The term sensitive in Persian—*hassās* (from the Arabic)—also means "quick, feeling, sentimental, delicate, precise, susceptible, essential" (Haim 1958:241). It signifies perception, sensing, and reaction, emotionally and physically. One is sensitive by attending to the words and behavior of others that affect one's social situation.

Being sensitive is a highly valued personality trait in Iranian culture. It delineates personal and social awareness as well as appreciation for the aesthetic aspect of life which is so much a part of Persian culture. This aesthetic aspect is represented by the arts decorating homes—carpets, inlay work, engraved metalwork, miniature paintings—and by poetry, read privately and recited publicly, by saying "bah-bah" while listening to Iranian music with eyes part-closed (indicating how the music is affecting one's internal essence), by going with friends or family on a picnic outside the city to commune with nature—to sit on a carpet, eat rice with *khoresh* (a sauce of meat and vegetables or fruits), drink tea, and talk about the meaning of life.

Sensitivity connotes social responsibility. Social interaction takes the concept of sensitivity into account. People ideally modulate their behavior vis-à-vis others, showing respect and making others comfortable (rāhat). In part, this has to do with ta'ārof and social distance, but respect and comfort are elements entering into social relationships that have to do with the concept that the inner core of the individual is sensitive. Thus, one speaks kindly, softly, and courteously; one is hospitable to others by offering tea to guests or to clients in one's office, making them feel more rāhat. The failure to portray this sensitivity would not only reflect back onto one's family and create an embarrassing social situation in the community, but could also engender nārāhati in others.

The negative side to sensitivity is that the sensitive person easily becomes nārāhat, with the possibilities of losing self-control and balance in the hierarchy of social relations, and of becoming sick from such reactions to nārāhati as not eating. With this in mind, the actions, reactions, and words of others are measured and evaluated by the parties involved in social interaction. If one thinks that another will become nārāhat if certain information is revealed, it is done so gently, perhaps with time, or maybe not at all. "Even if you want to cut off the head of a man," states a Persian proverb focusing on individual sensitivity and concomitant nārāhat, "do it with cotton and not with a sharp knife." So it is when negative information, such as someone's death, must be told to a relative abroad: this could take weeks, perhaps months, but decorum has it that the relative should not be alone when he or she hears of the death, since the person could become not only nārāhat, but could suffer from "fright" and thus become physically and, perhaps, emotionally sick.

Sensitivity depicts an indigenous character trait, one that is involuntary, as opposed to the more voluntary aspect of zerangi. Sensitivity implies the sociocentric aspect of personhood, while zerangi connotes the egocentric. Together, sensitivity and zerangi are two facets of personhood in Iranian culture, positively valued in some contexts, negatively in others. This double-sided view of the person shows not only that there are different concepts of the person cross-culturally (Shweder and Bourne 1982), but that different and contradictory concepts of the person can exist together in one person, in one culture.

Sensitivity and zerangi are two sides of the cultural understanding of the individual and human nature in Iranian society. These two aspects of individual personality are influenced by and in turn influence social relations. Zerangi, as the aspect of behavior concerning the outer public realm of relations, has within it an element of control, dissimulation, hierarchy, mobility, individualism, separation, guardedness. Separation and guardedness also are an aspect of sensitivity, but only in terms of the need to conceal one's sensitivity from others in a world where the zerang others are powerful and the sensitive person is vulnerable.

Insofar as sensitivity involves attending to others' words and actions, the zerang person is in a sense sensitive, but only in order to calculate his or her own behavior. The zerang person must hide this sensitivity, since its exposure means one is not in control. For relations to proceed smoothly, people must regulate their actions, ideas, and speech. But the exposure of personal sensitivity implies passivity in social relations. Unlike the zerang person, who can manipulate others and is thus seen as latently powerful, the sensitive person is seen as susceptible to the actions and words of others. This susceptibility implies powerlessness in the sensitive person, who feels and is influenced by such things as statements and deeds of others, something not said right, excessive noises, and sensations of physical pain. Therefore, in order not to appear powerless within a system of social relations, the sensitive person often tries to conceal personal sensitivity.

The vulnerability of the sensitive person is not the same as the ritualized vulnerability of ta'ārof, where participants in interaction know they are playing ceremonial courtesies. Rather, the vulnerability of sensitivity signifies not being in control: the inability to manage in a system of social relations where the individual has a particular status and role that must be maintained with others. To not be in control is to not be zerang. Instead, it is to be powerless (*za'if*) or weak (also *za'if*). Powerlessness and weakness indicate an inability to act within the system, and present a fear that one's weaknesses will be used against one, that other forces—political, social, familial, economic, spiritual—impinge on one's selfhood. (This is unlike the American conception of the individual in which the ideology suggests personal responsibility for one's position in life, to the extent that a cancer-stricken person is considered responsible to help stop death by controlling the tumor from spreading.)

Several Iranian friends of mine in Jerusalem mentioned that they never revealed their innermost thoughts to anyone—this in answer to my question why they said they would miss me when I return to the United States. They had confided in me, but not in each other, I found out. They did not want other Iranians, they said, to know they were weak. Weakness or powerlessness, as the sociopolitical side of sensitivity in social relationships, also has a physical aspect, in that sensitive people may also be weak regarding the physical environment and thus become sick. The combination of the social and physical sides of powerlessness and weakness are portrayed in a recent advertisement for a new translation of a book by the late Iranian writer, Jalal Al-i Ahmad, in which Mizan Press of California, an Iranian-owned publishing house, writes a short biographical statement about Al-i Ahmad, an intellectual dissatisfied with Iran's Westernization. They conclude, "He died in 1969, weakened by years of tireless intellectual, literary, and political activity." Here, weakness is illustrated as socially caused, with physical repercussions of sickness and death.

Because of the situation created by the concept that individuals are essentially sensitive, combined with the recognized social hierarchy and its demands of proper communication codes between individuals, and the everyday problems that individuals run into, people always experience some type of distress, or nārāhati. Things that one cannot control make one nārāhat. If someone is sensitive and cannot regulate the circumstances which engender nārāhati, the person is in more or less a powerless position regarding his or her sociopersonal situation. Being nārāhat exemplifies the social shame of being weak. If one shows weakness or powerlessness, others could take advantage of one in the nārāhat state. Thus, nārāhati is generated by and generates conceptions of powerlessness in the hierarchy of social relations. What constitutes and causes nārāhati, how and to whom people express it, depends upon an individual's relationships within the social hierarchy of intimates and non-intimates, and on the knowledge that others, too, are sensitive, and zerang.

"People Always Have a Nārāhati in This World"

Suzanne is a Western-educated multilingual Iranian woman whom I knew in Tehran and encountered by chance in Jerusalem after the Islamic Revolution. In discussing nārāhati, she explained it in English as "disappointment" and "depression." When I asked her what causes nārāhati, she replied, "People always have a nārāhati in this world. Obstacles always stop someone from reaching his goal, which leads to disappointment, which leads to depression, which leads to health problems, which makes someone be nārāhat all the time. . . . Things get in the way—where one lives, sickness, the difficult life one leads, change of place. Moving from Iran to Israel makes alot of people nārāhat." How does she know if someone is nārāhat? "Sometimes from the physical appearance. The person might not be as lively as usual. Or you can see depression on the face, or the person's face is pale." Her answer was similar to the doctor quoted in the beginning of this chapter, who said that he knows someone is nārāhat "from the face without speaking. The smile isn't a smile—the eyes aren't smiling."

Nārāhati—discomfort, distress, worry—is an undifferentiated dysphoric affect in Iranian culture whose meaning and expression relate to the cultural concept of the person as sensitive in a system of hierarchical social relations. Different events induce distress in different people, and culture determines what is perceived as distressful. The sensitive person who cognizes distressing situations—whether familial, economic, personal, political, physical, and so on—interprets and evaluates the experience and determines whether or not to express the feelings. Nārāhati as an emotion signifies exposed sensitivity, of being under the influence of social situations which engendered the dysphoric affect, and therefore being powerless, vulnerable, weak. When one feels nārāhat, the mode of expression is determined by the social relations in which the person is engaged.

Nārāhati must be guarded against by others and, if felt, expressed in specific verbal, nonverbal, or aesthetic idioms—or not expressed at all. The nonexpression of nārāhati is due to fear of exposing powerlessness, apprehension that others will take advantage of one, and care to avoid making others, especially those close intimates of one's family, nārāhat also. If they are sensitive, they will both perceive the nārāhati of another and, depending upon the relationship, become nārāhat too.

Sensitivity, as the perceptive and observant aspect of one's character as well as the reactive quality to one's personal and social situation, highlights peoples' observation of others' verbal and nonverbal communication: the eyes as indicating inner feelings; intonation of words as well as choice of words as manifesting thought and sentiment; gestures as connoting propriety and politesse or aberration and indecency. Regarding nārāhati expression, people consciously try regulating their behavior in front of others while watching for clues, searching for bits of information about the other's feelings, constantly on guard for the dysphoric affect of nārāhati to rise to the surface on the face of the other. People in Iran, and Iranians abroad, consciously and sometimes unconsciously mask their own nārāhati. This management of communication and information is the zerang aspect of people who are sensitive, nārāhat, and fear exposing the powerlessness they feel.

An individual's perception of his or her nārāhati influences whether he or she will manifest or hide it, express it verbally or nonverbally, or mask it consciously (or unconsciously). Revelation depends on the social context, where one is, with whom, and what the nārāhati is. This is related to conceptions of the sensitivity of the individual—one's vulnerability which is manifested in already being nārāhat, and the possibility of making others nārāhat—and to conceptions of social hierarchy with people of different statuses and different ranges of intimacy who can be trusted with information that may be personal. One can verbally reveal what I call a "public" nārāhati—something that others have also experienced—to one's intimates, and sometimes to one's non-intimates, depending on what the nārāhati is. With one's non-intimates, the closeness necessary to nārāhati revelation is nonexistent. To verbally disclose a "private" nārāhati, however, something which an individual feels is a personal, secret problem, to intimates or non-intimates of equal or lower status is a touchy matter. Once again, it could indicate personal weakness or powerlessness, about which others are not trusted, or it could induce nārāhati in others. Culture and relationships determine what constitute the social boundaries which govern emotion expression, who is to be trusted, and who is to be regarded with suspicion. Anything disclosed becomes a permanent part of relationships between people, especially with those intimates with whom one will be associated the rest of one's life. Where one can break relations more easily, such caution in revelation of information about oneself is not so necessary. Therefore, private nārāhati may be revealed to distant non-intimates of higher or totally foreign status, people with whom one has no vested interests, who are not in the network of intimates and non-intimates whose knowledge of one is potentially dangerous, appealing to the other's sense of noblesse oblige to help one get rid of the nārāhati or to gain sympathy.

The nārāhati that is expressed verbally is often a "public" or common nārāhati—some situation or happening that others could identify with, possibly feel, sympathize with, react to, or help ameliorate, such as being nārāhat from not receiving a letter, from waiting in line for buses, from hearing news on the radio, from new shoes which give blisters. In this situation people use the term nārāhat to define the feeling and the situation which causes it. However, frequently people will talk about their troubles and the problems bothering them without mentioning the word nārāhat in their conversations in reference to themselves, but do use it in reference to others' behavior. For instance, while I was in Iran during the Islamic Revolution, many Jews complained to me—the distant person of foreign status not affiliated with the community except by religious background—about the Jews being nārāhat because of the political situation. In the company of friends and relatives inside the walled compounds of their houses, people sometimes spoke openly about being nārāhat, but more often would talk about their problems and fears, never mentioning the word nārāhat. To non-Jews, of course, nothing was said because of mistrust that expression of their feelings would invite retaliation against the community.

More common than verbalizing nārāhati is expressing it nonverbally. The nonverbal expression connotes one's feelings, but it also creates an obligation in social relationships for sensitive others to respond to one's signals and act to ameliorate one's problems or to create a semblance of rāhati, comfort. The nārāhati expressed nonverbally is usually a private, personal problem, one that others cannot share or have not experienced in the same way as the person who feels distressed, such as specific family matters, economic troubles, embarrassment, and fear of failing school; or it may be a "public" societal situation of social or political events that one is powerless to resolve, such as war. Both types of nārāhati indicate personal sensitivity to social life.

Nonverbal expression of nārāhati is idiomatically expressed in three ways: (1) silence, quietness, and sulkiness, indicative of the sensitive person; (2) avoidance of food, signifying withdrawal from social interaction (as does the first) and potential physical danger; (3) sometimes, more among women than among men, crying, connoting emotionality, the exposure rather than concealment of feeling. "The wife gets upset immediately. She cries," explained an Iranian friend in Jerusalem. "The man goes to the crazy house (H., *beit mishuga'im*). He holds it in more and then he explodes."

Thus, without saying "I'm nārāhat," people express their feelings nonverbally, calling attention to themselves in the presence of others who could try to make them rāhat. The following three cases, in which I was involved, exemplify the nonverbal expression of nārāhati—the first two in Iran during the Revolution, the third in Israel after the Revolution:

[*Iran*] Mr. Ibrahimian was very upset when he came home from the synagogue, seeming quiet and agitated. He sat down at the table, which had just been set, and called his two young children who were watching television. But he did not wait for them to come to the table before starting the *kiddush*, the prayer over wine. They ran to the table. During dinner he lowered his head on the table, resting his forehead on the edge, saying nothing. The family knew he was upset but did not ask why since they knew that he, as father and head of the family, would tell them nothing.

[*Iran*] Firooz invited me for lunch. We sat and ate, listening to Iranian music on tapes and talking. Firooz ate very little, but kept telling me to "*bekhor*" (eat!). I asked why he doesn't eat. He is nārāhat. Why? Because of the situation. He told me that in yesterday's newspaper there was an article about Khomeini saying that the Jews have too high positions in Iranian society and that there are only 70,000 of them in Iran. And in today's paper there was an article taken from a Tel Aviv newspaper saying that Khomeini has sent flowers to the chief *hakham* [literally, wiseman (Hebrew); used in Iran by Jews as a title for religious leader] of Tehran. Since the two reports were contradictory in their contents, and in the implications of Khomeini's actions, the Jews are afraid, he said.

[*Israel*. Firooz and his mother, Mrs. Khalili, spent a month in Israel the summer of 1979. The following incident occurred at his mother's sister's house in a village near Haifa.] Firooz mentioned his mother hadn't eaten dinner or breakfast. When I was alone with Mrs. Khalili on the patio, I asked her why she hadn't eaten. She said she is nārāhat, and upon my probing, she said her daughter who lives in Israel and whom she hadn't seen in five years wants her to immigrate. But she said she can't since her husband is in Iran and they have their house which they cannot sell because there have been no buyers since the Revolution. When I asked why they cannot come to Israel without selling their house, she started to cry, and I felt terrible. I tried comforting her by asking about her grandchildren and by saying that things will turn out better in Iran. She stopped crying. Then Firooz walked out of the house and saw that something had happened to his mother. He asked what was the matter. She replied it was nothing, then walked to the edge of the patio and vomited. Firooz said, "What's this?" and put his arm around her and brought her back to sit down. He said this was happening because she didn't eat.

Her sister also said it was because she didn't eat, and she told her daughters, who were standing and staring at their aunt, to make tea and bring out some food. Sitting around the table, discussion turned to Mrs. Khalili's marriage. She was twelve when she married and her husband was twenty-five. She didn't want to get married, but she did not know what was going on, and she couldn't say no even if she wanted to. Her first child was born when she was fourteen.

Later I went with Firooz for a walk. He said he wanted to tell me why his mother was nārāhat. It had to do with his sister's husband who was married before and has two children, now fifteen and sixteen, from his first marriage, and the boys are crazy: they run away and steal. The mother is worried for her daughter and her grandchildren—maybe they will be crazy too or maybe the two crazy sons will be bothering her daughter.

The above three cases represent nārāhati expressed nonverbally: excessive quietness and sulkiness in the first case, not eating in the second, and not eating and crying in the third. In all three cases, the nārāhat person seems to have been powerless, not in control of the situation that was making him or her nārāhat. Mr. Ibrahimian, who often walked through the streets during the period of strikes and demonstrations of the Revolution, heard rumors and saw actions which he did not discuss with his family because he did not want them to be more nārāhat than they already were. But with his jewelery store forcibly closed along with other small businesses in the strike organized by the revolutionaries, he could not avoid showing his nārāhati since he was, as the doctor quoted at the beginning of this chapter said, "at the top of his nārāhati, and has passed all the borders." Firooz also felt powerless about the situation in Iran and showed his nārāhati to me by not eating; yet he admitted he was nārāhat when asked. Likewise, his mother was powerless concerning what she saw as her daughter's problems, which were family problems for her too, and she showed her nārāhati to her family by not eating. But to me, an outsider with whom association was transitory and thus safe, she verbalized her feeling nārāhat, while to her family she said nothing. In discussing her early marriage, she also revealed her inability back then to effect an outcome: others were making decisions for her. Here, too, she was powerless. Her son, aware of his mother's worries, knew her nārāhati and was able to talk to me about it, but not to his mother, nor to his relatives.

In addition to the verbal and nonverbal expression of nārāhati, people may opt to mask their dysphoria by neither talking about it nor displaying nonverbal signals. The rationale for camouflaging nārāhati is threefold: (1) the concept that nārāhati connotes personal powerlessness that distrusted others could exploit; (2) the belief that it sometimes signifies *qesmat,* or fate, the situation in life with which one is stuck and can do nothing about (this, too, is related to feelings of powerlessness); (3) the concern that exposure of nārāhati will make another person nārāhat. This silence regarding nārāhati expression usually occurs with intimates, when someone is living in close connection, emotionally and/or physically, with someone else who is unable to help the nārāhat person or who may already be upset about something else, or when one does not trust the other enough. The nonrevelation of personal, private nārāhati is illustrated in the following cases:

[*Iran*] In a discussion concerning nārāhati, Bahram mentioned two examples involving his family. One concerned problems his sister was having with her husband. They were living in Abadan. She called home in Isfahan and spoke to their father. The father and Bahram went down to Abadan to straighten things out. They did not tell the mother because they didn't want to make her nārāhat. There was nothing she could do about the situation, so why bother worrying her. Anyway, he said, she has diabetes, so they didn't want to make her sicker. Another example of nārāhati Bahram gave was of his father who was sick once a few years ago. For several weeks he went to a doctor and took medicine, but no one in the family knew, because he didn't want to make them nārāhat. He told them only when he was better.

[*Israel*] Monir, a twenty-nine-year-old married woman with three young children, came to Israel as a single woman seven years ago. She told me she feels alone, isolated, and quite nārāhat living in Jerusalem while her parents and siblings are in Tel Aviv. She said she was nārāhat in Iran because her family was poor and her father took a second wife. In Jerusalem she is nārāhat from being alone. She voiced being nervous and tired from having three children so close in age that all she was doing was washing diapers but she did not use the word nārāhat to describe the problems of motherhood. When asked if she talks about or shows her nārāhati, she replied, "No. I hide my nārāhati inside. Or I would make others nārāhat. I don't want others to know. Why should others know what problems I've got?"

The above examples of masking nārāhati pertain to the closeness of familial relations and to the sensitivity that others, also susceptible, perceptive, and unable to do anything to ameliorate the situation which caused the nārāhati, should not, also, become nārāhat. For several people in the family to be nārāhat would create a situation where the family as a unit, vis-à-vis other families as units in the society, might not function. Bahram's sister's marriage difficulties indicate familial and social problems for Iranian Jews, since divorce is a rare and dishonorable occurrence. She appealed to her father, as the most intimate high-status person she knew and who probably had considerable influence concerning her husband, for help. By keeping this problem from her mother, who is deemed already nārāhat with diabetes, and by keeping his own illness concealed from his family, Bahram's father prevents others from being nārāhat while simultaneously enacting his position as decision maker and head of the family. He exemplifies the strength of character which nārāhati revelation could weaken. Monir keeps her nārāhati inside, telling no one, since she feels there is nothing they can do, and it is considered disgraceful for others to know of her personal problems. The person who masks nārāhati creates an external appearance which differs from the internal state. This masking of nārāhati is zerang, as it prevents intimates from becoming nārāhat as well as preventing non-intimates from knowing one is weak or powerless.

In addition to masking personal nārāhati, people avoid telling someone about something that could cause nārāhati in the hearer. Because most people are considered to be sensitive, negative information which could engender nārāhati is often not revealed, especially if there is nothing that can be done. Over and over again I heard people say that they will not tell someone something because the person will be nārāhat. The prevention of nārāhati by noncommunication of what is perceived to be negative information is represented by the following illustrations:

> [*Iran*] Shireen said that one of her closest friends, a Muslim woman, had asked her if it is true that Jews send money to Israel. Shireen said no, that they give money to poor Jews in Iran, that if a family cannot afford food or clothing, the community will help them. Shireen said she would not tell her mother what her friend said because it would make her mother nārāhat.

> [*Israel*] Khosrow had invited me for dinner at his mother's house. He said that his mother was very nārāhat since his father's death three years ago, and for the first two years she wore only black and would not leave the house. But now she is just getting out of it. We had arrived at her house after seeing Shahla and Yossi, her daughter and son-in-law. She asked why they didn't come. Khosrow said that Yossi was tired since he had gone to the Dead Sea. She asked how he looks. I said that he is sunburned and Khosrow said that his skin is brown. I said it looked reddish to me. His mother hit the back of her left hand with her right hand and said, "*Heyf-eh*" ["It's a pity"]. Khosrow later told me he didn't want his mother to know about Yossi's sunburn since she would be nārāhat.

Shireen perceived her friend's question as antagonistic toward Jews helping Jews in Israel, and was afraid her mother would think so also, and thus opted not to tell her mother what her friend had asked. Khosrow's mother's reaction to my comment about her son-in-law revealed sensitivity for his condition. It also revealed, to me, that I had invaded private territory, having commented on something that I should not have mentioned. Had I been Iranian, I probably would have perceived and understood the cues Khosrow gave me, and would have mentioned nothing. However, as an American unfamiliar with the codes of conduct that are part of Iranian personal boundary regulations, Iranian conceptions of privacy, the cultural rules regarding expression of dysphoric affect and what causes dysphoric feelings, and how these feelings could be socially disruptive, I acted as I did.

The avoidance of telling someone something that could cause nārāhati includes several important features: involvement in intimate or protective relationships; responsibility for the rāhati (comfort) and well-being of others; concern for the sensitivity of the other person; knowledge that the other is powerless to do anything about the situation that might make him or her nārāhat; the possibility of making someone feel even more powerless. The relationship between masking negative information and nārāhati prevention, unlike my clumsy attempts in the letter incident related at the beginning of this chapter, concerns other problems as well. The person who is not nārāhat but who can prevent others from being nārāhat by controlling negative information is zerang. In the cases related above (the supposedly ill health of a son in California in the letter incident, the marriage troubles of a daughter, the contrary questioning of a close friend, the sunburn of a son-in-law), the negative information consisted of information which could induce nārāhati in someone else. In these cases the internal sensitivity of people is brought to the surface by the presumably negative or dangerous situations of someone close to them. This, then, is the danger of negative information: the disruption of the balance of rāhati, the balance assuring one's social, physical, and emotional well-being. But negative information has to do with other issues as well, issues which create a lack of balance in social relationships, such as ill health, loss, political trouble, arguments. As I had not quite understood the concepts of negative information and nārāhati causation, I had unintentionally made the Yaghoobis nārāhat because of the letter, and had also made Khosrow's mother nārāhat because I "un-zerang-ly" admitted her son-in-law was sunburned.

The situations which caused nārāhati in the cases above concern either macrosocial problems which create feelings of powerlessness in the individuals who are unable to do anything but who are affected by the goings-on (the Revolution, economic problems), or interpersonal, often familial, relationships which are troubled and which must be managed in order to insure familial efficaciousness and continuity. Socialization in Iranian culture demands that individuals consider family problems as primary, and personal problems as less important. To refrain from creating family problems in a social context where everyone is sensitive to the plight of others within the familial unit, and where familial units are in opposition to one another within the society, the nārāhat person will often conceal nārāhati from others in an attempt at self-control when actually fearing lack of control. Thus, nārāhati as an emotion is disruptive of social relations and it is communicated in culturally distinctive ways (quietness, not eating) or concealed.

The nārāhati which is not communicated to others exemplified in the last four examples differs from the nārāhati that is disclosed nonverbally. Disclosure initiates interpersonal negotiations in the familial or friendship setting in which others then become responsible for interpreting and ameliorating one's nārāhati. In a way, disclosure of nārāhati through excessive sullenness or refusal to eat creates, through revelation of sensitivity of problems in life, power in the ability to manipulate intimate others when one feels powerless about other things in life.

Only when nārāhati becomes a chronic coping style which disrupts family life through dysfunction of the distressed person do Iranians in Israel seek care; however, the care they seek is medical for somatic rather than for psychosocial problems.

Nārāhati, then, as a rhetoric of dysphoria, is both acute and chronic. People can be nārāhat for a few minutes, such as when a bus driver screams at a mother who permits her toddler to walk in the aisle; for a number of days, such as when one waits for a letter which doesn't come; for weeks, such as when a businessman loses money; or for months, such as when refugees or immigrants try to get accustomed to a new sociocultural system. The nārāhati that people feel and express depends upon their interpretation of the situation, an interpretation, as the examples above depict, which is culturally constituted. Undifferentiated nārāhati thus has different meanings and uses depending upon context, situation, and relationships. Its expression varies from verbally mentioning feeling nārāhat, to nonverbally showing it, to masking it altogether. In Iranian culture, where social interaction requires communicative control, nārāhati is an emotion showing that one is out of control—that one is sensitive, and possibly powerless and weak—if one's outer appearance fails to conceal that something is bothersome. Consequently, most people avoid verbalizing their nārāhati to non-intimates who could conceivably take advantage of them for their exposed vulnerability, or to intimates who could, as people sensitive to one's plight, also become nārāhat. For the most part, therefore, nārāhati is camouflaged so that others will be unaware of one's emotional state, or it is disclosed in an allusive way, appealing to others to be cognizant of how one feels. However, two types of emotion expression—sometimes referred to an nārāhati but more often further differentiated into anger (*asabāniyat*) and sorrow or sadness (*ghamgini*)—are not masked. These two emotions are acted out, in certain contexts, with certain people.

Differentiated Nārāhati: Anger and Sadness

The word for anger, asabāniyat, is derived from the Arabic word for nerve, *asab*. The term does not mean "nervousness" but, rather, the condition of the nerves not properly functioning which then creates anger. The adjective, angry, is *asabāni*. Another term is *nārāhati-ye asab*, "nerve distress," connoting the physical aspect of nārāhati as related to the expression of anger. This physical aspect was described once by an Iranian postal clerk in Jerusalem, who related the emotional and physical: "When I'm nārāhat I lose weight [from not eating—one of the signs of nārāhati]. It can make you lose weight. Nārāhati gives people nerves. No patience. When people feel really bothered by nerves they say, 'My nerves are very upset [distressed, troubled, bothered, etc.] (*asābam kheyli nārāhat-eh*).' "

To be angry is to be out of control. In Iranian society, where mastery of social communication is prescribed, the demonstration of anger could entail personal or familial embarrassment or shame, a possible breach in social relationships, or damage to one's reputation. The antisocial behavior manifested by the angry person stands in opposition to the ideal person who is sensitive to others, quiet and calm, who speaks gently, respects and honors others, is concerned about the social and physical comfort (rāhati) of other people, and is in control of himself/herself in social interaction. By contrast, the asabāni person displays a lack of sensitivity to others, loudness and agitation, screams, does not respect others and, in fact, makes those around him or her nārāhat, and is thus not in self-control in social interaction.

Expression of anger toward others depends on one's relationships within the hierarchy of intimates and non-intimates. Ideally, a lower-status person should not show anger by yelling or screaming at a person of higher status, whether intimate or non-intimate. A child does not show anger to a parent or an adult. Because women are considered to be, by nature, more emotional than men, they can display their nārāhati by crying, suffering in silence or, much less socially acceptable, by shouting. Men, on the other hand, considered rational, may keep their nārāhati inside them until they explode in anger, a feeling that is greatly feared because of its consequences (showing one is out of control, breach of social relationships, violent behavior toward one's family). Regarding anger in situations of high- to low-status relationships, we can generalize that a father can express anger to his children, as can a husband to his wife, or an employer to his employee. Although anger is sometimes expressed to non-intimates of all statuses, there is always the possibility that the ramifications of its expression will fall back on oneself, one's family, and one's position in society as a member of a certain class, ethnic, or religious group. It is because of the social danger of displaying anger in public that Beeman (1976b:41) writes that anger expressed by men in public is usually ritualized through "invoking religious oaths, trying to fight (and being held back by onlookers), turning red, being extremely vociferous, and proclaiming the entire reason for his anger to anyone who can hear."

Yousef, a middle-aged Iranian man in therapy for depression, explained the expression of nārāhati and anger:

> Only in the house they show nārāhati. They don't say it is nārāhati. They say it is something I'm nervous (*atzbani*—Hebrew) about. But usually I behave and manage alright. They don't know I'm nārāhat. It's a degradation. My wife and children know. They suffer. I yell and scream. In my family I can't tell my brother I'm nārāhat, but

friends will tell friends. Maybe because one brother has a better condition—I don't want my brother to be nārāhat because of me.[11]

Yousef's nārāhati—his degradation—is internalized, hidden from his brothers (status equals), and its causes kept hidden from his family. His wife and children (lower-status) know he is nārāhat because of his anger. His brothers and other people do not, he says, know he is nārāhat at all, and to them he would not show his anger.

However, in spite of the negative connotations of anger and the norms concerning to whom one may show anger, the person who displays anger is often not held responsible for his or her actions, as the outbursts may be blamed on "sick nerves." In spite of provocations or causes for anger—like a pent-up nārāhati—if one's nerves were not malfunctioning, one would not exhibit the antisocial behavior of anger. Anger is thus considered to be a somatopsychic phenomenon, with possible social precipitations, and definite social repercussions.

Sorrow or sadness, *ghamgini*, on the other hand, is a deeply felt nārāhati, one which can be "seen from the face." Sorrow, grief, sadness, worry—*gham* or *ghoseh*—are almost poetic feelings in Persian culture: sadness expressed as conveying the tragic of life is a valued emotion (see Good and Good 1985), and many times sadness is expressed verbally through poetry, just as poetry is used to depict the sadness of the human condition. Famous Persian poets employ the term *gham*—sad—over and over again in their poetry. Epic poems, such as *Layli and Majnun*, *Shireen and Farhad*, and the *Shahnameh*, portray grief and loss in terms of war, love, and family. Shi'ite religious tradition observes a month of mourning, Moharram, commemorating the death of Hussein, martyred by the Caliph Yazid at Karbala, and the reading of the story of Hussein's death at religious encounters known as *rowzeh*s, induce open ritualized weeping from the participants. And at funerals of all religious groups in Iran, ritualized weeping and expression of grief occurs. Grief and sorrow, then, are public and social as well as private and personal emotions.

Grief, sorrow, and sadness are indicative of a loss—the loss of a person, a livelihood, a country, a desire—and can thus be more long-lasting and fundamental concerning one's inner essence than a temporary nārāhati. Ghamgini is a private emotion publicly expressed, suggestive of the sensitive person in a positive, sociocentric, and aesthetic sense, connoting external expression of what is felt internally. Ghamgini, as opposed to undifferentiated nārāhati depicted in the previous section, is valued as expressing the tragic in life, which is so much a part of the Iranian religious, historical, and aesthetic traditions. To declare one's grief or sorrow, verbally and nonverbally, is not connotative of personal weakness, as with a private nārāhati. The issues one grieves or is sad about are the social problems deeply embedded in the Iranian social and cultural milieu and life in general (loss, death, separation), which everyone, at one time or another, experiences. It does indicate, however, the powerlessness of the individual person who cannot control the wheel of destiny. These sorrow-inducing social problems which engender ghamgini expression differ from the private existential problems which are best kept concealed to avoid familial disruption or disclosure of personal powerlessness or weakness. Ghamgini expression does not indicate such powerlessness, as does undifferentiated nārāhati, since it is valued as an expression of honesty (internal feelings revealed) and personal profundity.[12]

Poetry is used as an idiom, mostly by men, to express one's grief or sadness.[13] Reciting a line of Hāfez, Rumi, or Kayyām calls attention to one's internal state, which the poet and countless others have also experienced, and discloses a deep, sensitive, and pensive person. Two cases from Israel, one man who recites poetic phrases from biblical sources in Hebrew, and another who writes lines of Persian poetry, illustrate the connection between sensitivity, self, others, nārāhati, sadness, and poetry:

> Amir immigrated from Iran to Palestine in 1945 at the age of fifteen, later married an Iranian woman, and set up, unsuccessfully, a jewelry business in Jerusalem. When I saw him, he was in treatment for depression. "I am a very sensitive person," he said while explaining nārāhati. "I know when someone is nārāhat. I try to understand him. There is a phrase in Hebrew that I found last week in the synagogue when I picked up a book. I opened it to a page and saw the sentence, "There is no doctor like the experienced one" (H., "*Ain rofeh ke-ba'al nisayon*"). No one really understands another's nārāhati except the person who has it, but you try to understand him. . . . From the face you can feel it. The light of the face doesn't live. His cheeks fall down. There is a phrase either by Samuel or Kohelet [Ecclesiastes]: "Happiness of a person is portrayed on his face" (H., "*Simkhat adam tsiyer panav*").
>
> Iraj, a twenty-seven-year-old Tehrani who left Iran in December 1979, was living as a volunteer on a kibbutz, waiting for the appropriate time to return to Iran. Above his bed on the kibbutz was a photograph of himself sleeping, and next to it he pinned a quotation from a poem: "Sorrow of this sleeping one breaks sleep in my wet eyes" (P., "*Gham-e in khofte chand khāb dar cheshm-e taram mishkanad*"). He said that the Jews wrote this when Ayatollah Taleghani died (September 9, 1979) because they liked him. Under this quote was another, perhaps from Rumi or Khayyām, Iraj said. His uncle wrote it when he saw what Iraj had written: "For how long do you want to grieve this mean world. Drink wine. It's a pity that the wise one's heart would be distressed" (P., "*Gham-e donyā-i dani chand khori. Bādeh benush. Heyf bāshad del-i dānā keh moshavvash bāshad*"). When looking at the picture of himself sleeping, Iraj said, "That's Uri [his Hebrew name given to him by the kibbutz Hebrew teacher]. I'm no longer Iraj. That Iraj was someone with ideas who knew how to think and to work on

his ideas. Uri is a totally different person, someone who doesn't think and who just does the same routine."

Like many Iranians in Israel who translated Persian concepts into Hebrew ones, Amir resorted to biblical quotations rather than Iranian poetry to express his feelings to a non-Iranian. Iraj, however, drew upon the Iranian literary tradition of Sufi poetry to evoke his sentiments. The use of poetry as an aesthetic idiom to publicly express one's private feelings elicits sympathy in others and provides a way to communicate sentiments which are indicative of a cultural aesthetic of the person—one who is sensitive, and thus one who suffers. Recitation of Sufi poetry also signifies safā-yi bātin, inner purity. Iraj's sorrow is his loss of country and loss of self, expressed through lines of poetry which evoke tears, sleep, sorrow, the momentary world (the kibbutz), wine (the Sufi symbol of inebriation connoting the mystical path to God), and the distressed heart. Iraj felt powerless about his present position as he had planned to stay in Israel for only a month or two and was suddenly confronted with the possibility of returning to Iran to face being jailed, killed, or sent to fight on the Iraqi front. His nārāhati was one of loss and grief, sadness and sorrow, a nārāhati whose inner feeling, like anger, was expressed outwardly, both verbally and nonverbally.

Both anger and sorrow are types of nārāhati in which the external state reflects internal feeling: they are differentiated emotions as opposed to the undifferentiated term nārāhat. The undifferentiated nārāhati can be denied. Anger and sorrow cannot be. They are visible. Yet, like the undifferentiated, mostly masked emotion nārāhati, anger and sorrow are (visible) emotional expressions indicating the individual's powerlessness in social situations.

Anger and sorrow are thus indicative of the individual bound by a system of social relationships to whom these emotional expressions are revealed: anger disvalued as disruptive, sorrow valued as profound. These dysphoric emotions symbolize, for the persons experiencing, interpreting, and expressing them, the sociocultural conceptions of powerlessness of sensitive people experiencing situations and living in a world that they cannot determine, a world which subjugates them, to which they are subordinate. Expression of dysphoric affect, therefore, indicates that they feel this lack of control, powerlessness, weakness, in relations with others, with intimates or non-intimates, or as an individual trying to make sense of life and the world itself. Revelation of dysphoric affect indicates sensitivity, but concealment connotes control and cleverness, zerangi.

Powerlessness and Nārāhati

The difference between internal state and external action have been themes in Iranian religious tradition, both Islamic and Jewish, as well as in human interaction. The outward appearance, *zāher*, is the external conduct, in the religious lexicon, the exoteric meaning of a text; the esoteric meaning of a text is the *bātin*, the interior, the heart, mind, conscience. This is what Bateson et al. (1977) refer to when they discuss safā-yi bātin, inner purity, the Sufi concept. The constructs of the individual character as sensitive and zerang reflect the same concepts and constructs: the sensitive aspect of the person is the interior, and the zerang the exterior. The ethnopsychology of the individual in Iranian society as sensitive and zerang in a hierarchical world of distrusted others sheds light on the understanding of the meaning of emotions as informing, and being informed by, concepts of human nature and social relations in Iranian society.

These motifs of inner essence and external action, private and public, and sensitive and zerang relate to expression of nārāhati and to other aspects of social relations. What is of interest is not the verbal expression of nārāhati, through which the nārāhat person engages others in his or her problems by talking about them, gaining sympathy and/or help. Rather, the nonverbal expression of nārāhati, and even more so, its masking, are socially and culturally significant because of the ways in which masking nārāhati is related to the cultural values of the person. Masking in this context, unlike nonverbal expression, is a way of acting to disguise that one feels nārāhat by attempting not to display any dysphoric affect: if emotions such as nārāhati are not communicated or expressed, others do not know how one feels. In addition, the nonexpression of nārāhati is associated with the cultural values of the person (internally sensitive, externally zerang), hierarchical social relationships, and interpretation and communication of information in Iranian society. These values are depicted, as in the disguising of nārāhati, in the differentiation between internal state (nārāhat) and outer action (not nārāhat). Because of Iranian social hierarchy, the feelings of powerlessness that individuals have within the hierarchy, the knowledge of individual sensitivity, and the resultant self- and other-protectiveness, individuals conceal their nārāhati in order not to make others nārāhat or to expose one's weakness in being nārāhat which might invite exploitation by distrusted others. Thus, masking nārāhati conceals personal powerlessness, whereas nonverbal expression of nārāhati subtly enables the manipulation of others via their awareness of one's emotional state.

Messages concealed by individuals in the hierarchy of social relations in Iran reverberate into a world where people interpret situations, meanings, and actions as having hidden intentions. Thus, the differences between internal state and external action, as in the masked nārāhati, exist not only on the personal level, in transactions between individuals, but also on the societal level. Events are construed as having a symbolic meaning behind them. Two illustrations concerning the Islamic Revolution exemplify this focus on searching for hidden messages:

> [*Iran*, told by Muslims]: Israeli soldiers were used to kill people in Jaleh Square [near the Majles—parliament—where many people were killed on September 7, 1978, during an anti-shah demonstration]. Someone had seen them and they were blond, blue-eyed men who weren't speaking Persian, but some other language, which must have been Hebrew. Besides, Muslims wouldn't kill Muslims.
>
> [*Iran*] Discussions regarding Khomeini centered on the possibility of Khomeini being a fake. If he had been in prison for so long and then escaped to Iraq, maybe this is actually a younger man posing as Khomeini for the government. Perhaps the shah is having him say all these things in order to gain more control on the people and be more oppressive. Maybe Khomeini is a spy for Russia or the United States, being used against the Iranian regime.
>
> [*Israel*] Discussions concerning the shah's downfall focused on three reasons:
>
> a. The United States put Khomeini in power to make sure that Iran would not become a communist country, like Afghanistan, and they would ensure this by establishing an Islamic regime which would be strongly opposed to communism.
>
> b. In five to ten years Iran will become so backward that they would need the help of the United States, and so the U.S. would be gaining more in the long run than they are losing now.
>
> c. Iranians were getting too smart and soon would not be relying on American aid, and the U.S. would be losing a market. So the Americans had the Khomeini regime established in order to make the country backward, which would result in "b" above.

Such examples reveal a culturally determined way of conceiving underlying symbolic meanings in the world. Like the Persians described by Lady Sheil, my friends who voiced their political philosophies were "ever in the watch to discover . . . intrigues, falsehoods, and finesses." Like the individuals who conceal their private internal nārāhati or negative news in front of others, the internal meaning of events is concealed by external action. Like individuals who feel powerless in society, Iran is powerless in the world of nations. For example, most Iranian Jews believe that the Revolution was a creation of President Carter, not a result of sociopolitical forces within Iranian society. Iran is not controlled by Iranians; rather, external powers—England, Russia, the United States—have determined its fate.

The individual, as mentioned before, is also controlled by external forces—the family, the *jinn* (supernatural spirit), the evil eye, the political situation, economic problems.[14] But at the same time, the individual does control his or her own communication. Many scholars writing about Iranian society explain Iranian impression management, or dissimulation, as an outgrowth of *taqiyya*, the Shi'ite doctrine of concealing one's true religious beliefs to protect oneself and one's community from religious persecution to defend Islam and to expand Shi'ism, primarily against Sunnis.[15] Although dissimulation is a human universal, taqiyya as a concept of religious dissimulation is something known primarily by the Shi'ite religious establishment (non-Muslims and nonreligious or illiterate Muslims with whom I spoke were not familiar with the term). As a religious concept, it existed before Islam in Iranian Judaism: Gordon (1977) exemplifies how religious dissimulation is used in the Book of Esther, and the Talmud mentions that a Jew could declare himself a Zoroastrian in order to avoid paying the capitation tax during Sassanian rule (Widengren 1961:151–52).

Everyone "dissimulates" in Iranian society and, in varying degrees, in other societies as well. Rather than arguing that it is a result of taqiyya, which is a late development in Iranian culture, I would argue that concealing one's true beliefs and feelings is a way of protecting oneself and one's family in a situation where people feel powerless and where revelation of one's inner feelings could lead to adverse reactions, socially and personally. Concealment occurs with ta'arof on a public level concerning non-intimates, and with nārāhati on a private level concerning intimates.

In conclusion, we can see nārāhati as an emotion rooted within Iranian culture, generated by and generating a hierarchical system in which inner feeling differs from outer action and the sensitive interior differs from the zerang exterior. The interpretation of nārāhati shows that emotion expression and cognition, as well as events which generate emotion in individuals, reflect and are reflected by the concept of the person in society and in social relations. Nārāhati is not necessarily centered within the individual, as Western psychology would have it; nor is it an emotion which can always be detected facially or biochemically, as many psychologists and psychiatrists would expect. Rather, it is an emotion symbolic of the interface between personal and social experience, related to the concept of the sensitive individual. Nārāhati is an emotion held private, ideally camouflaged in front of others, rarely verbalized when deeply felt. As a consequence, in Iranian culture, which is filled with communicative and societal disjunctions requiring an individual to be in continuous self-control, nārāhati is an idiom metaphoric of personal powerlessness.

Chapter 4
Immigration, Communication, and Stereotypes

An Iranian refugee in Israel once told me:

> When I'm in Iran, when I'm talking to someone older than I am, I will say *shomā* [you, formal and/or plural]. We usually speak respectfully. Here I couldn't see it or feel it. The space between two people is not like it is in Iran. . . . They don't care about their children as we do. They don't say no—they say we shouldn't be afraid of anything because we have to fight the Arabs. They are ready to destroy everything. They have no moral borders or social borders. After two minutes an Israeli lets himself touch a girl he just met.

And an Israeli lawyer whose family came from Iraq five generations ago offered this view of Iranians:

> Iranians are not trustworthy. They will do anything and lower themselves to make a tiny bit of money. [He drew a ladder on a piece of paper and then drew a line under the ladder.] You can do business with anyone, and they won't go beneath this line—even an Arab. But a Persian, he will go below the line to get anything. Persians have no morals when it comes to making money.

In the two quotations, both the Iranian and the Israeli accuse the other of lacking moral standards, the Iranian saying that Israelis are devoid of respect for others, the Israeli saying that the Iranians are devoid of norms concerning money. Each judges the other in terms of his own cultural values concerning proper behavior. The stereotypes they hold of one another—no respect for others, no norms concerning money—are a result of perceptions, misunderstandings, and communicative conflicts of two peoples of differing behavior, attitudes and beliefs interlocked in social and cultural contact. In an immigrant society like Israel's, when two or more groups sharing the same environment have completely different systems and styles of communication and occupy different political and economic niches in the society, such impressions are heightened and reified, influencing relationships and interaction as immigrants learn how to behave in a new culture. Both the immigrants and the established citizens see themselves and others in a new light formed through cross-cultural contrasts. These contrasts may be seen as different culturally patterned communication styles of Iranians and Israelis, which engender the stereotypes that Iranians and Israelis have of each other. The stereotypes arise when Iranian immigrants, coming from a hierarchical society, confront Israeli society, which is ideologically egalitarian, and structurally differentiated. This will be exemplified by focusing on the experience of Iranian immigrants in Israel and their problems of identity adjusting to Israeli society.

The problem of identity of Iranians in Israel concerns both self-assertion (I am Iranian; I am Israeli) and assignment by non-Iranians (you are Iranian). Although immigrants usually accept their identity as being from their countries of origin, being an immigrant in Israel required developing and maintaining an Israeli identity. Unlike other societies based upon immigrant populations (the countries of North and South America, Australia, or South Africa), Israel was founded as a new sociocultural order based upon common religious traditions blended with symbols of Zionism, and immigrants were vital to create the new state and actualize the ideology. The ideology of immigration as ascent or elevation in a spiritual sense, absorption of immigrants, redemption of the land, conquest of the soil, and the ingathering and integration of exiles was developed by the Eastern European pioneers and disseminated to the new immigrants. As a result of the conscious effort to develop a sociocultural system different from any of those in which they lived while in the Diaspora, the immigrants were influenced to "forget" their cultures of origin and "become" Israeli, albeit to a society more Western in values and ideals than Eastern: cultures of origin were ignored, criticized, devalued, or ridiculed, and ethnic identity was made subordinate to civilian loyalty and national identity.

National and ethnic identity and ethnicity must be interpreted according to a country's or society's sociocultural circumstances. In order to understand the contexts in which ethnic relations occur, and why people view others in the ways they do, we need to look at the society or the nation-state and its ideology, or to the people in power and their attitudes and actions to maintain power: from the inside and the outside there are different mechanisms and sentiments to maintain or undermine ethnic identities. In the case of Israel, the Zionist ideology of the state's sociocultural foundation—in which those in power hailed from Europe with its biases of cultural superiority—has had a determining role in the creation of ethnic stereotypes of the immigrants and in the dissolution of ethnic identity among native-born Israelis.[1] Consequently, ethnicity and ethnic identity must be viewed as fluid social phenomena, shifting and transforming over time, as social, political, or economic conditions warrant. People negotiate their various identities (Israeli, Iranian, Isfahani, jeweler, religious) in various circumstances. Identity, ethnic or otherwise, is not a monolithic immutable badge.

The problems of ethnic stereotypes in Israel are based upon differences in communication styles, attitudes, and behavior of different immigrant groups. These differences, obvious among immigrants, dissipate among their children. However, the ethnic stereotypes, born out of the negotiation of behavioral norms and communication codes, represent structural problems in society, such as problems of power and powerlessness between groups competing for the same resources. The ethnic stereotypes then become symbolic of cultural being (of how others "are") and of interaction.

How the ethnic stereotypes of Iranians in Israel originated will be examined in relation to the immigrant experience and the differences in communication which lend legitimacy to ethnic categorization. These ethnic stereotypes will be exemplified by two very different illustrations of cross-cultural misunderstandings: a quarrel which created a breach in relationships, reinforcing previously perceived stereotypes, and a humorous bilingual Persian and Hebrew play produced by and for Iranians in Israel.

Immigration and Categorization

Immigration, whether to escape political or religious persecution, to eke out a better living, or to live according to some particular ideological principles, entails social and cultural changes which require individuals and families to cope with new demands in a new environment while simultaneously losing their traditional patterns of support and resort. The problems this poses for the immigrants are manifold. Families and individuals go through periods of transition, many of which are tense and trying as new communication patterns, roles, values, and goals are learned in conjunction with adjusting to a new society. In a country like Israel, in which immigration forms its raison d'être, immigrants are exposed to the ideology of the state: to acculturate, mix, become Israeli, strip off one's previous cultural heritage. For immigrants from North African and Asian countries, this was a policy of cultural ethnocentrism on the part of the European Zionist elite who developed the welfare state bureaucracy. People were to shed their cultures of the *galut*, the lands of exile, and adapt to that of the budding state, a culture based upon a Western world view, consisting of democratic ideals in state government, a bureaucratic rationality, lack of hierarchy in group relationships manifested not only in the breakdown of traditional roles associated with Jews abroad and with men and women in the family, but also in speech patterns (to reflect egalitarianism rather than hierarchy), employment (both men and women were to work outside the home), child care (children of working parents would be taken care of in daycare centers), religion (established religion was to be Ashkenazi or Sephardi Orthodoxy only; many people chose to remain secular, nonpracticing, or atheists).

New immigrants who arrived after the formation of the state faced a patent bureaucracy which housed them, fed them, gave them medical care, and assigned them work. Because of such a rapid influx of immigrants and lack of economic resources in the early 1950s, and because of the cultural differences between those who worked in the government bureaucracies dealing with immigrants, as well as differences among the immigrants themselves, many immigrants faced cultural degradation and economic disappointment upon arrival in Israel.

The cultural degradation signified the negation of the values, behaviors, and beliefs of immigrants whose cultures contrasted the most with that of the European founders of the state. It resulted from the state's goals of creating a Western-oriented unified culture and a social system modeled on the socialist idealism of the Eastern European immigrants of the turn of the century. They embarked on "absorbing" the new immigrants, persuading them to change their cultural traditions and adopt that of the country's veteran citizens (*vatikim*). The Ministry of Absorption was created to ease the experience of the new immigrants concerning housing, food, education, and employment. The new immigrants, many of whom had never faced such an elaborate network of governmental bureaucracies, were processed by office clerks who were frequently younger than the immigrants and more authoritative and commanding than were younger people in their countries of origin (see Handelman 1976). This created what Bar-Yosef (1966:63) calls "asymmetrical dichotomy" in the social structure of Israel. The veteran citizens became the officials, and the newcomers, the clients, the latter being older and less knowledgable about the rules and regulations of the society than the former. As a result, the bureaucratic interaction between officials and clients was one of "categorization" and "dis-aging" (Bar-Yosef 1966:63). Categorization concerns uniform treatment of clients, officials classifying them according to their cultures of origin. Dis-aging, a consequence of bureaucratic encounters in the welfare state, pertains to the lack of distinction between age groups as the bureaucracy takes on the role of partial provider of goods and services formerly provided by family members. Especially affected by this dis-aging factor have been older people, notably male heads of households, who lose status as authority figures in the family: not only does the bureaucracy take over some of his roles, but it also has the power to provide jobs, housing, and other needs. In addition, children who learn the language of the country more quickly than their parents become the cultural mediators between the officials and the families, replacing some of the social roles of the parents in their countries of origin. These cultural and social changes are resented by many families (especially by the older males) who immigrated from patriarchal cultures where the male head of the family was the decision maker, social mediator, and sole economic supporter.

For many immigrants who came to Israel in the 1950s and early 1960s, being processed by the bureaucracy was difficult, disappointing, and demeaning. Faced with so many people coming at once, and deficient in assets, the country placed its new citizens in transit camps while they awaited housing, in apartment complexes at the boundaries of urban areas, in border towns guarding the frontiers from enemy attacks and cementing settlements at the fringes of the land, and in rural farming communities (moshavim and kibbutzim). Jobs were given out according to what was needed by the government and by private establishments, differentiating between the educated and noneducated, skilled and unskilled workers.

For many Middle Eastern immigrants of the 1950s, the work situation was unfavorable: those men who were merchants, peddlers, or craftsmen in their countries of origin found themselves—without capital and without the communicative capacity to deal with the Western bureaucratic socioeconomic system of the Israeli welfare state—working as manual laborers, digging stones in quarries, tilling the soil for agriculture, working in factories, building houses, cleaning the streets, collecting garbage, painting buildings. The situation for the immigrants, as Eisenstadt (1954:137) put it, became "paradoxical"—they were granted basic equality and civil rights but were segregated in housing and occupation. Such structural differentiation contradicted the ideology of the state, the ingathering and intermingling of the exiles.

This paradoxical structural situation was intensified by cultural differences between the European oldtimers and Middle Eastern newcomers, in which the Western-oriented Israeli citizens viewed the non-Western immigrants, as European colonialists in other lands had viewed non-Europeans, as uncivilized. For the oldtimers, these new immigrants represented values, beliefs, and worldviews that contrasted with the prevailing socialist Zionist philosophy. The Western political and economic elite who established the sociopolitical foundations of the state became, by the late 1950s, the minority, and the non-Western immigrants—usually less educated and more religious than the Western Jews, with large families, many of whom immigrated as a community and lacked the socialist ideology of the Western immigrants—were the majority. The result of the quick contrast of cultural groupings of immigrants in such a short period of time was, on the one hand, an effort on the part of the Israeli establishment to settle them and to transform the immigrants' sociocultural orientation and behavior, to make them Israelis, and, on the other hand, the development of ethnic stereotypes.

Ethnicity materialized as a way of categorizing people in the 1950s during the mass immigration of non-Western Jews to Israel. Those immigrants whose culture contrasted the most with that of the European developers of Israeli society were disparaged with pejorative labels which reflected differences in communication and understanding between the immigrants and the established Westernized citizens. The perceived divisions between the Jews in Israel became one not only of religious and secular, but also one of Europeans, modern, advanced, cultured, in opposition to Orientals, primitives, backward, uncultured. Within these two categories, one seen as positive, the other as negative, ethnic stereotyping became even more specific, depending on the behavior and attitudes comprehended by those doing the labeling and those labeled, and on the process of acculturation of the immigrants to Israeli society: Moroccans, for instance, were—and sometimes still are—seen as troublemakers and were disparaged as "carrying knives"; Rumanians are thought of as "thieves"; Americans are considered emotionally dishonest, since they hide their true feelings behind a social smile. No longer were the immigrants labeled as Jews, as they were in their countries of origin. Now all Jews in one land, they were classified into specific groups by language or by country of national origin, such as all English-speakers, whether from England, the United States, Canada, South Africa, or Australia, being called "Anglo-Saxons."

In general, the Israelis divide themselves into two: Europeans and those of European background are the Ashkenazim, and the North African and Middle Eastern Jews are placed under the rubric Sephardim, a misnomer, since the Sephardim are the Spanish Jews (*sepharad* is "Spain" in Hebrew) who moved to North Africa, Italy, Greece, Bulgaria and Turkey during and after the Inquisition. In recent years, the term *edot ha-mizrach* (the Eastern ethnic groups, in English referred to as the Oriental Jews) has replaced Sephardim in reference to those from North Africa and Asia. Current lingo, even among social scientists, has shortened the term to *ha-edot,* the ethnic groups, in reference to non-Western Jews.[2]

Within the Ashkenazi and Sephardi segments of the Israeli population are the immigrants who came from various countries and cultures. In spite of the differences among them that they themselves observe, the immigrants from different countries are perceived by native-born Israelis and by other immigrants as an aggregate, and are labeled as such. For instance, Israelis know nothing of the regional differences and stereotypes that Iranians of different cities have of each other, that Yazdis are considered traditional and religious, Shirazis polite and kind, Isfahanis deceptive and untrustworthy. Iranians are seen as one group with specific cultural traits. The basis for such aggregate cultural stereotypes is twofold: contrasts in fundamental communication codes between the labeler and the labeled on the one hand, and the similarities in communication and behavior among the labeled on the other.

The situation of ethnic stereotyping and labeling is not, however, a one-way street. Immigrants, in addition to being labeled, are themselves labelers of Israelis, seeing them in contrast to the ways people "ideally" behave in the societies from which they came. Thus, for most Israelis, no matter what part of Iran an Iranian Jew comes from, no matter whether the person is educated or not, religious or not, Iranians are seen as stupid, stingy, and suspicious. And for the Iranians, Israelis are perceived as rude, impolite, and inconsiderate. These stereotypes, which will be elucidated throughout the chapter, construct interactions and transactions and are a result of verbal and nonverbal communication differences expressing values, ideology, worldview, and relationships.

Liminality: Being between Iranian and Israeli

As explained in the previous chapter, Iranian patterns of communication are based upon a vertical hierarchy of relationships that exist in Iranian society, in which different speech codes are utilized depending upon context, relationship, and situation, from the familiar person, to the respected, to the distant. In Iran people on different levels of the social hierarchy are expected to attend to, care for, and support those below them while competing socially and in largesse with their peers and trying to advance themselves and gain favor with those of higher status. Family and interpersonal relationships are ideally valued over personal goals, and private matters of the individual or of the family are concealed and protected from the outsider. This occurs through verbal strategies in interaction. Privacy, as the maintenance of interpersonal and familial boundaries, is also attained by silence on confidential matters, impression management, and through physical means such as houses protected by high walls.

In opposition to the Iranian social structure, that of Israel is *ideologically* horizontal: all Jews are considered equal and every child has the chance—so to speak—to rise from poverty to become a government leader. People relate to each other as equal in status, and speech codes reflect a pattern of familiarity even with strangers of different social, economic or age positions. In part, this has to do with the fact that Hebrew has no conventional grammar of colloquial formality, and this lack of formal grammar is reinforced by the lack of formality in speech and interaction. In addition, the Zionist ideology was to be free from the conventions of status and stratification which existed in the countries from which the immigrants came, where they were required to show deference to non-Jewish authorities and citizens while simultaneously keeping a low profile. Such patterns of communication were deemed unnecessary in the Jewish state where anti-Semitism could not exist. This then translated into interaction free from conventions of status and class: children call their teachers by their first names; a bus driver will impatiently yell at a member of parliament to get on the bus; a concerned citizen phones a politician during dinner hours at home to voice a complaint. Privacy and social distance, such as that valued in Iran, are hard to come by in Israel. People say what they think and value verbal honesty, and because of the tight housing situation and small apartments whose doors, walls, and windows do not afford familial seclusion from neighbors, people are familiar with the happenings of the families next door.

The Iranian immigrants in Israel face a society whose communication codes and concomitant social structure differ from the one in which they were socialized. In order to accommodate themselves to Israeli society, immigrants go through a period of "neo-socialization" in which a new language is learned, new ways of interacting are acquired, and new roles are performed. This is not to say that the immigrant experience is one of "desocialization" from the sociocultural system of one's origins, and "resocialization" to the society immigrated to, as Eisenstadt (1954) and Bar-Yosef (1966) purport. The immigrant is never entirely desocialized; interaction among immigrants from the same country reveals behavior and beliefs of the immigrants' culture. For instance, many Iranian immigrants in Israel who speak fluent Hebrew and behave, when interacting with non-Iranians, like native-born Israelis, will speak with the deference and respect of ta′ārof—the politeness code—when dealing with Iranians.

Neo-socialization is the process of learning a new way of behaving through acculturation to a novel and unfamiliar system of norms and values. It entails a period of liminality when the immigrant is no longer a member of the sociocultural system of country of origin, nor yet a full-fledged participant in the new culture. The liminal period is the point of transition between two states of being in which participants are temporarily released from previous norms and rules, a phenomenon, as Turner (1974:15) puts it, "in which all previous standards and models are subjected to criticism, and fresh new ways of describing and interpreting sociocultural experience is formed." Liminality, then, in a societal sense, is a state of being, a realm of action or thought in opposition to previously learned norms, actions, standards, and models. In the liminal state of immigration, former social status and attributes are removed as people are separated from their original society: the immigrant can no longer really behave in the old familiar style, and yet does not know how, exactly, to behave in the new, unfamiliar way. It is an in-between stage of a social process in which the immigrants become inwardly and outwardly transformed while accommodating themselves to the new sociocultural system.

The liminal period of immigration could take a few months or endure for years. It is the time when a person attempts to adjust to the new society, learning new rules, values, goals, and reevaluating the old, when the differences between old and new ways of interaction are exaggerated. People learn to see themselves and others in a new light during the period of adjustment as changes occur in relations with family, friends, neighbors, and strangers. These changes are a result of the inward and outward transition of neo-socialization.

Adjustment to the Israeli sociocultural system entails, among other things, learning Hebrew and how to communicate in Hebrew. This is not simply mastering the vocabulary, but learning the metalanguage, how to speak, what to do with the body and gestures, intonation, whether to show respect or familiarity. Immigrants learn Hebrew by attending *ulpanim,* intensive Hebrew language courses, or by picking it up on the streets, at work, from the radio and television, or through their children. However, communication in Israeli Hebrew requires more than a good command of the language and metalanguage. It also has to do with the ways people in Israel value relationships, as based upon Israeli cultural notions of honesty and idealism.

Accordingly, there are several ways Iranian immigrants speak Hebrew (we are not concerned here with accents, as each immigrant group can be detected by their peculiarities of pronunciation). Some people pick up the vocabulary, with all the nuances, intonation, and idioms, how to speak like an Israeli with Israelis—knowing how to question, argue, joke, be adamant, and interact with people of the opposite sex and different ages. Others pick up the Israeli style of communication, but have confused categories and thus make mistakes in interaction. Notable are the young men who learn the language fluently but who interact with women not as they would in Iran, with respect and distance, but in a way which is not quite Israeli either, a kind of instant familiarity, kissing and touching someone they just meet, confusing the "moral borders" and "social borders" (as the refugee quoted in the beginning of the chapter lamented) with levels of intimacy with different people. Some Iranians speak Hebrew well but reflect in their style of communication the social structure of Iran, such as showing respect to others in situations in which Israelis would not; and there are those who do not learn how to speak Hebrew at all, in spite of the availability of classes and the country's emphasis on learning the language. Among the Iranian immigrants I met, especially the refugees who came from Iran when I did, invariably the children learned Hebrew in school, the young adults learned the language at the ulpanim, and the older adults, those above the age of forty, oftentimes considered too old to learn in the ulpan, either never learn the language properly or, if they had studied in the Alliance Israélite schools or other Jewish schools in Iran, spoke a literary Hebrew without the idioms of Israeli discourse.

Those Iranians who learn to speak Hebrew and interact with others in the ways acceptable in Israeli society become, after a while, bicultural, at home in Israeli contexts as much as in Iranian contexts. Others may also become bicultural, but tend to be more comfortable socializing with Iranians. Even when socializing in an Iranian subculture within Israeli society, the Iranians, although they might speak Farsi with all the ta'ārofs and implications of status and class, become somewhat Israeli-ized in their communication. Hebrew words are incorporated into Farsi conversations, and the topics of discourse concern issues of importance in Israeli society (economic, social, military, and political problems) as well as topics concerning Iran.

How much of Israeli communicative behavior is incorporated into their transactions depends on age, amount of time they are in the country, and what kind of gathering people participate in. Three incidents exemplify communication within the Iranian immigrant subculture of Israel. One concerns a NoRuz (Persian New Year) party of Iranian university students in Jerusalem in March 1979. Many of these students were new immigrants, others refugees from the Iranian Revolution, and still others were in Israel for seven to ten years. Only Farsi was spoken. After dancing, singing Iranian songs, listening to Iranian music, telling jokes, and eating a well-liked Persian thick noodle soup (*āsh-e reshteh*), everyone went outside to participate in the ritual of jumping over a small fire. However, when everyone was jumping over the fire in this Persian ceremony, instead of each individual saying the traditional phrase, "My redness from you, your yellowness from me" (*sorkhi-yi man az to, zardi-yi to az man*—said to the fire), the students sang an Israeli song, "David, Melekh Israel" ("David, King of Israel"), and when everyone had jumped over the fire, they held hands and did the *hora*, an Israeli folk dance, around the fire. This example of new immigrants incorporating Israeli music and dance into a traditional Persian ritual is a conscious—albeit impromptu—way of mixing the two cultures.

Another incident of combined Israeli-Iranian behavior occurred in poetry readings presented by university students who had been in Israel from one to thirteen years. These took place in different students' apartments several times a year. The students prepared Persian food, played Persian music on cassettes, and recited the classical and modern poetry of well-loved poets, such as Khayyām, Hāfez, Sa'adi, Foroogh Farokhzād, and, after the Revolution, political poetry from books brought by tourists who had been in England. Yet, the language of interaction was mixed, both Persian and Hebrew. The students did not ta'ārof among themselves, nor did they engage in the formalized body movements—the rather reserved, controlled ways of holding one's head and torso straight in interaction with others. Instead, both men and women sprawled out on the floor, appearing relaxed and comfortable in each other's presence.[3] Only when special older guests were invited, such as an Iranian poet or musician, did the students resume a more traditional and formal posture of sitting on the floor with the legs tucked under, to the side, or crossed.

A third incident was an evening of Persian music at the home of middle-aged Iranians who had been living in Israel for over twenty years, having immigrated as teenagers or youths in their twenties. Invited to this soirée were relatives and friends, among whom were one of the directors of the Iranian Immigrant Association and a wealthy refugee. Interaction was very formal. People spoke only Farsi, and the formalized behavior of ta'ārof was observed by all. Guests and hosts referred to one another with the formal second person pronoun, *shomā*, and those of the highest status were seated at the head of the room. Two musicians played on traditional instruments (qānun, tombak, and violin) as others listened, sitting ceremonially in chairs lining the four walls of the room. During the intermissions the hosts offered food and drink to the guests, some of whom told Iranian jokes while everyone listened. This was followed by people talking quietly with those sitting nearby. Then the cycle started again, and again: music, food and drink, jokes, quiet talking. The interaction, both in style and content, could have occurred in Iran. Yet, in spite of the Iranianness of the parties, the children of the hosts and guests (except for the recent refugees) spoke no Farsi, and (aside from four grown children of one couple) were not interested in Iranian culture.

Iranian culture is alien for many Israeli-born children of Iranian immigrants, and even for some children who immigrated at a young age. They internalize the stereotypes heard about Iranians—their being stupid, stingy, and suspicious—and they harbor the same attitudes toward Iranians as an immigrant group as do non-Iranian Israelis. In a way, they negate their Iranian heritage to express their Israeli identity. And in another way, they express a generation gap, between parents socialized in one culture, and children in another. Those Israeli-born children of Iranian parents who grow up in neighborhoods which have a sizable Iranian population or who grow up hearing Farsi spoken may learn the language, but not fluently. Their accent is Hebrew, as is their intonation in speaking. In addition, few Israeli-born children of Iranian heritage speak Farsi with all the nuances needed to communicate like an Iranian: they do not know how to ta'ārof, or how to speak with others showing the respect one does for people of different statuses. Nor do they know the vocabulary necessary for discourse on a wide variety of subjects. They, like most people brought up in Israel, esteem and identify with the norms, values, and behavior of Israeli society, often finding fault with the traditions of their parents' past. Such attitudes were depicted by one woman who immigrated to Israel at the age of three, grew up in the Bukharian quarter of Jerusalem (which has a large Persian-speaking population), attended secular schools,[4] and spoke a not-so-fluent Persian with a heavy Hebrew accent. Because of the ways she was raised, she considers herself Iranian rather than Israeli, but her views express a negative attitude toward her upbringing which opposes the Israeli values she considers positive: "I grew up in an Iranian framework, with everyone speaking Persian and with a Persian culture, in a Persian neighborhood. But all the time I grew up I had the pressure and framework of the *primitiviyut* of Persians. I didn't feel the Israeli freedom—not to go out with boys, not to speak to them, not to go out—to guard the honor of the family." Note the term this woman uses to refer to Iranian culture: primitiviyut ("primitivity"). This is a term used by the Ashkenazi elite to refer to the "primitive" cultures of the Middle Eastern Jews which had to be modified to make them Israeli. People from the Middle East were frequently called *primitivim*—"primitives"—by the Ashkenazim and sometimes by children of Middle Eastern immigrants, such as the woman quoted above who, in evaluating her upbringing and comparing it to the relative "freedom" of her non-Iranian peers, took on the non-Iranians' negative stereotype of Iranians. Such negative stereotypes are effective ways of categorizing people, even for, or especially for, this woman who is in between being Iranian and Israeli.

Communication and Ethnic Stereotypes: The Case of Iranians in Israel

The stereotype of Iranians being stupid, stingy, and suspicious exists in all levels of Israeli society, among the educated and noneducated, among Oriental Jews and Western Jews, among the secular and religious, and even among some Israeli-born children of Iranian parents. These stereotypes have become reified in such a way that to call someone "Parsi"—Hebrew for "Persian"—or to speak Hebrew with a Persian accent connotes a whole series of negative cultural traits of being Iranian: greedy, devious, interested only in money, untrustworthy, passive, withdrawn, secretive, lazy, primitive, deceptive. Israelis see themselves, by contrast, as being honest, idealistic, independent, vigorous, scrupulous, direct. Iranians, on the other hand, see Israelis as rude, impolite, aggressive, selfish, and see themselves as respectful, kind, friendly, clever. The Iranians say the Israelis are the way they are because of the difficult years of economic hardship in the 1950s and early 1960s and because of the wars. The Israelis say the Iranians are the way they are because of their *mentaliyut*—their mentality—a term symbolic of a group's cultural background in the Diaspora, but connotative of traits, inherited somewhat as are physical features, traits which are difficult to lose in spite of years living in the country. All ethnic groups in Israel have their particular menṭaliyut, most of which dissipate with integration into the mainstream of Israeli social, economic, political, and cultural life. Thus, Israeli-born children of Iranian heritage who do not speak Persian and children who immigrated at a young age who, through the school system, radio, television, army, and friendship networks are socialized as Israelis often assume the same stereotypes of Iranians.

For Israel, the stereotypes are indicative of problems of classification in a plural society. Each immigrant group has its particular characteristics which influence its integration into Israeli society and its ethnic label. For Iranians in Israel, the stereotypes are indicative of the very real problems of identity. The problems of ethnic classification and of identity are seen here as issues of communication differences in an interethnic situation where interpretation of customary verbal and nonverbal signals engenders judgments of others' abilities, attitudes, and character.

The rude, impolite Israeli is derived from communication patterns in Israeli society in which the ideology that all are equal is reinforced by speech symbolic of that ideology. The stupid, suspicious, stingy Iranian is the consequence of a verbal communication problem in an interethnic setting where the Iranians' verbal and nonverbal behavior contrasts with that of the Israelis. By keeping personal, familial, and economic matters confidential, and by believing others do the same, as in Iran, and by questioning and interpreting the actions of others to know how to gauge one's own actions better, the Iranian creates the image of being suspicious, secretive, deceptive, devious, and untrustworthy. These traits, which represent an element of zerangi (cleverness) for Iranians, are exemplified in an expression some Israelis use to depict Iranians: "Every Persian is a poisonous snake" (H., *kol parsi nakhash arsi*).

Verbally, Iranians show respect of others through speech patterns, and speak Hebrew with a Persian accent marked by its sing-song intonation and by the mistakes in gender and syntax (the Persian language does not, as does Hebrew, differentiate between masculine and feminine with nouns, verbs, and pronouns). Thus, some Iranians have difficulty speaking correct Hebrew in the content or form that is considered proper in Israel, which makes the non-Iranian think the Iranian is stupid. In addition, many of the immigrants who came to Israel before the late 1960s were either uneducated, educated in the Persian school system with rote memorization the method of learning, or had studied in the Alliance Israélite schools. Few had a professional education. According to the Iranian immigrants, the lack of a Western education is the reason Israelis think they are stupid. As for the stereotype of being stingy, the Iranian Jew is the product of life in Iran which was plagued by insecurity and fear that showing wealth would invite riots and/or confiscation of property by others. Iranians see themselves as economical, as having priorities for spending. Since the first immigrants were poor, this was especially the case. But when Iranians, unlike other Oriental Jews, became a petty-merchant class owning many of the fancy clothing boutiques in the late 1960s and early 1970s and when they were not seen in places of leisure-time activity, such as cafés, restaurants, concerts, and cinemas, the stereotype became fixed (as it had for many minority ethnic groups who are small merchants in other parts of the world—Jews in Europe, Chinese in South Asia, Indians in East Africa).

The stereotype of Iranian stinginess is the subject of many Israeli ethnic jokes. When Israelis heard that I was studying Iranians, they inevitably asked me why Iranians are stingy or suspicious and would then proceed to tell me a joke. The jokes concern both the value of money for Iranians and social relationships among Iranians, exemplifying suspiciousness:

> How does a Persian change money from one pocket to another? He calls Brinks.

> When an Iranian takes out a hundred lira note, Herzl [founder of modern Zionism, whose picture is on the bill] blinks from the light.

> How does an Iranian sneeze? Aaaaaaaaa-*shtikhim*! ["carpets" in Hebrew; most of the carpet stores in Israel are owned by Iranians].

> When was the largest *aliya* [immigration] of the Persians? After they wrote "Jerusalem of Gold" [a song written by Nomi Shemer before the Six Day War; in actuality, there was an influx of Iranians for several years after this war, many of whom were involved in clothing business and other merchandising].

> A Persian man asked another Persian man the time. The latter said, "I won't tell you, because the next thing, you'll want to come to my house and then you'll see my beautiful daughter and you'll want to marry her. But I won't allow my daughter to marry a man who doesn't own a watch."

> A Persian man and his wife passed a falafel stand and the wife said, "Ummm—the falafel smells good." So the man took his wife back to the falafel stand and said, "Have another smell."

> A Persian man married a widow and before the marriage she asked about buying the tickets for the honeymoon. He only bought one. "Why," she asked, "only one?" "Because," he replied, "you've already been on a honeymoon."

The jokes are, as are many ethnic jokes the world over, a commentary on cultural perceptions of the "other." In Iran, the people from Rasht, a city on the Caspian Sea, are the brunt of ethnic jokes: because of the cool, moist climate and the cultural differences between the Rashtis and other Iranians, the Rashti men are considered stupid and the women preoccupied with sex. They are a foil for the rest of Iranian society who see themselves as intelligent and sexually moral in comparison with the Rashtis. Similarly, Iranians in Israel as perceived in the jokes are a foil for other Israelis. However, this is not to say that other ethnic groups are not subjects for ethnic jokes and slurs, for they are. A Rumanian joke, for example, plays on the image of thieves: how do you make a Rumanian omelette? First of all, steal two eggs.

Not only have the preconceived stereotypic notions of what people are and how they behave become the subject matter of jokes, they also influence social interactions. Frequently, the stereotypes that Israelis have of Iranians, and, to a lesser extent, that Iranians have of Israelis, govern their relationships. This is exemplified by an incident concerning an American man (Bob), his Polish-born but Israeli-bred wife (Anat), their two-year-old son (Yuval), and a middle-aged Iranian woman (Esther) who immigrated to Israel at the age of thirteen, married, raised three children, and works as a *metapelet*, a woman who takes care of several babies in her home during the day when the parents are at work. The incident concerns social negotiations and transactions which mirror and are thwarted by ethnic stereotypes that the couple has of Esther, and she of them.

Anat, Bob, And Esther: Stereotypes Influencing Interaction

Anat and Bob were looking for a metapelet for Yuval and called Esther, whose ad they had seen in a newspaper. Anat asked Esther if she is Rumanian, since she couldn't place her accent. Esther replied no, but did not say where she is from. Anat and Bob later found out from me that Esther is Iranian. Then, although they had felt that Esther's and her husband's "mentality" was very Iranian (they could not elaborate on what they meant by this, however), they decided to place Yuval in her care.

Nevertheless, Anat and Bob did not entirely trust Esther. They kept saying that she is not telling them what is happening with Yuval during the day. In fact, that did occur once when I was visiting Esther. Yuval had vomited after he was fed fruit juice. When I spoke to Anat later that day to tell her how good Esther is with Yuval, I also told her about Yuval's indigestion. Anat was upset that Esther did not tell her, and asked her why. Esther's response was that he did not throw up, but that she forced too much food down his mouth and he spit it out. Anat later told me that she was dissatisfied with Esther: "If Yuval falls, I should know about it, because if he vomits from falling, it is an emergency and not just as if he was vomiting for no reason, from an upset stomach. Also, meningitis is going around and I want Esther to tell me these things because they could be symptoms."

Six months after the incident of Yuval's vomiting, Anat and Bob had a falling-out with Esther which resulted in taking Yuval away from her care and placing him in a daycare center. When they had first placed Yuval with Esther, Anat had made an agreement with her that whenever she (Anat) would receive a cost-of-living increase at work, she would give the same percentage to Esther.[5] Their agreed-upon system was working satisfactorily until the last cost-of-living increase came through. According to Anat and Bob, Esther demanded 900 lira more than she was entitled to, which they computed to be 5,700 lira monthly. She wanted them to pay the same amount that the parents of other children in her care were paying, and she wanted retroactive pay for five months. Anat and Bob said that the other parents began paying her more to begin with. They refused to listen to Esther's requests, were yelled at by Esther's husband, and left her apartment. Anat declared, "Esther is a stupid woman who understands nothing about arithmetic or salaries, and what she is doing doesn't make sense." They determined to place Yuval in a daycare center with thirty children divided into four groups, which would cost 6,500 lira per month, 100 lira more than Esther asked for, rather than accept the terms Esther wanted.

Esther had a different version of the dispute. She said there were arguments about money, that she doesn't like arguments, but they were not at all nice to her. She and her son-in-law, an accountant, figured out how much of a cost-of-living increase she should receive, but Anat and Bob refused to pay it. They called her names and Anat ran out of the apartment without saying good-bye and slammed the door. The following day when Bob brought Yuval, he sat down to figure out how much they should give her, which would be 5,700 lira rather than the 6,300 she asked for. He then said they are giving her enough, and are actually giving her more than she deserves, and that she should think of it as "*kappara*".[6] She asked me if I think that what Bob said was not nice, that she isn't a charity case, that they should never had said to her it is kappara.

Esther mentioned that they will take Yuval from her. She said that it is bad to move him around so much, that he has no appetite in comparison to the other children. She kept repeating, in Hebrew, "It's a pity for the boy."

"Why are they so tight with their money?" she asked. "They get insurance and a pension, and I get nothing. Even a babysitter gets more than I do—40 lira an hour. But I take care of Yuval for 5,700 a month, six days a week. I should be taking care of him from eight to two-thirty, but many times they come to pick him up later, such as four or five, and on Friday they often pick him up after two, when all the other parents pick up their children at twelve."

She also mentioned that she did a lot for Anat and Bob. When Bob had pneumonia, he brought Yuval and they picked him up downstairs because he could not carry him up. But when she asked him to call her son when they went to the United States for vacation, Bob said they would not have time, that they would be in Washington, D.C. and not in Boston, where her son lives, and that they would not be able to post a letter for her because they would not be near a post office. "See what kind of people they are?" she said.

Two months later, Esther continued to dwell on the quarrel with Anat and

Bob, and the troubles they caused her: "They are going to pay. I have a lawyer. Bob thinks Israelis are stupid. He would always come late to pick up Yuval. Anat would always go home to rest after work. If I'd call her to pick up Yuval, she would say Bob will come later. But I'm going to show them that Israelis are not stupid. The lawyer will make them pay what they owe me. I want the law suit to get money from them to prove that Israelis aren't stupid. Why doesn't Bob serve in the army? He says he shouldn't have to. And Anat doesn't have anything Israeli about her. She has a Rumanian mentality that she picked up from her mother. I'll never say hello to them on the street. They treated me terribly and said awful things to me. And we ate salt together.[7] And I took care of Yuval like my own child. I have the feelings of a mother toward him."

Esther was hurt by the dispute with Anat and Bob. But what was at issue underlying their disagreement were the stereotypes coloring their perceptions of one another and, consequently, their interaction. Although Anat and Bob were not cognizant of the influence that their prejudices had on their transactions with Esther, their actions manifested their beliefs. They were at first hesitant about using Esther's services for the care of their son. Her "mentality" was Iranian, they said, and they did not quite trust her. The incident of Esther not telling Anat about Yuval's vomiting indicated her being untrustworthy in Anat's eyes. The stereotype of stinginess and concern for money was actualized for Anat and Bob by Esther's asking for a cost-of-living increase. The same request was also seen by Anat and Bob as not making sense, the conclusion being that Esther is stupid. Therefore, the stereotype of the Iranian being untrustworthy, stingy, and stupid played a part in the interaction between Anat and Bob and Esther, causing Anat and Bob to look for certain signs in Esther's behavior which would be indicative of what they expected her to be, and they acted and reacted accordingly.

On the other hand, Esther at first had no preconceived notions about Anat and Bob. At least, she said nothing negative to me about them. However, as her request for a salary increase was met with such adamant refusal by Anat and Bob, who discourteously departed her apartment, Esther saw them as aggressive, rude, and impolite. These characteristics were reinforced when Bob referred to part of the salary they were giving her as kappara. Esther was insulted. She then saw Anat and Bob in a completely different light, one which reflected Iranians'—and Israelis'—views of others. She insinuated that Anat and Bob are not good parents, placing Yuval in a daycare center where he would not get as personalized care as he does with her. Israelis, according to many Iranian immigrants, are not good parents and Israeli families are not considered as close and caring as are Iranian families. The refusal of Anat and Bob to give her a raise, whereas they have the employment benefits of insurance and pension, and their refusal to contact her son when they were in the United States, indicate to Esther the selfishness of Israelis in comparison to Iranians. But Esther, as an Israeli, breaks down the characteristics of Anat and Bob into specific ethnic stereotypes. Bob, as an American, is seen as spoiled: he thinks Israelis are stupid, yet he won't join the army to serve the country the way her son and husband have. And Anat is seen as a Rumanian, although by birth she is Polish: Anat steals what Esther thinks is her due by not giving her a raise and by taking Yuval away from her.

Another aspect of the quarrel signifies the problems of employer-employee relations, where the employers are Ashkenazi (American and Polish), the employee Iranian, and thus a member of the larger Middle Eastern segment of the Israeli population. The Ashkenazim, as mentioned previously, have been the powerful group in the society, those in control of resources. As exemplified by Esther's situation, a woman without the resources of pension and insurance, and without access to them, is dependent on the goodwill of those who hire her to give her salary raises. Although such situations are common worldwide, the problem in Israel is that the majority of people who lack access to certain resources are of the larger North African-Middle Eastern segment.[8] The position of the various immigrant groups within the socioeconomic and political structure is then exacerbated by the stereotypes which other members of the society have about them.

A Play on Being Iranian in Israel

With this background of the relationships between Iranians and Israelis, we can now look at excerpts from a bilingual Persian and Hebrew play that was written after the Iranian Revolution by an Isfahani living in Jerusalem.[9] It was performed in a theatre in Jerusalem in May 1980. Its title: "To Jerusalem with Love."

The story takes place in the customs area of Ben Gurion Airport several months after the Revolution and symbolizes the problems of Iranian immigration and acculturation to Israel. This is exemplified through verbal and nonverbal interactions of three characters: Mulla Davut, a religious Isfahani Jew who just arrives, loaded with luggage and dressed in the garb of a Shi'a mulla; he speaks Persian with a heavy Isfahani accent; an Israeli customs official who speaks Hebrew only; and Nissan, wearing a kibbutz hat and pants too short, like those of the poor Iranian men who clean the *joob*s—the sewers—in Iran, revealing by his dress a mixture of material culture; he is an Iranian janitor who, although he barely understands Hebrew and speaks with a typically Persian accent, becomes a temporary translator and is thus the mediator between two cultures, Iranian and Israeli, a position in which many Iranians in Israel find themselves to be.

The characters are stereotypes of Iranians and Israelis, imposed from the outside, accepted from within. Mulla Davut is a characteristic Isfahani: he is polite, to a point; he is traditional and zerang—clever—and can outwit anyone; yet, he is innocent to the workings of the Israeli bureaucracy which he tries to outmaneuver. He is the quintessential Iranian immigrant. The customs official is a non-thinking bureaucrat, cold, does what he has to by trying to find out all the things that newcomers try taking into the country in order to tax them. And Nissan is the fool. Partially acculturated, he does not know Hebrew very well, but he speaks it with an intonation of impatience, rudeness, and *khutzpah,* so characteristic of the Iranian stereotype of Israelis. He, too, is a typical Iranian immigrant, but at a later stage of the game, a person who is no longer really Iranian nor yet Israeli, although he tries. Culturally, he is caught between two worlds and because of his language incapacity, is in somewhat of a liminal stage, a cultural non-entity entangled in an alien environment.

The play's introduction is a humorous commentary on other social subdivisions in Israeli society—the religious, represented by a Hassidic man—and the secular, a sexy young woman. The customs official tries talking with the Hassidic man who knows only Yiddish, making him seem even more ignorant than Nissan. The official asks if he knows English, French, or Hebrew, and the Hassid replies, "Vus? Vus?"—Yiddish for what? what?, and, in the context of modern Israeli ethnic stereotypes, a Vus Vus is a noun meaning an Ashkenazi. A modern sexy woman comes on stage and the Hassid runs away screaming and spitting phew! phew!—for she is an infidel in an obscene sense. After that (the audience loved the Hassid), there is an announcement that a flight is coming in from Athens. The customs official says that there will be alot of Iranians on that flight. And onto the stage walks an Iranian wearing the clothes of a mulla, with a blanket covered with a sheet over his shoulder (we find out later that it is actually a carpet that he is trying to pass tax-free). He gets on his hands and knees, kisses the ground, says a blessing, calls his wife Ta'oos and starts to leave. The customs official puts his suitcase on a counter and Mulla Davut tells him, in Persian, "I'll sacrifice myself for you. Don't bother yourself. I'm embarrassed. I'll take it myself." The customs official and Mulla Davut engage in a Hebrew-Persian dialogue which neither understands. The customs official asks him what language he speaks. Mulla Davut talks about wanting to go to the holy city Jerusalem. Finally, Mulla Davut exclaims, "Put dust on your head! What are these things you are saying? Speak the language of human beings. Farsi! Farsi! Khomeini!"

The customs official understands, goes out and returns with Nissan, who speaks to him with utmost impatience and lack of respect, "Boss, what do you want? I have work." Nissan's impatience and hand gestures indicate his awareness of Israeli communication patterns which he tries emulating to show how

Israeli he is. The official tells Nissan that he might be able to help this man who just came from Iran. Nissan and Mulla Davut talk, recognize one another from Isfahan, then greet each other with a kiss and hug. Nissan asks Mulla Davut why he is dressed like an *ākhund,* the term that Iranian Jews use to refer to Muslim clergy. They refer to their own clergy as mullas. He replies, "Don't touch my stomach (you don't know all the problems that are within me). They've turned the wheel in Iran around, said that they'll give everyone money who will be an ākhund. I myself have taken on this appearance and each month I receive many tomans [Iranian currency]. Now I told them I'm taking a trip. They gave me a considerable amount of money, they got me a ticket, they cleared me, and I came." Mulla Davut shows his cleverness (zerangi), his ability to outwit the system for his advantage, while simultaneously ridiculing the incompetent new regime of Iran.

The rest of the play is based upon two sets of dialogues, the customs official and Nissan, and Nissan and Mulla Davut, with mistranslations from Hebrew (H) to Persian (P) and series of puns. One sequel of dialogues exemplifies the communication problems between the three characters:

Customs Official (H): Tell him to show me his passport. [*The Hebrew word for passport is* darkon. *A similar sound in Persian means "in the ass" and that is what Nissan thinks is said*.]
Nissan (P): Your excellency, Mulla, excuse me . . . ah . . . excuse me.
Mulla Davut (P): What are you saying? Why are you hemming and hawing?
Nissan (P): Forgive me. Excuse me. He says take off your pants and show him your seat.
Mulla Davut (P): What does he want from doing all this? Maybe you're making a mistake again?
Nissan (P): Ask the customs official. (H) What do you want to see?
Customs Official (H): The passport [*darkon*].
Nissan (P): Did you see what he said?
Mulla Davut (P): Good. Now that it's by force [*and he starts taking off his pants*].
Customs Official (H): What are you doing? I asked for your passport.
(English) PASSPORT!
Mulla Davut (P): Deaf! He wants the passport!

The customs official takes the passport, writes something on it, opens the suitcase and takes out a tape recorder. He previously had asked if Mulla Davut had any electrical appliances to declare and Nissan told him to declare nothing.

Customs Official (H): What's this?
Nissan (P): He's asking what's this.
Mulla Davut (P): Is he blind? It's a radio and tape recorder together. Haven't the Israelis ever seen anything like this?

Nissan (H): This is a (P) *zabt-i sot*. Don't you know what this is? [*He turns it on and talks on the tape*.]

The customs official starts pulling out objects from the bags of Mulla Davut and writes them down for tax purposes: copper vessels, henna, eggplants, tomatoes, electrical appliances, herbal medicines. He finds out that Mulla Davut had been in Israel before, bought a house, sold it illegally, and now is returning with all these things and owes 30,000 lira to the government. The play ends with Mulla Davut going with his suitcases to the police station, thinking they are taking him to the central bus station.

The play is an Iranian-Israeli cultural creation whose protagonists typify different stereotypical characteristics of Iranians and Israelis as seen by Iranians in Israel. Not only do they make fun of themselves through the characters in the play, but the play itself is a vehicle for positive Iranian identity in a society which knew nothing about and negated their cultural heritage and which, at the same time, made life difficult economically with all the taxes, rules, and regulations that are more easily outwitted in Iran. Consequently, the play is a discourse evoking a whole series of problems—economic, social, cultural, linguistic—that Iranian Jews have in Iran and in Israel. The play is for Iranian-Israelis only. Those of Iranian background who do not know the Persian language are as good as lost when it comes to understanding the play. They have become Israeli-ized, more so than Nissan, and no longer speak the language of human beings, as Mulla Davut says. And those Iranians who do not speak Hebrew, who have not been able for one reason or another to accommodate themselves to Israeli society, also cannot understand the play. Thus, the play delineates the negotiation of identity of being Iranian in Israel, expressed by one man to me, "I consider myself an Israeli, but my heart and eyes are toward Iran."

Ethnic Stereotypes and Cultural Identity in Israel

Since the children of different immigrant groups learn how to communicate in Hebrew as Israelis, the ethnic stereotypes which are based initially upon communication differences of immigrants do not in reality hold for them. When asked what their background is, the reply often sounds like this? "My mother is Yemeni and my father's family is from Poland and Germany," with an underlying assumption being, if not actually stated, "but I'm a *sabra*" (a native-born Israeli). Most sabras, having imbibed the patterns of behavior and aspirations of the society, devalue their families' cultural background in favor of their own culture of Israel. Many assume that the culture of the immigrants represents somewhat of a corruption, a culture from the Diaspora which they see as Jews living in fear of persecution, condescending to non-Jews because of fear of reprisal if they do not, keeping a low profile, not saying anything. Israeli society—a society where people can say what they think, when they think it—is seen as the opposite of the "Diaspora mentality." Therefore, Israeli-born children of Iranian parents, and even many Iranians who immigrated at a young age, consider themselves Israelis and negate Iranian identity. The negotiation of their Iranian heritage has to do with both the negative stereotypes and images about Iranians that exist in Israeli society and the impetus of the ideology to forget the Diaspora culture and be Israeli.

Children of immigrants identify themselves as Israelis, with Israeli culture, not with the culture of the immigrant group, although they often concede that in the home there are distinguishing family features from the cultures of origin—foods that the parents or grandparents made might be cooked, certain religious rituals might be performed, ethnic music might be played. These family and regional traditions which had been seen as cultural expressions derived from the Diaspora are now exploited, often publicly, for political and cultural aggrandizement. There is even a word in Hebrew to connote different traditions based upon having lived in different societies in the Diaspora, *minhag*. The meaning is "manner, custom, usage, way, conduct, habit" (Alcalay 1963:1371), but it is used to refer to religious practice as well as family traditions, connoting custom as law, an accepted way of behavior which is often unchangeable. The *minhagim* (pl.), once scorned as superstitious or appreciated as unique folkloristic practices, are now emblems representing cultural heritage, customs to be enacted as signifying a certain type of Israeli: there are Moroccans who pray at the tomb of a revered rabbi; ultra-Orthodox Ashkenazim who celebrate a wedding for seven days; Iranians who observe the annual commemoration of someone's death with a meal for the family. Although many native-born Israelis dampen their connection to the past in favor of developing their place in the culture of the present, others are using minhagim specifically to place their mark in the present.

The culture of the present is changing in Israel. In the past ten to twelve years Israelis began to reevaluate Diaspora cultural markers as badges of background pride, worn to assert recognition of cultural traits which were previously ridiculed as primitive but always were there and practiced. This reevaluation is also exemplified by the development of ethnic-political movements based on political and economic inequality which derived from cultural differences between the immigrants (especially those from the Middle East) and the Ashkenazi establishment in the 1950s. For instance, Tami, an ethnic political party developed in 1980 by North African immigrants and their descendants, and headed by Aharon Abu Hatzeira, of an eminent Moroccan family, confronted the socialist Zionist ideology of absorption of immigrants and asserted full participation of

Oriental Jews in the political and economic structure of the state. In addition, there is a new ultra-Orthodox Sephardic political party which appeared at the time of the 1984 elections, *Shas*, an acronym from "Shomrei (Torah) Sepharad—"Sephardic (Torah) Guardians". This party, created by doctrinal rabbis and other extremely religious individuals of Middle Eastern and Sephardic background as a counterpart to the Ashkenazi ultra-Orthodox political party, Agudat Israel, often utilizes concepts of divine punishment to propagate moralistic behavior. An example is a collision between a train and a schoolbus from the city of Petakh Tikva, which caused numerous casualties. The accident came at a time of a secular-religious struggle to open—or continue to keep closed—movie theaters on Friday evening during the Sabbath in Petakh Tikva. Yitzhak Peretz, Minister of the Interior who represents the Shas Party, blamed the collision on "desecration of the Sabbath" (*khilul shabbat*).

The reappraisal of ethnic heritage springs from changes in Zionist ideology from the socialist Zionist universalistic orientation of the 1940s which dominated the country until 1967, to a particularistic and nationalistic orientation beginning after the Six Day War.[10] The transformation, a consequence of Israel's successful defeat of the Arab nations in 1967 and their unsuccessful battle in 1973, combined with the failure of the state to integrate the numerous Oriental Jews into the social, economic, and political structure of the society, elicited a new search for meanings among the populace. Different manifestations of Jewishness have become salient means to assert ethnic identity and to claim the right for full participation in societal institutions. Some Ashkenazi youths from secular families embrace ultra-Orthodox Judaism, whereas different Oriental communities, such as Moroccans and Kurds, are developing folk festivals to exemplify their cultural heritage as worthy of respect and recognition.

One such observance is the Maimouna, a Moroccan festival commemorating the philosopher Maimonides on the day after Passover. In Jerusalem the Maimouna is observed in a public park near the Israel Museum. There is a large platform on which musicians play, politicians talk, dancers perform; there are people selling kebab, falafel, ice cream, and drinks; families come, set up tents, prepare picnic lunches, play Moroccan music and dance; some women wear traditional Moroccan clothing. I attended two of these festivals, two years in a row. The first one had mostly Moroccans as participants. The second, in the year of the 1981 elections, had tents and booths of several other Middle Eastern immigrant groups, each marked out in its own place, with the Moroccans occupying the large central area surrounding the platform. In an area behind the platform were the tents of Kurds, Georgians, Iraqis, and Iranians.

The Iranians who attended Maimouna, immigrants with their children, brought picnic lunches and sat under the tents with family or friends. In Iran, on the last day of Passover, and also in Israel, families go to gardens for picnics, a day known as Ruz-i Bāgh, Garden Day. In Jerusalem of 1981, for the first time they participated in Maimouna. The Iranians had their own exposition at the opposite end of the park from the Moroccans. There were tents which housed displays of Iranian handicrafts—carpets with Jewish themes, metal plates engraved with a picture of Moses holding the Ten Commandments, an ingraved silver *megillah* cover (the Book of Esther in scroll form), Hebrew and Judaeo-Persian miniatures, needlework, and old clothing. One woman was dressed in an Iranian Kurdish costume and sat on a carpet next to a tray full of tiny tea glasses. The Iranians also had a food-tasting contest for the best cook of Iranian foods and an Iranian dance contest for twelve to seventeen-year-old girls. The prizes for the contests were the newly published Hebrew-Persian dictionaires (for the refugee market), donated and presented by the publisher, a man who came to Israel at the age of sixteen in 1949.

On the main platform in the Moroccan section were performances by different immigrant communities and municipal groups, such as an Israeli folk dance troupe and a police band, and speeches by different politicians. One performance exemplified the social status of the performers by the audience's reaction. A group of Soviet Georgian immigrants performed several Georgian folk dances. The Georgians are one of the newest immigrant groups and in the context of Israeli stereotyping, are considered to be criminals (thieves, murderers, rapists; several crimes were committed by Georgians who had difficulties adjusting to Israeli society; the stereotype that they are social misfits stuck). After the young Georgians danced, the announcer told the audience to clap, since the dancers came all the way to Jerusalem from Nazareth especially to perform at Maimouna. Instead, the audience was silent. However, the audience booed, hissed, and threw food at Shimon Peres, the Labor Party candidate for prime minister who spoke at the festival. For many Jews of Middle Eastern origin, the Labor Party represents the Israel which denied them their cultural heritage, stuck them as settlers at the borders of the state, and placed them in a low socioeconomic position vis-à-vis the Ashkenazim. Shimon Peres was not welcome. But Menahem Begin was. When he spoke, the audience shouted "Begin! Begin!" and some started to sing the Hebrew song, "David, King of Israel", as "Begin, King of Israel". Begin, although Ashkenazi, represents nationalism, distinction, and separation to those citizens whose cultural identity was denigrated by the Labor government and/or whose Israeli identity is intensified and manifested by the ultranationalistic ideology of Begin's brand of Zionism. Those Israelis of Middle Eastern origin, exploited in the 1950s to develop the industrial and agricultural economy, are now no longer at the bottom of the sociocultural hierarchy since the Arabs do the manual labor they used to do. Instead, they focus on their identity as real Israelis while claiming that the predominantly Ashkenazi members of Peace Now would like to relinquish the land to the Palestinians and therefore are not true Israelis.

Rather than the above being a diversion from the discussion of identity and stereotypes in Israeli society, the occurrences at the Maimouna festival exemplify the complexities of ideology and ethnicity in Israel. The ideology, which people take to heart, concerns the ingathering and intermingling of the exiles, and the development of one sociocultural system. The Maimouna festival gathered many of the Middle Eastern ethnic groups. The individual members of these groups, in terms of behavior, goals, attitudes, values, speech, and social relationships, are more similar to one another and to Ashkenazi groups than they are to those of their families' countries of origin. They exhibit the national culture based upon a common code of communication which expresses attitudes about and models for human relationships and behavior, and a common heritage emphasizing the need to be powerful because of the consequences of powerlessness in the Diaspora. Except for some of the immigrants, the majority of those who attended the Maimouna, the participants as well as the observers, identify themselves as Israelis, not as Moroccans, Iranians, Kurds, Russians, or what have you. Their identity as Israelis was reaffirmed by the support they presented Begin. Yet, the particular ethnic differences of the participants of Maimouna were maximized by the purpose of the festival: to observe a Moroccan celebration. This celebration has been enhanced to include the pageantry of what Keyes (1979) calls "symbolic expressions"—food, dance, music—of the different Middle Eastern immigrant groups in Israel, the same groups who were told in the 1950s to forget their cultures of origin. The Moroccans are the largest Middle Eastern immigrant group in Israel with political clout, courted by politicians who now recognize, as opposed to the politicians of thirty years ago, the validity of immigrants' cultures, and who try to foster the display of ethnic differences in terms of folkloristic characteristics, the quaint customs that differentiate one group from another, and which are being lost due to the quest on the part of the society and the immigrants themselves to become Israeli. *In becoming Israeli, it is not so much these quaint characteristics which are dropped as invalid representations of Diaspora culture, but, rather, ways of behaving, communicating, and thinking about human relationships, the family, the individual, and the state.*

Ethnic identity in Israel is a way people categorize themselves and others. On the one hand, there are the immigrant identities based on culture of national origin which, in confrontation with the Israeli sociocultural system, engender ethnic stereotypes. On the other hand, there are the identities of Middle Eastern and Western, aggregate geographical-cultural and economic groupings, where the Middle Eastern immigrants and their descendants have been relatively poorer, less educated than Western immigrants, culturally disregarded and scorned, and economically exploited by the ruling Ashkenazi elite. Such divisions are the roots of present-day political antagonism as both groups compete to be more "Israeli," aspiring more to the ways they understand Zionist ideology. The Middle Eastern and Western segments of the population create their own ethnic stereotypes of one another, which do not take into consideration the culture of national origin but which, instead, look at the ways people of the two segments view nationalism, politics, and access to resources. What has happened in Israel is an obfuscation of ethnicity as representative of culture of national origin in favor of Israeli identity and the expansion of ethnicity as membership in either Ashkenazi or Sephardi-Middle Eastern segments of the population (or in both, as the exogamy rate between the two segments is 20 percent).[11] Added to this are the minhagim, the customs, of different immigrant-ethnic groups, such as a Yemeni woman having a henna ceremony before her wedding, an Iranian woman preparing rice and *ghormeh-sabzi* for Passover, a Moroccan woman dancing at the Maimouna festival wearing a long brocaded gown, an ultra-Orthodox American woman breaking a plate before her marriage: although each is observing a minhag representative of varied cultural traditions, some of which, like Maimouna, may be employed publicly for political purposes, all identify themselves primordially as Israelis, secondarily, if that at all, from Yemeni, Iranian, Moroccan, or American background.

The differentiation, therefore, must be made between ethnicity or identity as self-ascribed and as other-ascribed, and when and why they are articulated. Although descendants of different immigrant groups consider themselves Israelis, Israelis still harbor stereotypes for the different ethnic groups, in spite of the fact that the descendants of these groups in terms of behavior, communication, ideals, and goals can seldom be differentiated, although racially, some groups, such as Yemenis, may be distinguishable.[12] Yemenis are still considered rooted in their cultural traditions, Iranians stingy, stupid, and suspicious, Moroccans aggressive, Americans spoiled and dishonest about expressing their emotions ("they smile when there's nothing fully to smile about"). The Yemenis, Iranians, Moroccans, and Americans do not view themselves with such stereotypes. The question of stereotypes and ethnic identity then becomes a problem of relationships and categorization, in which certain attributes, such as ways of communicating, are developed and contrasted as representative of group characteristics, influencing interaction and transactions. We saw this problem in the relationship between Anat, Bob, and Esther, and we recognized the way the stereotypes are used and made fun of to enhance immigrant identity in the play about Mulla Davut.

The sociocultural situation in Israel concerning relationships between different immigrant groups is a result of the original structure and ideology of the state, which fostered immigration, developed a state bureaucracy to deal with the new immigrants, and manned the offices with Western immigrants or sabras who helped process the newcomers to a completely different sociocultural system from the ones they left. Following the immigrant experience and cross-cultural contact were both the creation of ethnic stereotypes based upon mutual misunderstandings in the realm of communication, and a culture of the nation-state which stressed shedding the values, beliefs, and behaviors of the Diaspora and adopting new ones based upon a nonhierarchical society in which relationships would be grounded upon honesty, idealism, independence, and scrupulousness. Children of immigrants want to have as little to do with their parents' traditional behavior and values as possible, although observing certain minhagim are appreciated as distinctive folk and familial practices. Israeli identity is valued over Diaspora regional ethnic identity. Yet, at the same time, the stereotypes which were developed at the time of immigration remain and oftentimes form barriers to successful social transactions and interactions.

Who knows what will happen concerning ethnicity in Israel in the next decade or two. As it stands now, many native-born Israelis do not look toward their Diaspora past as anything to be proud of,[13] although minhagim symbolize bonds with the past as connected to Israeli peoplehood and dramatize differences in the present. Perhaps this will change, and it will be interesting to discover what happens in the society to foster such change. In the meantime, communication forms relationships between different ethnic groups and inspires ethnic stereotypes. In addition, when people from different immigrant backgrounds start communicating in the same styles symbolic of newly learned relationships, norms, and values, their previous differences are homogenized into a new cultural entity, although the ethnic stereotypes remain.

The problems of ethnicity and ethnic identity are expressed through ethnic stereotypes on the one hand, and denied by maintaining Israeli identity on the other. Each group tries to be more "Israeli" than the other, while often looking for the trait which will indicate something about the ethnic stereotype in others. Resulting from these contradictions in self- and other-ascribed identity are problems in cross-cultural communication, especially between people of an immigrant group and Israelis, where stereotypes and communication differences influence interaction.

Chapter 5
Iranian Immigrants in Israel: Sociocultural Dissonance and Personal Distress

Leaving one's homeland, voluntarily or unwillingly, and settling in an alien environment necessitates socialization to a new symbolic structure of behavior, actions, values, goals, and beliefs. Often this entails an identity crisis, problems in coping with a new reality, changes in an individual's role system and in social relationships, and disintegration of the immigrants' cultural patterns of behavior and beliefs.[1] At other times, immigrants settle in the new society practically problem-free. What kinds of situations are perceived as especially distressing depend on the immigrant's culture of orientation, which is used as a reference point from which to compare, contrast, and understand the alien and unfamiliar society in which the immigrant chose to live.

If we define, as Geertz does (1973:144–45), culture as "the framework of beliefs, expressive symbols, and values in terms of which individuals define their world, express their feelings, . . . make judgments, . . . interpret their experience and guide their actions," and social structure as "the form that action takes, the actual existing network of social relations," then when the form of social relations changes and the symbolic meaning of experience and action does not, a situation of incongruity is created. People have difficulties interpreting and making sense out of the action of others (often in relation to self) as problems of meaning of beliefs and behavior come to the fore. Such problems of incongruity between changing social structure and culture are frequently the experience of immigrants.

Many immigrants who experience the unavoidable social changes prompted by adjustment to a new environment do not encounter cultural changes at the same rate. Their ideas, beliefs, and values about the ways people should behave, and how relationships, whether within the family or with nonintimate outsiders, should transpire, are based upon those of their culture of orientation. Accordingly, Iranians in Israel perceive certain social situations as distressing because their social relationships are changing faster than are their conceptual categories about the transformations they are experiencing. These social and cultural transformations, which are influenced by certain social stressors—events, dilemmas, or situations in society which are problematic for the people experiencing them—generate the dysphoric affect nārāhati. Although the stressors experienced by the immigrants are social products of the economic, familial, and environmental transitions wrought by reconciliation to a new society, many Iranians in Israel experience these stressors as personal, rather than social, problems.[2] The incompatibility between the patterns of social relationships formed in the new society and the cultural underpinning of the former society engenders sociocultural dissonance which calls for resolve. Here, the resolution for the nārāhatis of immigration for many Iranians in Israel is sickness.

Sociocultural dissonance is a term I use to connote a condition or situation of incongruity between beliefs, values, behaviors, and feelings favored and experienced by people from one culture living in, confronting, and trying to make sense out of those of another. When there is a lack of fit, a discord, between core cultural values, questions regarding proper behavior, self and other, the good and the bad of the "us" and the "them" arise: How should I behave? What are they doing? Why do they act the way they do? What's happening to my family? What's happening to me? Why is life so different? The contrast between external social stressors, those problems and situations in society which induce feelings of pressure or stress on individuals, and internal cultural values exacerbates sociocultural dissonance and engenders distress. The distress comes about because of the lack of harmony between the individual's values, goals, expectations, and beliefs, and those of the society in which he or she lives, and the consequent changes. How individuals manifest the distress created by sociocultural dissonance is culturally dependent and frequently reflects images and associations of the values called into question. The sociocultural dissonance experienced by Iranian immigrants in Israel, those stressors in Israeli society which are particularly difficult for Iranians to get used to, are attributed not to societal differences and sociocultural stressors, but to the sensitivity of the particular persons involved. Individuals regard the changes which occur in their lives not as a result of social transformations due to adaptation to a new social and cultural system, but as personal problems that they are incapable of resolving.

For Iranian immigrants in Israel, issues of distress include changes in societal role definitions, behavior, relationships, and physical, environmental differences. These changes are manifested structurally in problems of interpersonal transactions, disintegration of traditional familial roles, economic problems, work dissatisfaction, feelings of powerlessness vis-à-vis the state bureaucracy, and inadequate housing. Perceptions and experiences of these stressors are not uniform among the Iranian immigrant population, as the population itself varies in levels of attachment to Iranian cultural patterns on the one hand, and accommodation and adaptation to those of Israel on the other. In addition, there are intergenerational, intraethnic, familial, regional, religious, and individual differences among members of the same immigrant group. For instance, among the Iranian population in Israel are parents who are attached to Iranian cultural norms, whereas their children not only know little about the Iranian heritage (frequently I heard Israeli-born children of Iranian heritage referring to Muslim Iranians as "Arabs"—a misnomer that offends Iranians), but also communicate and behave like Israelis, showing the lack of respect and rudeness which Iranians see in Israelis. Other social differences exist among the Iranians: educational, from illiterates to academics; regional, with Isfahanis, Yazdis, Shirazis, and Mashhadis in Jerusalem affiliated with their own ethnic synagogues; religious, ranging from very religious to traditional to secular—with intergenerational differences creating tension between parents and children. These elements of diversity make generalizations about acclimatization to Israeli society difficult. Furthermore, Iranians in Israel may be classified as having different adjustment and cultural characteristics depending upon time of immigration and reasons for immigrating.

In spite of the differences among the Iranian immigrants, and their different rates of adjustment to Israeli society and "becoming" Israeli, several stressors stand out as being of paramount concern to them in assessing their lives in Israel and comparing them to life in Iran: changes in the family; economic difficulties; loneliness; communicative difficulties; unfulfilled expectations.[3] These stressors, a consequence of social changes which proceed more rapidly than peoples' values, feelings, judgments, and beliefs with which they order their world, give rise to sociocultural dissonance and personal distress.

Comparing Iranians and Israelis: The Good and the Bad

The Iranian cultural values which maintain and are influenced by the hierarchical structure of Iranian society and by the social relationships which compose the hierarchy, such as respect (ehterām), honor and respectability (āberu), privacy, zerangi (cleverness), and sensitivity (hassāsiyat), are the paragons of propriety by which people govern their behavior. Iranian immigrants invoke these cultural values while trying to explain and evaluate their lives in Israel. However, their lives in Israel are not based upon the hierarchical social relations and communication codes that are intrinsic to social interaction in Iran. In Israel such forms of behavior which recall hierarchy are culturally disvalued. The Iranian social boundaries of economic class, personal-familial status, and relationships of domination and subordination, which form the basis for interpersonal relationships with nonintimates, and sometimes with intimates of different ages and gender, become blurred, muted, or abrogated in Israel. For some Iranian immigrants in Israel, the incongruity between their Iranian cultural patterns and their Israeli social relationships creates a situation of sociocultural dissonance and distress, engendering feelings of powerlessness to act effectively within the new social system. This will be exemplified in the following two sections by case studies of three families with different reactions to the immigrant experience. First, however, we will evaluate the discourse of Iranians regarding the good and the bad of Iran and Israel, articulated on themes of the sociocultural stressors they experience while adjusting to Israeli society.

The Jewish family in Iran was essentially a patriarchal one in which the father was the principal decision maker, primary money-earner, purchaser, and public agent in negotiating with other families and other institutions. The mother worked within the confines of the walls surrounding the yard and the house, cooking, cleaning, and child-raising, sometimes constructing relationships with other families through contacts with other women, such as marriage arrangements. Children's relationships with parents were characterized as one of subordination and respect, listening to and carrying out the desires of the family in order to ensure the survival of the family as a unit and to maintain familial honor and reputation in the society.

Upon immigration to Israel, such familial relationships are subject to change as women enter the workforce and as children learn Hebrew and adapt to Israeli values. Iranian women who perceive the participation of Israeli women in the economy as instrumental for vacating their small apartments, developing a wider network of relationships, and earning more money for the family's expenses, frequently obtain employment. For traditional men, this change in the social role of their wives is threatening, undermining their own position as the head of the family: with the woman bringing into the household extra income comes increased power in decision making, thus corroding one of the role functions of the male head of household. Consequently, when one or more members of the family hold traditional cultural values concerning patterns of social relations within the family, and when such patterns change due to the intentional acts of others within the family, such as the case of a wife working, the incompatibility between the cultural categories and social patterns creates tension among family members.

The traditional structure of the Iranian family in Israel is also undermined by changes in the child-parent relationship. Parental dominance is dissolved as parents become dependent on their children to carry out activities within the community that require a knowledge of Hebrew that some adults never properly learn. A generation gap is thus created between parents whose cultural values vary from those of their children who are socialized, outside the home, to the core cultural and social patterns of Israeli society. Children in Israel are seen by Iranian immigrants as being too free, spoiled, and lacking respect and honor for their parents. The Israeli-socialized child learns a different way of relating to honor, respect, and power than had the Iranian immigrant parents. The parent expects honor and submissiveness from the child. The child exemplifies honesty and egalitarianism learned in school, in the army, and with friends. Children may talk back to the parents, say what they think, do what they want. For the children such communication represents honesty as a characteristic of the good Israeli, but for the parents it represents disrespect and rudeness of the child not honoring the parents. Moreover, many children of Iranian immigrants make fun of their heritage and laugh at the Persian language. That, in itself, is a grave insult to the parents who value their cultural background.

Iranians appraise the changes in familial relationships in Israel by contrasting the family in Iran and in Israel as two opposing types. In Iran, the family is seen as closer, warmer, and based upon relationships of respect and honor. In Israel, the family is seen as distant, sometimes nonexistent, living apart, and lacking relationships of politeness and respect between children and parents. For Iranian parents dealing with their Israeli children, and for traditional men dealing with wives who voluntarily transform their roles, such problems are stressors, creating discord as one or more people in the family prefers the traditional role while another prefers a new role. The family as a unit the way it was in Iran becomes transformed and undergoes stresses of transition in Israel.

Economic difficulties of immigration generate social changes in relationships with intimates and non-intimates with regard to work and housing. Compared to life in Iran before the late 1950s, where many Jews were confined to life in the mahalleh (the Jewish ghetto), life in Israel was an improvement economically, as well as socially and politically. However, there were years of economic hardships after immigration. This was the case for everyone in the 1950s as well as for Iranians who came to Israel after the Iranian economy began to prosper in the 1960s. People left large houses, carpets, and other goods in Iran along with their jobs, whether they were petty-merchants, workers, craftsmen, peddlers, housewives, or professionals. The men in the first decades of the state were given jobs which were usually insulting to their pride: not only were they not independent providers, as most of them had been in Iran, but they had become, in Israel, workers under an employer in a semi-socialist economic system that was alien to them. In the first years of the state, work was what needed to be done, and many, powerless and unable to obtain employment by themselves, or without capital to start a business, accepted the positions given to them by public and private bureaucrats who were working for such organizations as the non-profit Jewish Agency, or profit-making establishments such as banks and textile firms. For many Iranians, the jobs were not only lacking in status (guard, post office clerk, painter, stone cutter), but they paid less than they had been earning as self-employed wage-earners in Iran in comparison to costs of food, clothing, and housing.

Since housing is expensive in Israel, most families live in apartments, although some do own private villas, costly and limited in numbers. For families who lived in the mahalleh in Iran, housing in Israel has been an improvement, but for those who lived in large private houses surrounded by walls separating the family from the neighbors and the street, apartments in Israel are small and lack the privacy they were used to in Iran.

Economic problems are further exacerbated by high income taxes deducted from workers' paychecks, lowering the already low wages even more, whereas in Iran, one often did not pay taxes. Salaries are perceived as restricted, and food, clothing, utilities, and other goods are seen as more expensive than in Iran. Moreover, food is considered healthier in Iran, more natural, and devoid of chemicals. Thus, the economic situation, with low status jobs for some, low salaries for many, high taxes for all, and high cost of living in comparison to Iran, is stressful for Iranians, as well as for others living in Israel. The zerangi (cleverness) which could be mustered to circumnavigate such economic problems in Iran does not work in Israel, and many immigrants therefore feel powerless regarding their economic condition. This powerlessness in the economic realm of society working with non-intimates is reminiscent of the powerlessness in relations with non-intimates in Iran. However, the egalitarian ideals that characterize communication among people in Israel, fostering a kind of communicative closeness among non-intimates which is nonexistent in Iran, engenders ambiguity in relationships among new immigrants accustomed to more structured hierarchical relations.

The differences in relationships between intimates and non-intimates, egalitarian and hierarchical, magnified feelings of loneliness among Iranians who immigrated to Israel without their families. Loneliness has been a profound and disturbing social and personal condition for the several thousand teenagers who came on Youth Aliya[4] in the late 1940s and early 1950s, for the young men and women who left their families to pursue studies or work in Israel after the Islamic Revolution, and for couples who immigrated without their extended families. Without their families for social, cultural, economic, and emotional support and nurturing, lone immigrants perceive their social situation as devoid of the relationships necessary to prosper in the new environment. This is aggravated by not knowing the language at first, not being able to communicate with those around them. In addition, not having a group of friends with whom to socialize—*khevreh* as it is called in Hebrew—adds to their predicament. Israelis socialize with and entertain the same group of friends whom they know from school and the army, and to be an immigrant not part of such a group, whether of Israelis or other immigrants, can enhance loneliness. Loneliness is also enhanced by the Iranian cultural values of separation, distance, privacy, and distrust of non-intimates. Lonely Iranians often search for non-Iranian friends to reveal their burdens (*dard-i del*), rather than confiding in nonintimate (possibly zerang) Iranians. Those Iranians who perceive themselves as weak and vulnerable, which may carry the social stigma of shame for oneself and one's family, frequently distrust other Iranians who, they fear, could take advantage of them personally or spread confidential information about them within the Iranian community, thus jeopardizing their social standing.

The period of loneliness, a time of liminality when learning the sociocultural system of Israel, lasts for a few years, my informants say in retrospect. Iranians negatively value the position of being alone; family members or friends will stay with someone in order that the person will not remain alone in a house; young people do not, for the most part, live alone; people are more apt to be afraid when alone. Therefore, the loneliness of a lone Iranian immigrant, without a family, without a friendship network, without knowing the rules of the society or the regulations of communication, is intensified by the cultural values of sensitivity, respect, privacy, and distance in relations with non-intimates which inhibits, for some, the ability to form new intimate relationships.

Finally, when expectations of life in Israel are thwarted by the reality of life or are unfulfilled, Israel is seen as negative in opposition to Iran which is valued as positive. The social and cultural traits compared are not material ones, although people always refer to the better houses and cheaper foods in Iran. Rather, what is contrasted are human relationships, by which the two societies are characterized as opposites.

One particularly bothersome feature of Israeli society for Iranians involves the conduct of men and women in the public domain. In Iran, the public domain is one of distance and formality between people. In Israel, the public domain is seen by Iranian immigrants to be lacking "moral borders" and "social borders": Israelis lack both respect for others and politeness necessary for public behavior with people one does not know. To a certain degree, the lack of formality between people and the relaxation of sexual codes in the secular population of Israel negate the concept of Israel as a "Promised Land" to many. One refugee who arrived in Israel in December 1979, after experiencing religious revival in Iran and the public institutionalization of what is considered proper behavior between the sexes in Islamic law, expressed his dismay at his expectations of the "Promised Land": "Israel as promised land or a country of Jews—wow! To see it as promised, you have to look at the religious side. It is not from the Bible. There is no religion. In the promised land you shouldn't see kissing on the street. I believe in sex freedom, but the promised land is not that. This isn't the promised land." Sexual freedoms of Israeli youth are condemned as lacking "moral borders." This is also observed in the style of dress, which is seen as sloppy in comparison to the Iranians, who are well-dressed when outside their houses in Iran. "Iranians dress well over there," said an Isfahani well integrated in Israeli society, "But here, Israelis walk around with half their behind sticking out of their pants." This lack of "moral borders" and "social borders" and the breakdown of separations between male and female (premarital sex among teenagers, pornographic magazines in shops, public display of affection, coeducational youth groups) are as distressing for many immigrants as is the change of relationships within a household: social categories are blurred and called into question, creating sociocultural dissonance as the immigrants' core cultural values conflict with the external social situation.

Iranian Jews are also disappointed by the stereotypes that others have about them in Israel. They feel as if they are not respected by other groups in Israeli society. Being called "Parsi" or "Parsi midunid" (Persian for "do you know Persian," a phrase which many Israelis know; apparently, during the first large wave of immigrants from Iran in the late 1940s and early 1950s, many Iranians had asked people on the street if they knew the Persian language; the question stuck and had become an ethnic label) is reminiscent of being called "Johood" in Iran and for some, feels worse. Expectations were that discrimination against them, as Jews, would not exist in Israel. But they were disillusioned at being distinguished negatively as Persians. They attribute the negative label to the first waves of immigrants who were uneducated in the Western context and were thought of as ignorant. However, most Iranians deny the existence of social or institutional discrimination against them in Israeli society, although they do admit that in daily interaction ethnic slurs are common. Others say there is discrimination against Iranians as a group of Sephardim, that there is nothing on television about Iranians, that there are few Iranians in government, that there is only one member of the Knesset who is Iranian (and some say he became a member of the Knesset because his wife is Ashkenazi).

One Iranian friend of mine whose family heritage is Iraqi explained the attitude of Israelis toward Iranians and toward herself. Although she differentiated herself from other Iranians by taking on Israeli attitudes about Iranians, she was labeled as Iranian by Israelis: "Here Iranians are cheap. They are dirty, like they are living with Gruzim [Georgian Jews, in the late 1970s the lowest ethnic group on the Israeli status totem pole]. That's because the high class don't come.

Only the low class does. They are cheap in their appearance and they speak cheap. Israelis have more character than Iranians do. Here Iranians are put all on the same level. So I say I'm an Iraqi Jew born in Israel who has lived in Iran when I'm at work. But what they see is Iranian in me, the way I talk and act. They call me 'Khomeini.' "

Immigrants who face the loss of previous problem-solving strategies for mastering social situations feel powerless in the new social and cultural milieu. In Iran such mastering often depended on whom one knew in terms of influence for granting favors, a system of patronage known as *pārti-bāzi,* in which favors were granted in exchange for reciprocal favors or social support. Many newer Iranian immigrants see the Israeli system of favor-granting, *protectzia* (from the English, protection), as being one-sided, not open to everyone, whereas pārti-bāzi is available for anyone who could take advantage of it. Other immigrants, the ones who came before and during the first years of the state, value protectzia (good and open to all) and contrast it with pārti-bāzi, which they consider bribery in Iran (bad and open to the rich only). What is at issue is not the differences between the different forms of favor-granting in Iran and in Israel, but the feelings of relative powerlessness that immigrants often have in a new society.

Relative powerlessness, personal or social, stems from a discrepancy between cultural values about the social system and the reality of the social system itself. People are told that they should be able to participate in various segments of the social, economic, and political structure of the society, but are simultaneously excluded from it, whether by education, lack of access to resources, prejudices, or poverty. In Israel, relative powerlessness first arises from being processed through the bureaucratic chain of offices dealing with immigration, welfare, absorption, and customs, which do, in actuality, help the immigrants settle. It was previously mentioned that the people working in these offices were often younger than the immigrant clients who became dependent on the clerks for certain goods and services. In comparison to the people in control of these goods and services, the immigrants, incapable of action, need to develop a relationship with the bureaucrats or clerks to get what they want. Those citizens who are familiar with the goings-on of other governmental agencies (those not dealing with immigration) often are able to use protectzia to influence the solution to their problems—faster, with ease, sometimes with less pay, sometimes with greater benefits. However, new immigrants who have no connections with people in the bureaucracy, or who have no connections with people who do have such connections, are at a disadvantage (see Avruch 1981 for a witty account of American immigrants' encounter with protectzia). One new immigrant, a refugee who was a resident in surgery at a Jerusalem hospital, looked at the problem of protectzia for Iranians as the dearth of Iranians in governmental positions, attributing this absence to the lack of educated Iranian immigrants during the early periods of immigration to Israel who, had they come, would have been in positions of power.

In actuality, Iranians are not as deficient in protectzia as they perceive they are. One instance of protectzia relates to Iranian refugees who came to Israel with Persian rugs after the Islamic Revolution. These were taxed as luxury items by the customs office. However, after numerous refugees appealed to various established Iranians who had been living in Israel for years, the problem of taxed carpets was alleviated. Iranian officials of the Iranian immigrant associations who had governmental connections convinced the customs department, by demonstrating that Iranians' savings are their carpets, to allow Iranians to bring into the country a certain amount of square meterage of carpet. Whereas other immigrants are permitted to bring into the country certain electrical appliances tax-free (refrigerators, televisions, dishwashers), the Iranians who quickly left Iran because of the political turmoil took out of the country their carpets and perhaps a number of other local arts. Taxing them was then perceived by the refugees and by the Iranians involved in politics as unjust. Iranian protectzia therefore changed the customs regulations on behalf of the new immigrants.

Although direct personal contacts with governmental clerks and officials through whom protectzia is procured may be lacking, indirect personal contacts in different aspects of Israeli society are to the Iranians' advantage, although not realized as such: workers at the Iranian immigrant organization call up Iranian acquaintances at banks asking for positions for new immigrants; Iranian clerks in the produce department of the supermarket save the best produce for Iranian customers; some Iranian residents in Israel do not take out Israeli citizenship in order to avoid paying exorbitant taxes and having male members of the family drafted into the army; Iranian owners of clothing stores give discounts to Iranian customers.

The protectzia that is lacking is the ability to circumvent various aspects of the system that were, as mentioned in the play about Mulla Davut, more easily outwitted in Iran. Many Iranians in Israel, in that respect, see themselves as powerless. This perception of relative powerlessness in comparison to the other major ethnic groups in Israel—the politically dominant Ashkenazim, and even the numerically dominant and vociferous Moroccans—is seen as a disadvantage and as something caused by and perpetuated by others, something for which the Iranians themselves are not responsible.

Such social and cultural stressors as depicted above indicate the reference point that Iranian culture has in the thoughts of the immigrants. What are perceived as negative in Israel are social and cultural qualities which differ from their counterparts in Iran. However, not all differences between the two sociocultural systems are seen as negative. There are characteristics of Israeli society which are valued as positive when compared to life in Iran. These characteristics are depicted in the framework of life in Israel being freer than life in Iran. Although part of this freer feeling pertains to being in a country where they do not have to worry about discrimination against them as Jews as they did in Iran, most of the discourse on freedom in Israel refers to values and traits which are, in themselves, part of the stressors which people complain about as being worse in Israel. Several examples explain this contradiction.

Iranians complain about the Israelis being rude and impolite compared to Iranians being polite and respectful. Yet, they admire the self-confidence of the Israelis, the fact that there is no ta'ārof, that people speak together more willingly, not realizing that these valued aspects of Israeli behavior are correlated with the rude and impolite characteristics: the fact that people say what they think is good on the one hand (no ta'ārof) but bad on the other (rude and impolite). This is contrasted with the negative aspect of communication in Iran, in which people flatter others too much, often say one thing and mean another, and do not speak freely: behind the distance and politeness people often do not know what the other is thinking. Iranians also complain that the Israeli families are not close and that the Iranians have close caring familial relationships, but another trait admired about Israelis is that they are individualistic, "live for themselves," as one friend of mine put it, not caring what neighbors, family, or strangers think. However, because individuals often do what they want without regard to the family as a corporate unit whose dignity and reputation must be maintained, Iranians think that Israeli families are not as close as Iranians.

Women immigrants mentioned that life in Israel for women and children is better than life in Iran: freedom to walk in the streets without being bothered; education and work opportunities; independence for boys and girls to interact without proscriptions for separation in school and extracurricular activities. Furthermore, in spite of the complaint that Israelis dress slovenly and Iranians dress neatly when walking on the streets of Iran, many immigrants voice approval of the comfortable style of dressing in Israel: young refugees from the Islamic Revolution who in Tehran would dress differently when outside the walls of the house than when inside familial, private space, in Israel wear whatever feels comfortable, usually T-shirts and jeans. No one worries what neighbors or strangers think about their dress style, as countless young people in Israel wear the same clothing.

Another salient contrast mentioned by several immigrants is that Israelis are never very depressed, implying that Iranians, in opposition, are more often depressed.[5] Israelis are characterized by Iranians as not caring much or worrying much about their future because of having to contend with the uncertainty of war; rather, they enjoy the present. Daily problems which Iranian immigrants see as significant (children not listening; premarital sex; lack of respect in relationships), they feel Israelis see as unimportant compared to the all-important problem of war. Accordingly, Iranians see themselves as more sensitive than Israelis, more concerned about family relationships, more worried about the future, deeper in terms of thinking and feeling about such issues, and therefore, more depressed. Yet they admire the Israelis for not being depressed since there are so many matters about which to be depressed.

The above examples in which the good of Israeli culture is contrasted with the bad of Iranian culture are fraught with inherent ambiguities. People often make comparisons of the good life in Iran with the bad life in Israel, the good life in Israel with the bad life in Iran. However, what is not articulated is that the traits valued as good in Israel are correlated with the traits that are valued as bad in Israel. For instance, the freedom of women and children (good) is interconnected with the lack of close familial relationships (bad) that are perceived about the Israeli families by Iranians; the self-confidence and freedom of speaking (good) is correlated with the rude and impolite Israeli (bad). Such ambivalence of values and behavior no doubt is distressing for immigrants.

The ambivalence felt—and, partially, the stressors inducing it—are a consequence of sociocultural dissonance which pits one culture's ideals and norms against the other's: the internalized (Iranian) opposes the external (Israeli), generating questions of behavior, status, roles, self, other, values, goals, and beliefs, and raising conflicts in families, within individuals, among neighbors and strangers. Questions are social issues—how should one think and behave, like an Iranian or an Israeli? The feelings of relative powerlessness, changes in family relations, work difficulties, economic worries, loneliness, negative stereotypes about them that Israelis have, and being called "Parsi" or "Parsi midunid" produce feelings of nārāhati among many Iranian immigrants in Israel. Added to this nārāhati is the distress brought about through sociocultural dissonance, a condition about which individuals are not quite cognizant, nor quite ignorant, a kind of hovering situation in which the actors are somewhat out of harmony with the surrounding system, but not so out of harmony as to be unable to participate in it.

Responses to Stressors of Immigration

Perhaps most stressful for Iranian immigrants are those problems pertaining to changes in the family. In Iran, family membership is one's fundamental source of identity, others being religion, neighborhood, town or village, province or profession. Individuals behave to ensure family honor and respect vis-à-vis other families in the society. Individuals also ideally interact with intimates and nonintimates to maintain one's repute and that of the family while showing respect to others. Status, honor, and respect of self and others, as well as consideration of the essential sensitivity of people, form the basis of communication and interaction in Iran. However, all these ways of being—sensitive, respectful, hierarchical in relations, motivated by familial honor—are called into question upon immigration to Israel. In interaction with Israelis whose social structure and communication code reflect not a society based upon hierarchy but one based upon egalitarian ideals, honesty (especially verbal) in relations with others, and self-confidence of the individual, often the sensitive Iranian immigrant comes face to face with communicative conflicts which are difficult to understand. The consequences of these conflicts are difficulties in adjusting to the new society.

Personal distress of Iranian immigrants in Israel is manifested by social discourse on the difficulties of life in Israel, by exemplifying nārāhati verbally or nonverbally, or by becoming ill. Illness is a medium through which social and cultural discomfort can be expressed when it is disapproved of or inconvenient to disclose one's nārāhati (to do so would indicate personal weakness or reverberate onto the family and make others nārāhat) or when one is not quite cognizant about the impingement of personal, social, and familial stressors on one's situation. Illness may be a reaction to social and personal problems that a person has, signifying a person's being out of control, or powerless, concerning personal or social predicaments, such as those confronted upon immigration. For the sensitive Iranian, polite and considerate, sometimes passive with respect in interaction with others, confrontation with rude Israeli bureaucrats, ill-tempered clerks, or children who are unsympathetic to the parents' culture of orientation, is personally disturbing.

Some Iranians who are sensitive to the social and cultural peculiarities of Israeli society complain with friends (Iranians; Israelis wouldn't understand) about the difficulties, whereas others rarely say anything unless questioned. Some people have difficulty adjusting to Israeli society and blame the Israelis, while others do adjust to being in Israel and harbor little, if any, resentment toward the Israelis. To exemplify the adjustment and reconciliation to life in Israel, sociocultural dissonance, personal distress, and illness, we will look at two families who came as refugees from Iran after the Islamic Revolution. One, a large family from Kashan with eight children, ranging in age from six years to twenty-six years, blended into Israeli society within months. Another, a Shirazi family with four children, did not.

The Kashani family came to Israel in two steps: first, in December 1978, the mother, six of the children, and the paternal grandmother arrived; then, after Khomeini took over the government and the Islamic Police burned the father's liquor store with the father and one of the sons caught in a back room, the father and the two oldest sons came, in March 1979. The family brought with them carpets, copper and silver trays and utensils, several fine miniature paintings in *khātam* (inlay work) frames, jewelry, and other arts from Iran. They bought a house in Jerusalem and the entire family, including the parents, studied at an ulpan (intensive Hebrew language course). The attendance by the parents was unusual, since the majority of Iranian adults over the age of forty in Israel who came after the Revolution (and some who came before) consider themselves too old to learn. Since this family intended to stay in Israel, they resolved their position as immigrants by taking advantage of the opportunities offered by social and governmental agencies to help with assimilation. The two older daughters who were attending different universities in Iran decided to go to trade schools in Israel. The older sons, who worked with their father in his liquor store in Kashan, helped the father establish a gift store business in Jerusalem. At times they were assisted by other children in the family.

This Kashani family maintained close contact with relatives in Jersualem who visited them often. They became active participants in a local Sephardic synagogue of the neighborhood (the synagogue services were performed in the Sephardic rite, and the people who attended were from various Middle Eastern and North African countries). After they were in Jerusalem for a year, the grandmother died. They mourned her death, but their lives as Iranians in the process of becoming Israelis were not disrupted. Except for the father, who survived the trauma of almost being burned with his shop and who had difficulties launching a new business in Jerusalem, the family members did not complain about life in Israel, how much nicer life was for them in Iran, or how difficult life became for them after the Revolution. Rather, they managed, through their family strategies, to integrate themselves socially and economically into Israeli society.

The Shirazi family, on the other hand, mourned Iran and the difficulties of life in Israel. The father of the family was a businessman in Shiraz. The children, all in their twenties, were either working or studying at one of the universities in Iran. In Israel, the family rented a furnished apartment in a modern building on a commercial street which, by default, afforded them neither a sense of neighborhood nor privacy. They had brought some of their household items from Iran, such as carpets and trays, which they used to make the atmosphere more habitable.

Unlike the Kashani father, the Shirazi father did not seek employment or business opportunities in Israel. He kept talking about returning to Iran when the situation would improve, or joining relatives who had moved to Los Angeles before and after the Revolution. Although both parents had relatives in Jerusalem and Tel Aviv who immigrated to Israel between ten and sixty years ago and who became successful professionally and socially (in the extended family were rabbis, teachers, businessmen, dentists, doctors, electricians), they looked toward California rather than Israel as a place to succeed socially and economically. Their relations with their extended family in Jerusalem were good; their apartment was always filled with relatives. They also had many friends visiting, most of whom had fled Iran for Israel and fantasized returning to Iran. Among the other refugees, they complained about life in Israel. Among their relatives they did not.

The parents, unlike the Kashani family, did not attend an ulpan. They considered themselves too old to study, and, because they did not want to remain in Israel, they thought it unnecessary to do so. The children, however, did learn Hebrew and became, as had children in many immigrant families, cultural mediators between the parents and the clerks, officials, doctors, teachers, store owners, and others: traditional family roles were beginning to break down. The father, an authoritarian figure who was the prime decision maker for major family affairs (such as choosing which pictures from his daughter's wedding the photographer should develop, which ones his daughter would keep and which she would send to relatives in Iran and the United States), had to rely on his children for developing extrafamilial connections and interactions. The older daughter found work as a kindergarten teacher. The older son found no work. The younger son attended a university in Israel. The younger daughter, who had been in her fourth year studying for her B.A. in history and economics at Pahlavi University in Shiraz, opted not to continue her studies in Israel, but to work. She attended a training program to become a secretary and worked in a travel agency.

Like the Kashani family, the Shirazi family was religious. However, they did not attend, as a family, a neighborhood synagogue. Although the father, whose family is originally from Mashhad, frequented a Mashhadi synagogue in the Bukharian quarter, the women did not go with him. The father would spend his days visiting friends and relatives in the city. The mother stayed home. The daughters worked; the younger son studied; the older son stayed home. He, like his father, did not search for employment or for the possibilities of opening a business, and refused to attend a university or trade school.

The mother, the younger daughter, the older son, and the father spoke often about Iran, how good their lives were there, easy and secure, and how difficult it is for them now in Israel, economically, socially, with people who are impolite, noisy, insensitive, and fanatically religious (they contrast the black-coated Hassidim with religious Iranian Jews who are indistinguishable in appearance from nonreligious Iranians and who are not excessive in their religious practices). They spoke often about being grieved and becoming sorrowful—*ghoseh khordan*, literally, "eating sorrow." Everyone in the family, except for the father, lost weight in Israel. The mother became physically sick (suffering excessive uterine bleeding and requiring a hysterectomy) and the older son suffered from flank pains and leg pains, attributing the discomfort to kidney stones and blood clots, although no pathological findings were reported by the physicians. The family was at a loss to explain why they all became sick after leaving Iran. Some blamed sickness on weight loss. Others blamed weight loss on ghoseh khordan, on grieving, "eating sorrow," and therefore, having no appetite. No one blamed the sicknesses on ghoseh khordan, however.

The parents and older son frequently talked about grieving for Iran. Although the other members of the family also grieved for their previous life, they did not speak about it in front of the rest of the family, "in order not to make them more nārāhat" as the younger daughter said. She, in fact, wanted to continue her studies in Iran and disliked her family's situation in Israel, but did not want to add to the burden of her parents' sorrow by her complaints. She was silent in her grieving, and she lost weight. Her mother, however, attributed the daughter's weight loss to ghoseh khordan.

The discourse on ghoseh khordan, mostly verbal, sometimes silent, is exploited by people who suffer loss of person, friend, family, job, house, or country. Concerning refugees such as the Shirazi family, loss of culture, previous social relationships, identity, and status are things that are grieved. The grieving for Iran is experienced as intense sadness. Unlike the private feelings of nārāhati which might show weakness in the self or create discomfort in others, loss of Iran is expressed openly. It is a social and public loss: all Iranians in Israel feel it. Even some Iranians who had been in Israel for thirty years or more, many of whom used to vacation in Iran, do business with Iran, had family in Iran, or planned to return to Iran to live, often spoke in terms of ghoseh khordan when discussing their feelings about the Revolution. However, the grief of the refugees is stronger and more deeply felt, more real, than that of the immigrants who had voluntarily decided to settle in Israel. The refugees expressed their grief by verbalizing it with other refugees, by deep sighing, and by becoming ill. The poem that my friend Iraj wrote and pinned to the wall above his bed in the kibbutz is another way of expressing sorrow—quoting poetry exemplifying one's internal state.

The feelings of loss and bereavement due to being uprooted from one's country of origin create what Marris (1980:97) calls "interruptions of the continuity of structures of meaning"—those understandings of one's physical and social surroundings formed out of experience and shared knowledge. Grieving for their lost culture and country is a way of resolving the deprivation of customary meaning and disruption of identity and community. This is particularly the case with involuntary immigrants, that is, with refugees. Bereavement is a way of coping with the changes they go through upon leaving their countries of origin and acclimating themselves, if possible, to their new countries of residence. Intense sadness, sometimes crying, thinking about the past, inability to engage in new types of relationships required in the new society are all part and parcel of the bereavement process, as are certain physical manifestations of depression, such as disruption of sleep and lack of appetite. This explains how the Shirazi family, many of whom "ate sorrow," lost weight.

Not all new immigrants and refugees grieve for their lost country and cultures. Those Iranians who came to Israel as refugees but who had always had an orientation toward Israel as a place of potential settlement, such as the Kashani family, were hastened on their way by the events in 1978–79. How families decide to rearrange their lives influences their settlement in Israel and their grieving for Iran. Some, like the Kashanis, determined their social, economic, and familial situation in Jerusalem through decisions to establish themselves in Israel. The family settled in their neighborhood, socializing, working, praying, studying. By contrast, the Shirazi family, unhappy having left Iran, knew no one in the apartment building in which they lived, met few Israelis, were unable to engage themselves economically in Israel because they focused on returning to Iran or leaving for Los Angeles. Unlike the Kashani family, the Shirazi family did not feel in control of their situation. They tried to secure visas to go to the United States, but were blocked by the American Embassy, which said that because they are Jews and safe in Israel, there was no reason to give them visas for the United States. They felt stranded in Jerusalem, unable to control the political, social, economic, and cultural events which had occurred to them, and did not know what to do. Their social situation had changed: the family no longer functioned as a corporate unit in society; the parents became dependent on their Hebrew-speaking children who worked to support the family; they experienced financial problems and housing inconveniences. But their cultural values did not change. Thus, because they grieved for Iran and refused to settle permanently in Israel, creating a self-imposed endless liminal state, they "ate sorrow," lost weight, and several of them became sick. The Kashani family, on the other hand, reconciled themselves to their refugee situation, made every attempt to adjust culturally as well as socially to the new society, and did so with few, if any, adverse reactions: everyone worked or studied, they participated in some neighborhood religious and social activities, the house was filled with guests several times a week, and no one lost weight. On the outside, the family seemed to adjust to living in Israel quite well. If anyone in the family felt nārāhat about their new social situation in Israel, the feeling was kept silent to outsiders and to family members. The only problem that seemed to bother the family concerned the health of the father, who had frequent headaches and leg pains, which, although he also suffered from them in Iran, were intensified in Israel.

Although Iranian immigrants, voluntary or involuntary, may not openly grieve about Iran and the losses of their past lifestyles—and some do not grieve at all, being glad to leave Iran for Israel—they all experience the social and cultural constraints of immigration which impinge on the individual, sometimes creating stresses which may be personally disturbing. How people react to the stressors of the social system and to changes in relationships depends on the culture and personality of the individuals, as well as on the kinds of relationships maintained with family and friends. Because Iranians who experience such stressors are often reluctant to express their particular personal nārāhatis, (such as saying "I'm nārāhat because my children don't treat me with respect" or "My wife working makes me nārāhat"), they complain instead about general impersonal social occurrences (such as "Israelis are rude" or "You can never make as much money in Israel as you can in Iran"). By revealing personal nārāhati, one also indicates personal powerlessness, which could be demoralizing individually and socially as the family transforms to become more or less Israeli in norms, behavior, and values. Since individuals frequently mitigate their personal feelings for the good of the family, often individuals hide their feelings of being upset, worried, or depressed, in order that the family as a unit function in the society. Undoubtedly, this occurred in the Kashani family, while it did not among the Shirazi family. Both families, however, had episodes of sickness which were without organic or physical abnormalities according to the physicians they saw.

Because many parents who were born and grew up in Iran have Israeli-born-and-bred children, they must contend with a family situation which is unlike that of Iran: the family in Israel is not an unindividuated unit but is a group of individuals. For many parents, this transformation of the family is one of the most stressful situations in Israel. Unable to verbalize their nārāhati, many will resort to nonverbal means (not eating or sulking) to express their dissatisfaction with the familial state of affairs in order to manipulate children, spouses, or siblings to their advantage. Others, not quite aware of the stressors impinging on them and unable to cognize the conflicts and contradictions of their lives, cope with social and cultural stressors through illness. Illness, then, becomes an idiom of distress, a way to manifest the nārāhati that one is incognizant of, or that one cannot express for fear of showing weakness. This is especially the case with people who are sensitive (hassās) to the words and actions of others, are aware of what goes on around them, and are influenced by events that seem beyond their control. Such is the story of Amir, a man who experienced numerous sociocultural problems—familial, work, economic, religious—about which he felt unable to do anything. His problems were further amplified by sickness which was influenced by and also aggravated his social and personal situation.

Amir: Social Stressors, Cultural Values, and Personal Sickness

Amir is a short, overweight, religious man with a serious demeanor, who at the age of sixteen immigrated to Palestine in 1945 by way of Lebanon. His father and brother had established several handicraft stores in Beirut and Damascus, in addition to Isfahan, the family's home city. He went to Jerusalem by foot, illegally, during the time of the British Mandate, paying various Arabs to help him cross the border.

Life in Palestine was difficult for him at first because of loneliness: his parents were still in Iran, although a brother and several aunts and uncles were in Jerusalem; he did not speak Hebrew; he had no group of friends (H., *khevreh*). He was given manual labor work (he did not say what or by whom) which he disliked, saying he was not "built" for that kind of work. Although Amir also disliked a jewelry-making course in which he enrolled, he was familiar with the jewelry business from working with his father in Iran, and he therefore decided to pursue the same business in Israel. He began his trade as a jeweler, fought in the Army in the War of Independence in 1948, and then his parents came from Iran, after which he felt more at ease in the country.

In 1951 Amir had seen a psychiatrist at one of the local psychiatric hospitals as an outpatient for outbursts of anger and violence. It must be recalled that anger, especially with violence, is an antisocial and denigrated form of behavior, sometimes considered to be somewhat of a malfunctioning of the nerves. Although he did not elaborate on what induced his outbursts of anger, his irascibility was troubling enough to him and to his family to inspire them to seek help for him. And because of his psychological condition, he was released from further army service, an action which intensified his sense of loneliness and undermined his sense of self-worth.[6]

At the age of twenty-four he married a fifteen-year-old young woman whose family had also immigrated from Isfahan. The fathers of the couple arranged the marriage. For the first year and a half of their marriage they lived with Amir's parents in a small apartment, during which time their first son was born. His wife pressured him into moving to their own apartment. Although they moved into a two-room apartment in the same building as his wife's parents and brother, the privacy they desired was thwarted: a number of tenants in the building shared some of the same services, including a central kitchen. They lived there for approximately fourteen years, during which time five other children were born. It was at this time that Amir set up his own jewelry shop, making and selling different items. His wife was interested in the business but he considered it his pursuit and would not accept or listen to any advice from her. His wife wanted to move from their two-room apartment, which housed eight people, into a larger one, but Amir did not. Nevertheless, family pressure from his wife's parents and his wife forced him, so he said, to sell his store and supplies in order to put a down payment on a new and larger apartment. The wife did not want the store sold, but rather their old apartment. Amir, however, thought of the old apartment as property which could be used for their son as capital (*nedunya*, Hebrew for dowry, the word he used) for his future marriage, and decided that selling his store and inventory would enable him to buy the new apartment, save the old one, and set up facilities for making jewelry in the new apartment.

After moving into the new apartment, Amir could not work. He suffered from rheumatism, kept thinking of all his debts, made lists of what he owed whom, had quarrels with his oldest son who was showing signs of psychological disturbance (distancing himself from his friends, feeling repelled by women), was unable to stand the noise and commotion of the younger children, and had occasional outbursts of violence toward his wife and children, hitting them and screaming. Neither he nor his wife knew why he did so. He felt he was not in control of himself. Amir also felt he had lost his position of independence as a businessman with his Isfahani businessmen friends. Working at home was inconvenient and troublesome, and he felt demoralized going from store to store like a peddler selling merchandise. He accused his wife of the loss of his store and supplies whose worth went up on the market (albeit several years after he sold the store, and he did not consider inflation when talking about the present-day value).

Amir perceives his wife as indifferent to his situation. He considers himself sensitive (hassās) and nervous from birth and expects her to know what he wants, and when, to prepare him tea or other foods and drinks without his having to communicate his desires to her. He also feels that since he basically freed her from living within the confines of a small apartment, she owes him everything but does not want to show it. Instead, she has become more independent. Several years ago, when they first moved into the apartment and rheumatism prevented him from working, his wife obtained employment to help support the family. His wife's working had undermined his sense of self and created conflicts in role expectations concerning status and behavior for husband and wife. He was no longer the proper husband and father, nor was she the proper wife and mother:

> She was working all day at the university. No one cleaned the house. The children came home from school and there was no food. I couldn't make them food all the time. Once, twice, maybe. But she wasn't being a wife. And she was spending the money on

> the things she wanted. I told her not to work, that she should stay home and be a wife. She wasn't being a good wife, working, not cleaning the house, not cooking, and not obeying *nida*.[7] I told her and told the children that I am no longer her husband. We lived together but we didn't talk. Then she went to live with her father. I even washed my own clothes then, and sometimes cooked for the children. Sometimes they stayed with me, sometimes with her. So I made some phone calls to her sister and to her father and told them not to listen to that woman who is telling stories about me and that she can return to me if she wants, that I have no expectations of her, as long as she is a proper wife. She came back. Things are good now, thank God. Now she is working, but only four hours a day. She took some kind of course and goes around to old and poor people to see if there is anything they need. And she doesn't spend money the way she used to so things are good.

Before the wife went to work, she depended on Amir to give her money for household and personal expenses, but he would not give her money regularly, and often not as much as she needed. Her working and his failure to work intensified the problem of disintegration of traditional familial roles by making Amir dependent on his wife, whose influence in family matters surpassed that of Amir, whose cultural values upheld the father's domination in the family. This incongruity between Amir's Iranian cultural values and his Israeli social relationships was further aggravated by generational problems between Amir and his children. Amir and his wife spoke Hebrew to the children (between themselves they spoke Isfahani, the Jewish dialect of Isfahan), brought them up in a religious household, and sent them to religious schools. The oldest son, the one with psychological problems, was unemployed and was attending a yeshiva, but was foundering academically, and was sending all his living expenses to his parents to pay. His oldest daughter quit her studies at a religious teachers academy; one of the younger daughters who refused to study in the religious girls' school in Jerusalem resided at Kfar Habad (located between Jerusalem and Tel Aviv), an educational and religious community run by the Lubovitcher Hassidim. Amir feels that his strict upbringing by his authoritarian and well-to-do father was beneficial, and bemoans the fact that he cannot give his own children the kind of education and rearing that his father had granted him and his siblings in Iran. "Today," he kept saying "people lack the upbringing of another time—children don't have discipline and respect regarding parents and teachers." Family relations in Israel are "shameful" and "disgracing" in comparison with family relations in Iran.

His relations with his wife were also influenced by conflicts imposed by religious law. Amir practiced as many of the religious regulations as he knew. Both husband and wife are responsible for observing the religious injunctions concerning sexual relations. Amir mentioned that when his wife was working fulltime she was not observing nida. However, he and his wife engaged in sexual activities which are proscribed by religious law, namely, mutual masturbation which, if the man achieves orgasm, is a transgression against the biblical and Talmudic injunction of not "spilling seed."[8] In addition, many followers of the Kabbala, the Jewish mystical text of the Middle Ages, believe that sperm ejaculated outside the woman's body is potentially harmful, becoming spirits which haunt the man and his family for years. Besides engaging in masturbation with his wife, and thus "spilling seed" which he knows is against religious law and which therefore makes him feel guilty (and which might create spirits to haunt him), Amir sometimes suffers from impotence. In addition, his wife uses birth control pills which, like "spilling seed," is against the decree of being fruitful and multiplying. Thus, Amir faces the conflict between the religious laws which he tries hard to observe but in the realm of sexual relations violates, and economic reality, the inability to support more children.

Amir, as a sensitive solemn man, does not vocally express what he thinks about his personal and familial situation to his wife, relatives, or friends. He keeps his nārāhati inside himself until he explodes in anger and violence. He is especially disturbed when his wife is angry at him, and a few times when she did express her anger, he attacked her sexually. Although it is certainly not uncommon for wives to express their anger against their husbands, it is considered improper to do so since wives are subordinate to husbands in the familial-social hierarchy. In Amir's case, where his status as husband, father, worker, and wage earner had been so transformed as to put him in a position of relative powerlessness vis-à-vis his wife and her family, his outbursts were inevitably a way of expressing his anger and procuring some sort of power, albeit temporary.

Amir's powerlessness was reinforced on a personal level by the interactions with his wife, her family, and his own children, as well as by the difficulties he encountered in his work relationships with other jewelers who continued to work in their stores after he sold his. He also felt powerless in relation to the society as a member of the community of Iranians as opposed to the politically dominant Ashkenazim. He told me about a friend of his who, having been fired from his job, went every day to the employment office to ask for work and every day was told to come back, but they gave out all the jobs to Ashkenazim. He also said one of his daughters finished a teachers seminar with a grade-point of 9 (out of 10), but could not get a job, while her Ashkenazi friend who had a 6.5 was hired. In addition, he mentioned that he went to look for work at an employment office but they gave him nothing; then he sheepishly said that it was probably his fault because he began to cry when he was in the office, demonstrating his sensitivity in a particularly Iranian way (to place himself in a lower position and inspire pity from those in a higher position in order to manipulate himself and others for his own advantage, here, to procure employment), but his methods did not work in Israel, where clerks consider such behavior erratic. He rationalized: "I'm not built to ask people for work, or to ask people for anything."

Amir also depicts himself as physically sensitive, suffering from what he calls "severe rheumatism" all over his body. Rheumatism is one of the reasons he could not work after he sold his store: he had pains in his back, shoulders, and legs (his wife also suffers from pains in her legs). He visited doctors in several primary care clinics and Hadassah Hospital for pains of rheumatism, tiredness, lack of strength in his hands, and sleep difficulties. One of these doctors referred him to a local mental health clinic where I met him. It was there that he had undergone treatment for depression and was able to express to the members of the staff, through their questioning, the plethora of personal problems which had been distressing him. But it was not for depression, or for any of his personal, psychological, social, economic, or existential problems that he chose treatment. Rather, it was for rheumatism and other physical complaints, through which he was able to express the difficulties of his life as an Iranian immigrant in Israel.

Why Amir focused on rheumatism rather than other problems distressing him concerns the metaphoric expression of nārāhati bodily. The body as the focus and locus of distress (see chapter six) enables individual distanciation from sociopersonal problems. What are these problems in Amir's case, and how do they relate to the issue of sociocultural dissonance?

To understand the creation of sociocultural dissonance and personal distress for Amir, we must evaluate the sociocultural stressors experienced by immigrants to Israel, indicate their association with Amir's personal problems, and show how the problems are related to the corrosion of core cultural values. The incongruity between the core cultural values and the social changes experienced by Amir in the form of personal problems is the sociocultural dissonance which engendered his personal distress.

The stressors of immigration, independently or together, produce social and personal problems for individuals and families, many of whom are unaware of the relationship between the social and cultural stressors and their own particular personal experiences. In Amir's life, many of the problems he experienced are a result of the stressors of immigration pitted against his traditional values, standards, and beliefs. For instance, his first outbursts of anger in 1951, which he attributes to nervousness (H., *atzbani*—could be a gloss for "angry" in Persian, *asabāni*), exemplify problems of interpersonal transactions. These interpersonal problems were exacerbated by his dismissal from army duty due to his psychiatric state. The dismissal then intensified his feelings of powerlessness and loneliness, since he was no longer participating in the primary social organization that is the focus of male adult life and societal responsibility.

Economic and work problems, inadequate housing, the disintegration of traditional familial roles, and unfulfilled expectations aggravated Amir's feelings of powerlessness and engendered his quarrels with his in-laws and wife, who pressured him to purchase a larger apartment. Because he sold his jewelry store to finance the purchase of the house, he inadvertently intensified his loneliness (with respect to his relationship with other Isfahani jewelers) and his economic and work problems, further aggravating the disintegration of his traditional familial role as male head of household and prime decision maker. For Amir, the breakdown of familial roles, from which his wife, working, earning money, spending without consulting him, gaining power in the familial setting while he, unemployed and sick with rheumatism, became more powerless, was distressing. Added to this was his poor relationship with his children who did not exemplify the respect and honor to him that he expected. To enhance his distress were the Iranian values which he held concerning the hierarchy of husband-wife relations, the respect and honor of parent-child relations, the sensitivity of the individual, the expectations that life in Israel would be economically and socially better than it was in Iran.

Amir's outbursts of anger and his rheumatism signify individual sensitivity, socially and personally as well as physically. His personal distress, spawned by the difficulties of his first years in Israel, the changing familial relationships, work problems, and religious issues, and ultimately, rheumatism, results from the incompability between his conceptual categories of behavior and relations, rooted in Iranian patterns of meaning and ethnopsychology, and the reality of his social relations in Israel. The consequence of sociocultural dissonance, individual personality, and personal vulnerability, his distress is symbolized by outbursts of anger and violence, to which he attributes physical causality (nervous from birth), and rheumatism. Thus, illness for Amir, as for many other immigrants, is a vehicle for contending with the problems of sociocultural dissonance.[9]

Sociocultural Dissonance and Illness

The stressors of immigration and the peoples' perceptions of them, how the new and old symbolic meanings contrast and sometimes are contradicted, have been exemplified by examining changes and differences in human relationships in Israel as compared to Iran. We have seen how Iranians in Israel perceive family, husband-wife relations, issues of respect and status, economic and work difficulties concerning questions of independence and pride, loneliness, housing problems, and stereotypes. We also see how the good and bad in Iranian culture are reference points for the good and bad in Israeli culture, and how certain contrasts concerning communication differences (no ta'ārof is good, but Israelis are rude and impolite) generate ambiguities which engender ambivalence regarding proper behavior. Also, differences in pārti-bāzi of Iran and protectzia of Israel are perceived as inherently different means of gaining access to power. Iranians in Israel view themselves as relatively powerless as an immigrant group in Israeli society. This relative powerlessness at the social level is augmented by personal feelings of nārāhati as individual immigrants experience the social stressors of immigration as personal problems. Perhaps the major stressor for many Iranians in Israel is the breaking up of the family unit into individuals who comprise the family. The Kashani and Shirazi families did not yet undergo such a familial breakdown of traditional roles, except for the Shirazi children becoming the mediators between the parents and Hebrew-speakers in the society and working to help support the family. In both families the cultural values of relationships remained essentially the same as they had been in Iran, with honor and respect marking interactions between parents and children and between the dominant husband and subordinate wife. In contrast, Amir's family experienced transformations in husband-wife relationships and parent-children relationships, engendering distress in Amir whose conceptual patterns of familial relations were based upon those of Iran.

Among themselves, Iranians in Israel complain about their social situation as an immigrant group, about difficulties communicating with Israelis, about economic hardships and work complications, about small apartments. These are all experienced, to a greater or lesser extent, by most immigrants. To complain about them is concurring about life difficulties with others who experience the same difficulties. People willingly express such nārāhatis, since they are social, rather than private, problems, experienced by all.

However, personal problems which result from the social, economic, and cultural issues outlined above, such as those of Amir, are usually not cognized as derived from the social and cultural transformations that immigrants undergo. Instead, they are seen as personal difficulties which require personal and/or familial strategies to overcome. Dilemmas which induce feelings of personal weakness, powerlessness, being out of control, such as problems originating from one's wife working or one's children not giving the respect due to parents, are not communicated to others outside the intimate circle of relationships. Sometimes they are not even communicated to those within the intimate circles. Iranian immigrants, faced with constraints of adjusting to a different social structure and culture from the one in which they were raised, and having expectations, as Jews, that Israel would be more of an ideal society than it is, are frequently reticent about expressing personal nārāhati in many cases. They would be expressing the vulnerability that they feel, making them appear even more vulnerable. This is not to say that the immigrants do not recognize their problems. Many do. But many do not perceive them as a result of social forces encroaching on their traditional ways of being. However, since they are channeled culturally not to express certain feelings and thought in verbal terms, they sometimes express dissatisfaction with their personal relationships or situation nonverbally by being excessively quiet, sullen, or refusing to eat. And often, what does get expressed, aside from complaints about the new society, are complaints about not feeling well.

The nārāhati that Iranian immigrants talk about in Israel has to do with issues which call into question the values and ideals that they upheld in Iran. Because immigration entails social and cultural transformations of behavior and beliefs, learning a new way of being or of becoming could be stressful for some immigrants, especially when changes in family, work, communication, community, environment, and self are involved. We have seen how particular stressors of immigration and stereotypes of Iranians in Israel result from differences in communication, culture, and social structure of the two societies, Iranian and Israeli, and how these differences are manifested in judgments and standards concerning the ways human beings should ideally behave. The contrasts between the preconceived ideal behavior in the old society and the real way people behave in the new society, along with all the socioeconomic problems induced by immigration, generate sociocultural dissonance which is experienced by the immigrants as personal distress. How Iranian immigrants react to the social and cultural changes created by immigration varies individually and familially. Some adjust to life in Israel with enthusiasm and with few problems. Others suffer major crises. Some speak continuously about the difficulties of life in Israel. Others are silent about the things that bother them. And there are those who, for a variety of reasons, physical, social, personal, emotional, or environmental, become ill.

Illness becomes a subject that immigrants have in common with one another. Discourse on not feeling well, medication, doctors, clinics and hospitals becomes part of many interactions, joining ghoseh khordan about the situation in Iran, economic problems in Israel, and insensitive Israeli clerks and bureaucrats. It is my contention that social and cultural problems among Iranians in Israel which induce sadness (ghamgini), sorrow and grieving (ghoseh), stress, anxiety, depression, nārāhati, and other dysphoric affects are expressed verbally if others experience the same problems, and somatically for individuals who are not conscious of their existential situation, cannot do anything about it, or who have no other means of relaying their distress since certain types of nārāhati are culturally disapproved of to manifest verbally. Illness becomes one way of coping with personal and familial distress that is produced by sociocultural constraints of immigration and change.

The illnesses resulting from socioenvironmental stressors may be termed sociosomatic illnesses, as differentiated from psychosomatic illnesses which signify internal personal conflicts. Sociosomatic illnesses are socially produced (cf. Kleinman 1980, 1985), influenced by and influencing individuals' social situations, personal problems, interpersonal transactions as members of immigrant, ethnic, socioeconomic, or familial groups within the social structure. How individuals manifest their illnesses, what symptoms they present, are tempered by the culture in which they were socialized, by beliefs of illness causation, by the world around them and by being members of families which have certain ways of behaving about illness and when ill. Consequently, illness expression depends on cultural conceptions of the body and illness causation.

Illness, rather than or in addition to complaints about Israelis' behavior, changes in the family, economic worries, small apartments, becomes part of many immigrants' conversations and transactions: going to the doctor, taking pills, buying herbal medicines, and talking about how they just do not feel well. Ill health, then, becomes a coping mechanism for dealing with the stressors of immigration and a communicative device for expressing the distress of sociocultural dissonance. How Iranians symptomatize their illnesses, what they think causes them to become sick, and how they use the body to communicate dysphoric affects are determined by cultural conceptions of illness, health, and the body, and are examined in the following chapter.

Chapter 6
Physical Nārāhati: Cultural Conceptions of Illness

Often Iranian doctors initiate clinical transactions with their patients by asking them, "*nārāhati-yi tun chi-eh?*" What's your nārāhati? What's bothering you? The answer given, in this context, is a physical, not emotional, problem. Although the term used is the same, physical nārāhati is dissociated from emotional nārāhati in the clinical setting as patients visit physicians for physical ailments in need of treatment. The physical ailments could be anything from a broken bone to generalized or specific aches and pains. Talking about the nārāhati of aches and pains is more common than verbalizing private emotional nārāhati: articulation of bodily discomfort is prevalent in social discourse as people complain about their physical problems and receive sympathy and advice in return. These aches and pains will be examined in relation to cultural perceptions of the body, for based upon these cultural constructions are illness behavior and transactions involving carers and curers.

Somatization

Somatization is the conscious or unconscious expression of social, personal, psychological, or emotional problems in physical symptomatology. People who somatize either have no pathological disease and recurrently present with physical complaints or, if they do manifest physical problems, their symptoms are amplified and they frequently use physicians' services.[1] In Iranian culture, somatization may be a means of expressing distressing emotions when it is inappropriate or disapproved of to verbally or nonverbally express one's nārāhati or anger. The body thus becomes a metaphor for personal distress. Coding distress in physical symptomatology enables a person to distance himself or herself from personal problems and not assume responsibility for them, as the problems often are either not cognized or are not considered to be related to the bodily symptoms.

Somatization, as a category of illness, must be viewed as an individual and cultural expression linked with a system of meanings within which it is perceived, sensed, sustained, and treated. These meanings maybe varied, shared, or not always understood in the same way by everyone within the culture; they may be consciously expressed or not, explicit or implicit. Somatization allows the individual to use the body as an idiom of expression in which physical problems supplant psychological or social ones. By somatizing one's problems, the sick person could avoid disruptions of social relationships, manipulate others, control interactions, evade stressful situations, and express discomfort.

The study of somatization concerns the interconnection between the social and cultural conceptions of the individual in society and the ways of understanding, sensing, and signifying biological and psychological experiences. Somatization, as illness, is socially precipitated and consonant with cultural conceptions of illness causality and treatment. Cultural interpretations of the body, how it works, how it is injured or harmed, and what to do about it bear on the illness experience, as the physical part of a social and cultural individual. Although somatization pertains to physical feelings, culture determines and molds concepts of the body, physical symptomatology and expressions of it: people learn how to respond to their social and physical environment, how to be sick, and how to complain.

In Iranian culture, where people are so reticent to express private nārāhati, complaints about bodily discomfort—stomach aches and other digestive problems, pains in the limbs, chest pains (Good 1977)—are commonplace. The bodily complaints may be consciously utilized to manipulate others in distressing social situations. They may be actual pathological problems. Or they may be real physical sensations through which individuals somatize their affective states. In order to understand the relationship of the sociocultural to somatization, problems of somatization within Iranian culture will be elucidated by looking at four issues which influence the relationship between the cultural conception of the human body and the individual manifestation of illness: hot and cold food categories, climatic effects on the body, the supernatural and sickness, and verbal expressions concerning emotions and pain. These four issues are related to the conception of the individual as a physically sensitve being as well as an emotionally and socially sensitive (hassās) person. The individual, in the physical sense, is also considered to be sensitive, hassās. The body is sensitive to various elements in the environment—climate, heat, moisture, food. An imbalance in any one of these elements, such as an oversupply of heat or moisture, or the eating of too much of one category of food, causes the body to react with some type of discomfort, some type of nārāhati.

Physical and emotional sensitivity are not necessarily causally connected in terms of etiology of illness. There are those who say that feeling nārāhat emotionally can cause certain illnesses, whereas others state no causal relationship whatsoever. Of interest here is the interaction between the two concepts of sensitivity and nārāhati, on both emotional and physical levels. On the emotional level, people continually monitor actions and reactions of themselves and others in order not to create or to show nārāhati. On the physical level, many Iranians monitor their bodies, interpreting bodily change and reacting accordingly, asking for advice from relatives and friends, treating oneself, or visiting healers, either folk or biomedical physicians, for treatment. Emotionally and physically, people are seen as sensitive to the world around them.

In Iranian culture, the personal, existential complaints of nārāhati are muted, disguised, or denied. To focus on them could be detrimental to the social situation of the individual and to one's social relationships. Physical complaints, however, are enhanced and focused upon. The constant attention to the body postulates concepts of the self as "somatic functioning" rather than as an "existential process" and is dominated by somatic symptoms rather than existential complaints (Marsella et al 1973; Mechanic 1972, 1980). Not only do physical complaints form a viable alternative to expressing emotional nārāhati, but the concept of the body in interaction with the environment forms the basis of understanding and interpretation of illness. Personal and social problems rank secondary to other conceptions of illness causation, and most of the time are not considered to have any causal connection. Rather, cultural concepts of the body as a sensitive entity in the physical world are central to explanations of sickness. Two models of illness causation in Iranian culture are an imbalance of physical elements in relation to the body, and the evil eye. The first pertains to the individual as a biological being in relation to material factors of the cosmos. The second concerns the individual as a biosocial being in relation to other people in the community and to the supernatural. Both models elicit attention to the well-being of one's sensitive physical self. Accordingly, concentration on the body in relation to the environment is a factor constraining and molding sickness in Iranian culture, its physical manifestations, and social expression.

The Individual in the Cosmos: Classical Theory of Humoral Medicine

The popular system of health care in Iranian culture is based upon the Galenic-Islamic tradition of humoral medicine,[2] perhaps best elaborated by Ibn Sina (980–1037), an Iranian of Hamadan who wrote in Arabic, a physician, philosopher, and poet who developed his system of medicine from Arabic, Greek, Latin, and Indian philosophies. Ibn Sina's medicine survives today in Iran and among Iranians abroad in the form of the hot/cold food system, conceptions of climatic influences on health, and notions of individual temperament.

Ibn Sina's philosophy disclosed the existence of two worlds, the perfect outer sphere of the stars, planets and celestial beings for which there was no generation or decay, and the sublunary world of generation and decay, in which human beings, animals, plants, and minerals exist. Their existence is dependent upon compounds of the four elements of fire, air, water, and earth, and different proportions of the qualities of hot, cold, wet, and dry. The physiology of human beings, in addition, was determined by the balance between the four humors with their concomitant qualities: blood—hot and moist; red bile (bilious humor)—hot and dry; phlegm (serous humor)—cold and moist; black bile (atrabilious humor)—cold and dry. The humors are derived from nutrition, in which food is digested and transformed into blood and other humors. According to classical theory, the food first goes to the stomach where it undergoes the first step in digestion. Then it goes to the small intestine where it is further diluted, and afterward, to the liver, where the four humors are formed through transformation of aliments: blood, which is the basic constituent of the body and the principal factor in nutrition; red bile, which abets digestion by residing in the gall bladder where it is secreted into the stomach and intestines, helping expel wastes, and by being in the blood where it aids nutrition in the lungs and general tissues; phlegm, which maintains the moisture of the body and resides in the joint tissues, saliva, and mucus, and, when mixed with the "innate heat" of the blood (which is provided by the heart), a portion of the phlegm is transformed into blood; black bile, which goes to the spleen and blood where it contributes to the formation of bones, hair, and nails.

In classical medical theory, an imbalance in the humors creates disease, as do climatic and environmental influences and an inadequate functioning of the three faculties, the properties or potential powers manifesting life. The three properties (or faculties) are the vegetative or natural, which resides in the liver, and whose functions are nutrition and reproduction, the animal or vital, which resides in the heart and whose functions are to provide "innate heat" or "vital breath" to the body, and the rational faculty, which resides in the brain and whose functions are sensation and rationality. Innate heat protects the body against external or foreign heat and is a primary force in digestion of food. The heat is stronger in the liver than in the stomach and intestines, and is provided by the heart. The breath, or *nafas* in Arabic, is an immaterial constituent of life dependent upon a material basis to subsist, somewhat but not exactly like a "soul" or "spirit." Gruner (1930:125) describes the breath as "that which binds the vegetative and sensitive life into one connected whole. It is common to, and like in, *all* living things." The breath is active, changes in quality and moves from place to place in the body, varying in rate, time, person, family, and race, waxing and waning in different parts of the body at different times, in correlation with the waxing and waning of the innate heat. Both the breath and the innate heat are related to the physical feelings of the emotions, the seat of which is in the heart, the producer of innate heat and breath:

> If two motions of the mind occur simultaneously, the breath may move in two directions (contraction within itself, and enlarging) at once. This happens (1) when there is fear, dread, and anxiety about the future (2) when anger and gloom occur simultaneously. The two opposite movements may produce a sense of shame, because there is first the confinement of the breath in the interior parts, and after that the power of reason returns, and resolution appears, allowing the contracted breath to expand again, and bring heat to the surface. The skin how becomes red. (Ibn Sina 1930:213)

> when the breath residing in the heart is plentiful (as it is when there is plenty of that material from which it is rapidly and constantly being generated); when it is balanced in temperament; when it has a luminous, beautiful and bright substance—then there is a strong tendency to joy.
>
> When the breath is scanty (as occurs in convalescents, in long-standing illnesses, and in old persons); when it is not balanced in character (as in morbid states); and when it is (a)very dense and coarse in substance (as in melancholy and old people)—it cannot arouse joy; (b)very delicate in substance (as in convalescents and in women), it will not allow of expansion; (c)confused (as in melancholy people)—in all these cases there is a very strong tendency to depression, sadness, and grief. (Ibn Sina 1930:538)

Here we see the body influenced by the individual's mind in relation to the external environment in the first case, and by internal characteristics in the second case. In the first case the emotions create a physical reaction, the red skin due to the movement of the heat and the breath in the body. In the second case, the quantity of the breath, here being a physical entity, causes the emotions. Both cases relate to a holistic view of the individual functioning in the environment in which there is no separation between body and mind as exists in contemporary Western thought. In fact, traditional Galenic-Islamic medical theory postulates the interrelationship between the mind and the body in which an imbalance in the emotions or in any of the faculties can induce physical sickness. In addition, an imbalance in the climate or temperature in the environment is also conducive to sickness, as weather effects individual temperament through the qualities of hot, cold, dry, and moist.

Each individual has a different temperament derived from a distinctive balance of the four humors. Temperament is considered to be the physical constitution, not the personality, of the individual. Temperament varies according to age (youths are warmer, old people colder), sex (females are colder, males warmer), race, and climate. Ibn Sina writes that temperament is moister in people living in northern countries and colder for those living in southern countries. He also correlates temperament with geographic zones:

> Of all races of men, those who live in countries within the equinoctial circle, away from mountains and seas, approach the ideal equable temperament more closely than others, and those living in other countries.
>
> In the case of peoples living in the equinoctial zone, the states of the body are in all cases more like the ideal; the atmosphere in these regions exerts no evident deleterious effects, but is always in harmony with their temperaments. (1930:61)

> There is a special equability peculiar to the race, climate, geographical position or atmosphere. The Hindus, in health, have a different equability to the Slavs, and so on. Each is equable in regard to their own race, but not in regard to others. So if a Hindu were to develop the temperament of a Slav he would probably fall ill, and might even die. (1930:60)

Although Ibn Sina writes in detail about health and climate, he does not refer to the term "temperament" when discussing the effects of the air, the winds, and geographic regions on the body. Rather, he writes about bodily reactions to the environment, such as the physical accommodation to living in high altitudes where people "are healthy, strong, and capable of much physical work; they are long-lived" (1930:208), or somatic responses to changes in atmosphere, such as the north wind which "braces and hardens the body; . . . prevents the flow of visible excretions; . . . closes the pores, strengthens the digestion, causes constipation, increases the urine, and makes septic pestilential atmosphere healthy" (1930:204). In spite of the influence of climate and geographical zones on large populations, no two individuals have the exact same combination of humors even though they might be of the same sex, age, race, parentage, and living in the same vicinity: thus no two individuals have the same temperament.

The theoretical framework of the classical theory of humoral medicine delineated by Ibn Sina is not part of today's popular medical knowledge in its entirety. The theory of innate heat and vital breath is no longer articulated, and the functions of the four humors physiologically and in regard to individual temperament have been filtered to concentrate on the functions and importance of blood (see M. Good 1980), and to a lesser extent, red bile, phlegm, and black bile. The qualities of hot, cold, moist and dry in maintenance of health are articulated not in terms of the humors, but in terms of food and climate as they affect individual temperament.

Individual temperament in contemporary Iranian discourse refers to the natural constitution of the individual in terms which denote both physiology and personality. One way of referring to temperament is the term *tabi'at* (Arabic), meaning "nature" in both a personality sense and in a physiological sense, as a form of socialized temperament, a way a person is with others, the way a person reacts to others and with the environment. The term tabi'at is used in the same way that the term "nature" is used in English to refer to an individual's make-up or to the world of nature. Another way of referring to temperament is the term *mezāj* (Arabic), meaning condition of health, referring to how one feels physically. Mezāj is used when having a physical reaction to food eaten, or to the climate where one lives or has been, or in inquiring after someone's health. Both tabi'at and mezāj are concepts which vary with each individual, according to sex, age, race, and climate, as does the concept of temperament in the sense used by Ibn Sina. However, concerning individual health, the term mezāj is expressed more often in such phrases as the following:

Vaz-i mezāj-i tun chehtor ast?
How are you feeling?

Vaz-i havā-yi kharij-i fārs be mezāj-i man namisāzad.
The climate at the Persian Gulf doesn't agree with me.

Khorāk-i keh diruz khordam be mezāj-i man nāsāzegār ast.
The food I ate yesterday doesn't agree with me.

Each individual has a different temperament and constitution, and what may be beneficial for one in terms of diet or climate may be harmful to others. Conceptions of the way the body reacts to certain aspects of the environment form part of the cognitive framework, which then influences physiological reactions: people who believe certain elements in the environment cause or cure sickness will be more likely to get sick or well from these elements. The aspects of the environment considered here are categories derived from the concepts of hot, cold, moist, and dry as practiced in terms of diet and conceived of in terms of climate.

The Individual and the Elements: Contemporary Concepts of Illness and Health

Similar to the ways in which the individual is considered sensitive to social and personal difficulties, the body is sensitive to elements in the external environment. This sensitivity is in part a recognition of the interrelationship between human beings and the rest of the world, both cosmologically and materially. It is also a recognition of the fact that some people react differently from other people to physical surroundings. In addition, the physical sensitivity is related to a constant concentration on the body, focusing on physical sensations in case sickness occurs and taking preventive measures if feeling somewhat out of sorts.

In order to control the proper functioning of the human body to maintain health, diet should be regulated in reference to consumption of hot and cold foods. In Iran all foodstuffs are categorized into hot and cold, with a number of foods classified as neutral, having neither a hot nor cold valence. The terms hot and cold refer to qualities, the essence or character of things. The ingestion of food should balance the hot and cold qualities, or sickness could occur, arising from intake of too much of one quality of food or the other. Health is maintained by diet as long as a person's individual equilibrium of hot and cold is not upset. Eating too many hot foods (or cold) can create a reaction which may be ameliorated by eating foods or herbal medicines of the opposite quality.[3] Precaution is taken concerning consumption of foods in order not to produce adverse reactions.

The reactions attributed to an imbalance in the hot/cold equilibrium of the body have to do with digestive problems, skin eruptions, sore throats, and headaches. Although articulation of exactly how the digestion of hot or cold foods creates such unfavorable reactions was neither detailed nor uniform among informants, the consensus was that the hotness or coldness itself created pain or discomfort of one kind or another.

Consumption of too many cold foods in one day or at one meal, such as too many mulberries or several pomegranates, without eating the compensatory amount of hot foods—and these amounts are judged according to the quantities of hotness or coldness contained within each particular food—can induce nausea and vomiting. To counteract the nausea, tea, which has the quality of hot in addition to the hot temperature, is drunk with *nabāt*, crystalized sugar akin to rock candy, which is considered to be very hot and thus alleviates the nausea brought on by cold foods.

Eating too many hot foods at one time can cause headaches, rashes, pimples, sore throat, and sore mouth, although not all necessarily simultaneously. Which reaction one gets from eating too many hot foods depends on one's constitution. To counteract the effects of eating too many hot foods one ingests some cold food or drink, such as oranges, pomegranates, or *āblimu*, a sour lemonade. Certain physical problems resulting from overconsumption of hot foods can be ameliorated by specific foodstuffs: headaches, citrus fruits and āblimu; pimples, āblimu; sore mouth, thickened pomegranate juice; sore throat, āblimu; sweet lemons (a fruit native to Iran), hot milk.

Thus, diet in Iranian culture is deemed particularly important for the maintenance of health by balancing the hot and cold qualities of the foods consumed, creating a diet which is balanced in nutrition.[4] Overconsumption of any one type of food is deemed unhealthy and is rarely done. Unlike many Americans, who may eat a box of cookies in a day or two, most Iranians will limit their intake of sweets to one, two, perhaps three pieces at a time, as otherwise they would come down with a headache, sore throat, or pimples. It was surprising to my friends to hear that I could eat ten or fifteen cookies at once. They wondered how it was that

I didn't get a headache or sore throat from eating so many sweets—and I wondered how they did get sick when they ate half as much as I did.

Sickness causation is not solely attributed to overconsumption of one category of food, however. If someone does not feel well, with a sore throat or stomach ache, for example, the family first questions what foods were eaten that day, or the day before. If no dietary difference can be ascertained, such as whether the person suffering from the symptoms devoured too much from one category or another, then food is ruled out as the causal agent of discomfort. Although foods might not have caused the symptoms, special foods and herbal remedies are used to treat the problems. These problems, or symptoms, unlike those of Latin American cultures that also have a hot/cold food categorization, are not in themselves classified as hot or cold. In other words, for the symptom of a cough, which may or may not be due to the common cold, some foods must be avoided as bad for coughs and colds, such as pickles, which are cold, and sweets, which are hot, whereas other cold foods, such as turnips, are considered beneficial for coughs. Stomach aches and nausea, which could be attributed to eating too many cold foods, may not necessarily be attributed to diet, and may be caused by a malfunctioning of the gall bladder, which secretes too much bile into the stomach (an example is nausea from motion sickness). Whatever the cause of the ailment, however, the same herbal teas or infusions are given: tea with nabāt (rock candy) for a stomach ache or nausea, āblimu for a headache or sore throat.

The utilization of herbal remedies is a major part of Iranian popular medicine. These are dried flowers, seeds, leaves, and berries seeped in hot water (or sometimes cold) and drunk for a variety of ills, ranging from digestive problems of nausea, stomach ache, diarrhea, and constipation, to the more refined aspect of digestion, cleaning the blood. In addition, there are herbal remedies for gas, coughs, sore throat, bone aches, fevers, nerves, fear, and cleaning the kidneys. Some of the traditional medicines are utilized to treat a variety of sicknesses which may be categorized as having different etiologies. Two of the most common of these all-inclusive medications are dried purple flowers called *gol-i gāv zabān* (foxglove, *digitalis*) and flat brown seeds called *khākshir* (London rocket-seeds, *Sisymbrium irio*). Gol-i gāv zabān is seeped in hot water and sometimes drunk with nabāt and is used for nerves, fear, pains of unknown origin, and blood. One man described his using gol-i gāv zabān, "For blood and fear. My wife's brother-in-law died of a heart attack. The whole family drank it because of fear and crying alot. It is also good for blood. When the woman gets her period she drinks gol-i gāv zabān. It gives strength." Although the problems for which this herbal remedy is given may be considered as having different causes, it appears that there is a relationship between blood, strength, and emotional behavior of nerves and fear. Thus, a dichotomy between the emotions and the physical is at times not as prevalent when issues of blood, strength, and social relationships are involved. This will be further elucidated below in the discussion of blood, weakness, nerves and anger.

Khākshir is used for stomach aches, diarrhea, constipation, nausea, fever, and dirty blood. These tiny brown seeds are rinsed several times in water and then drunk with the water. They go through the digestive system undigested, expelled whole, thus working as an abrasive, taking out with them the various poisons that are believed to cause the symptoms. This water-and-seed combination is also drunk after fasting, such as after the fast on the Jewish holiday of Yom Kippur, to prevent cramps or vomiting, which are believed to be caused by eating on an empty stomach.

In Iran, the traditional medicines are sold by vendors in the bazaars, by private traders in stores, or by peasant men and women who sit on cloths on the sidewalks near produce markets selling herbs, dried leaves, or seeds of plants. Most households have a variety of traditional medicines stored in cloth bags or glass jars, to be used when needed. Iranians who immigrated to Israel often took traditional medications with them: they are known, they work, they are trusted, and they do not, so people say, create adverse reactions. "These medicines are good," explained a middle-aged Iranian man in Jerusalem, "much better than modern pills. There are no after-effects from the herbal medicines. They don't have the poisons modern medicines have." The virtues of the traditional medicines were also extolled by an Iranian physician in Jerusalem: "Gol-i gāv zabān is good for the heart. It is a treatment for tachycardia, nerves, and neuralgia. It has a lot of vitamin B and is the basis of digitalis."

Iranians in Israel who finished their supplies of traditional medicines before the Islamic Revolution either asked relatives or friends to bring some from Iran if they were going for a visit, or they used to ask family to send them from Iran. Now, with a freeze on communication and transportation between Iran and Israel, acquiring traditional medicines from Iran is nearly impossible. Some of the medicaments, however, are available in Israel in specialty stores catering to the Middle Eastern immigrants. These stores sell spices, grains, legumes, dried fruits, some candies, and nonmedicinal teas. In addition, some store owners also engage in the merchandising of traditional medicines. One of the merchants in Jerusalem who has such a business is Itzhaq, one of the three or four traditional medicine sellers in the city. His store, the only one of its kind in northern Jerusalem, is in the Bukharian quarter, an area of Persian, Bukharian, and Afghani cultural, residential and religious orientation since the end of the nineteenth century. Customers from various Middle Eastern backgrounds crowd in the store, buying, asking questions, giving advice. Itzhaq—short, overweight, unkempt—is often asked by customers what kind of remedy he could recommend for certain sicknesses. Among the burlap bags filled with grains and beans, piles of boxes of candies, sweets, dried fruits and nuts, jars of spices, empty bottles, empty boxes, papers, dust, and dirt, he finds what people seek.

Itzhaq's store is a focal point in the Bukharian quarter for people who want some kind of traditional medicine. People come there, listen to others' problems, volunteer which medicaments are good for what, and leave purchasing something, whether nuts, sweets, spices, or medicines (once when I was there, a Moroccan woman, sitting against a burlap bag and listening to me ask Itzhaq some questions, volunteered the information that one can take *hilbeh*—fenugreek seeds—for stomach aches). Itzhaq is a clever merchant and a good listener. Not only has he picked up the medical traditions of the different ethnic groups in the area, but he also has picked up different languages: Turkish, Persian (in various Jewish dialects—Isfahani, Mashhadi, Hamadani), Bukharian, Arabic, Kurdish, and Hebrew. He was born in Israel to parents whose families came from Iraq, Bukhara, and Iran (Mashhad and Hamadan). Before the Islamic Revolution he traveled to Iran, but was reticent to say whether he brought back any traditional medicines, perhaps fearing the Israeli customs taxes. He would only talk about his adventures in Iran, avoiding all questions I had about where he purchased his merchandise and how he learned about which medications are good for what. "Where does anyone learn anything?" he remarked shrewdly, and continued talking about his experiences in Iran.

Itzhaq is a well-known person among the Iranians in Jerusalem. He is not considered to be a pharmacist or an herbalist, but is a wise merchant who knows what traditional medicines one should use to treat which illnesses. Now that it is impossible to return to Iran or to receive visitors or packages from Iran, Itzhaq's business with the Iranians has skyrocketed. New immigrants in Jerusalem know about his store after a few weeks, and many Iranians who visited from the United States purchased spices, gol-i gāv zabān, and khākshir from him, and bemoaned the fact that he does not carry all the traditional medicines that they used to be able to buy in Iran.

Following a diet deemed proper for health maintenance in Iranian culture, as among other peoples (Chinese, Indian, American health food enthusiasts), creates a continuous concern of the individual's relationship with food, which is seen as directly related to health, sickness, and treatment. If the diet must be balanced in terms of food categories, then the concept of balance of food intake, although not necessarily articulated, becomes an everyday consideration. Among many Iranians this is the case. The result is a healthy diet, few obese people, and a discourse revolving around health. This is not to say that everyone all the time talks about feeling ill. But illness often becomes a topic of conversation in which not feeling well elicits suggestions and support from significant others—what foods to eat and avoid, what medicines to take, whether one should see a doctor or not, how weather or climate could affect health. In Jerusalem, illness discourse among Iranians usually focuses on three ailments: *kam khuni* (lack of blood), nerves, and pains in the arms, and sometimes, legs.

Kam khuni is deficiency of blood, developed from improper diet, thus not creating enough blood, or from excessive bleeding, as in menstruation or from an accident or surgery. The main symptom of kam khuni is weakness (za'ef, noun; za'if, adj., the same word used for showing weakness while exhibiting emotional nārāhati). The weakness is due to the fact that there is insufficient blood to nourish the body. A well-nourished body, one not too thin, is deemed healthy and thus not considered to be prone to kam khuni, although women of childbearing age are liable to develop it due to menstruation. In addition, thinness is associated with kam khuni, as thinness is a sign of improper nutrition. A secondary outcome of kam khuni is weak nerves, not in the sense of feeling lethargic, which is a sign of lack of blood, but in the sense of being asabāni, the nervousness which easily provokes one to anger or excitability, as there is insufficient blood to nourish the nerves; the nerves malfunction and one angers easily. Another outcome is headaches due to lack of blood in the head.

Gila, a young woman whose parents were my neighbors, was considered by her parents and by herself to be suffering from kam khuni. She was very thin and complained of weakness, often being too tired to do her housework, and often she suffered from headaches. The mother of a one-year-old boy, and married to an Israeli whose parents were Kurdish Jews from Iraq, she spent most of her days at her parents' house, lying on the couch or bed. Both parents expressed concern to her that she does not eat enough, that she should eat liver, which is good for kam khuni since it is considered to be concentrated blood and will easily enrich one's blood supply—but she would not eat it. They suggested vitamins, but these too she would not take. When Gila complained to me of being thin and asked what she could eat to gain weight, I suggested eating some cookies or ice cream each day. "No," she said, "I'll get a headache or sore throat." When she had a miscarriage in her second month of pregnancy, this was partially attributed to her being weak and thin by her parents, and to her lacking blood by her brother. Lying on a bed at her parents' house after the miscarriage, Gila complained about feeling weak—here her weakness intensified by the lack of blood from the miscarriage—and asked her mother to make her some gol-i gāv zabān, the infusion good for building strength, assuaging fears, and helping increase the blood.

Gila's family cared for her kam khuni and the consequent miscarriage (also partially blamed on the evil eye; see the following section) by conferring assiduous attention to her desires. They attributed her illness to an inadequate diet, and their treatment for her involved food, vitamins, and herbal medications as cures.

The foods most salient to treat blood deficiency include liver, lentils, and spinach—three foods high in iron. These foods in Western popular medicine are used to treat anemia. It may be possible to conceive of kam khuni as anemia since both involve blood and weakness. However, the Iranian discourse of kam khuni is not concerned about the structure of the blood in the way anemia is. Rather, it concerns an entire range of ailments involving weakness, thinness, headaches, and nervous disorders. Kam khuni is considered a physical ailment, and its manifestations are due to physical causes. In other words, weakness and lethargy, agitation and irritability, are considered somatic ailments, originating sometimes, but not always, in the lack of blood. Kam khuni thus provides the etiology for a range of illnesses, from physical to emotional, in which certain affects, such as irritability, anger, and lethargy, are attributed to lack of blood, as are headaches, pale skin, tiredness, and weakness. The treatment with foods and infusions involves the family and sometimes outside agents, such as pharmacists or physicians, to procure vitamins and tonics which are also seen as beneficial for treatment. Thus, kam khuni is an illness whose cause is seen to come primarily from an inadequate diet or physical loss of blood and whose effects are other symptoms ranging from physical to emotional.

Irritability is one of the possible outcomes of kam khuni, although it is not always caused by lack of blood. Being agitated and quick to anger in a culture which values quietness and compatibility is socially disruptive. Although social situations can provoke anger, individual temperament, such as one whose nerves are weak or are not functioning properly, can create a disposition prone to anger and irritability. Anger is not only socially disruptive, but at times is considered physically disruptive as well. An incident that happened to a friend of mine exemplifies this connection:

> Manizheh left Iran during the Revolution as a single woman in her early thirties and came to Jerusalem, where she studied Hebrew and then worked as a receptionist. She met an Israeli man and after one month they decided to get married. The celebration was attended by her relatives in Israel, but her parents and siblings were unable to leave Iran and were thus not at the wedding. Manizheh became pregnant within a month following her wedding, and in the beginning of her second month of pregnancy, a sixty-year-old French woman, a friend of her husband, came from Tel Aviv to visit him and to meet her. According to both Manizheh and her husband, this woman was quite a busybody and kept telling Manizheh that she was not acting like a proper wife and that she was a wicked woman. At this, Manizheh said she became angry, her heart stopped beating, and she fell on the floor. When she felt better, she accused the

woman of making up all the denunciations, and later told her husband she never wants to see that woman again. A week later she began to stain blood and went to the hospital for tests. She was so upset that she could not eat anything all that day, and she blamed the bleeding on her anger at her husband's friend. She asked the doctor if anger could have been the cause of the bleeding and he told her they do not know what the cause is, but that anger could have added to it. Manizheh stayed in bed for several weeks, and her husband, neighbors, and uncle's wife came over to keep her company, some arriving with a blood-strengthening soup, *āsh-e anār,* made from various fresh green herbs and pomegranate juice. While in bed, she kept moaning about how much her stomach is cramped, but did not know why. After a few weeks, she returned to work and worked until the baby was born, in spite of continuous nausea which she attributed to the pregnancy.

Perhaps Manizheh's case is an uncommon one, but it does exemplify the interconnection regarding lack of blood (due to pregnancy), weak nerves, anger, bleeding, again creating the cycle of lack of blood, which is broken by proper diet prepared by relatives, friends, and herself. And it also indicates that anger is an emotion which is dangerous physically as well as socially.

So far, it has been shown how food becomes a major factor in maintenance of health and in treatment of illness with the hot/cold system in Iranian culture. Food is also part of the discourse of showing one's nārāhati: avoidance of food indicates that one is emotionally upset. Avoiding food too much will thus endanger one's physical health. Whether emotional nārāhati can endanger one's physical health, however, is a question which receives equivocal answers. Some people say that feeling emotionally nārāhat cannot cause one to be sick, whereas others say that thinking and worrying can cause headaches, and perhaps stomach aches. Some people said it is because all the nerves are in the head. Others said it is from not eating and being weak, such as Mrs. Khalili in the third chapter who threw up from being nārāhat. Other aches and pains are not considered to be caused by emotional nārāhati but to cause it: one worries about being ill, especially if one does not know its cause or cannot be cured. Thus a cycle can be created. One has pains or some other physical ailment—backache, high blood pressure, insomnia (this is considered physical by several patients at the clinics where I worked), heart problems—which then cause one to be weak and from this weakness one can become nārāhat. The prevailing view, then, is that physical illnesses cause emotional nārāhati more often than emotional, social, personal, or psychological problems cause physical illness. Consequently, a somatopsychic view of the workings of the body is more prevalent than a psychosomatic view. In fact, we may say that a somato-psycho-somatic view of illness prevails. Amir, from the previous chapter, is a case in point:

> Amir was being treated for depression. His explanatory concept for his illness combined both Iranian and Western models. Before he was depressed (by this he meant diagnosed or labeled as depressed by the physicians in Israel) he had seen many doctors who had given him numerous pills—"all kinds of valiums: librium, valium, glorium"—but when I had talked to him he was taking only a few. "I have kidney stones and *atzabim*. I have seen several doctors for atzabim. Because of my kidney stones I had to drink sixty-four glasses of water a day. And I have burns in my shoulder, pains in my leg—rheumatism—and pains all over my body. I had backaches before I was depressed. After my depression, I felt a pounding and burning and alot of pain on my back. That is from atzabim. Because I have rheumatism, I can't have much wind on me. So I close the windows, and that makes other people nārāhat, and then that makes me nārāhat."

Amir's use of the Hebrew term *atzabim*, "nerves," is a translation of the Persian/Arabic term *asāb*, meaning "nerves." Both terms are derived from the same semitic root. The sounds are similar and the words are used interchangeably by Iranians in Israel. For Iranians, the term *asāb* connotes "weak nerves"—being prone to weakness and anger. In the Israeli biomedical sense, like the American, the term "nerves" (atzabim) is used by physicians to refer to pains whose origins cannot be physiologically or biologically determined. When Amir said he had seen several doctors for "nerves," he used the Hebrew term *rofeh atzabim*, "nerve doctor," which is a Hebrew translation of a Persian concept of either a psychiatrist or a neurologist, both of whom give medicine for "nerves"—the *doctor-i asāb*.

Amir's interpretation of his illness was that his atzabim caused him his pains and because of his pains of rheumatism, and the discomfort it caused others when he had to close the windows, he was nārāhat. Although he did say that he was unhappy with his working conditions, that he had to sell his store because his wife wanted him to buy an apartment for his family, and that he could not work at home, he did not attribute his atzabim to his social, personal, familial, or economic situation, although, through therapy, he took on the therapist's model of social attributions of depression. He differentiated between depression and atzabim, seeing no causal connection between the two. Nārāhati, for Amir, was a by-product of his rheumatism, not the source of his pains. It was the pains in his shoulders that got him the referral from the primary care clinic to the mental health clinic where he was diagnosed as depressed. For Amir, the existential condition of depression is unrelated to his physical condition. He attributes his atzabim to physical exertion and to weakness, saying that when he rests he feels better. His explanation is that shoulder pains are derived from weakness of the nerves. The atzabim and his familial problems make him depressed, and then he gets more pains in different parts of his body. But his nārāhati comes from his having rheumatism and making others nārāhat. Thus, his conceptual model is a somato-psycho-somatic one, with nārāhati coming in secondarily as a result of interpersonal interaction concerning a different illness which is considered to be purely physiological in nature, rheumatism.

Many middle-age and older Iranian men and women suffer from rheumatism. It is believed to be caused by living or working in damp, windy, cool places. As derived from traditional Greek-Islamic medicine, the climate is the causal factor in this illness, moisture being the culprit. Moisture is associated with coolness and with winds. Winds (*bād*) can enter the body and create pains, cause rheumatism or aggravate it. Therefore, Amir closed the windows when he felt the wind disturbed his rheumatism. Also, certain foods or food combinations are known to cause winds in the stomach and abdomen, such as eating yogurt and melon together.

The term rheumatism entered the Persian popular medical discourse, almost replacing the traditional term, *bād-i mafāsal,* wind of the joint. Any sudden pain, such as a cramp in the stomach, can be attributed to winds. Chronic pains in the joints and the bones of limbs are considered to be from rheumatism, caused primarily by moisture, secondarily by winds. It is treated traditionally by applying layers of cloth or clothing to the afflicted area, applying heat, or taking herbal medications.

Middle-aged Iranians in Iran and Israel commonly complain about the pains in their limbs. When they were children, they say, and throughout their lives in Iran, they slept on a mattress on the floor, and the floor was cold and damp. Or they would bathe in the *hamām* (public bath) or in the *hoz* (the small pool which is in the family courtyard), catch a wind, and get sick. In Israel, people go to doctors for pains in their limbs, not always telling the physicians what they think the matter is, but wanting some legitimate excuse for their pain, and medication to take for it—and show for it. Legitimation of rheumatism, when the physician does put a label on it (several physicians told me that they tell Iranian patients who want a sickness label that their pains are rheumatism), enables the person afflicted to gain ease in work.

For some women who work with water doing their housework, the label of rheumatism allows them to take time off washing clothes and dishes, leaving the responsibility to others, or leaving the work undone. Women are particularly prone to pains in their arms, and it is customary to complain about the pains in a high-pitched voice and rub the afflicted arm with the one that feels normal, and to attribute their pains to years of housework for their families, or to an unknown agent. Many younger woman, when I asked, said yes, their mothers or grandmothers suffer from pains in their arms, but they, too, attribute it to doing dishes in cold water for years. When I mentioned that my mother and grandmother and all the women I know of in the United States who have washed dishes and clothes in cold water do not have pains in their arms, my informants either shrugged their shoulders and shook their heads wondering how this is so, or expressed judgment that Iranians are more sensitive physically than other people, and that is why they feel the pains.

The example of an Iranian friend of mine in Jerusalem comes to mind. Esther, the metapelet (child-carer) whose request for a raise inspired a quarrel with Anat and Bob, is a woman in her mid-forties, middle-class, married to a cousin who is a bitter and demanding person and who is very concerned about his heart. She has one son who is married to an American woman and lives in Boston, and three daughters in Jerusalem, one of whom is married and has two children. My friend was orphaned at a young age and left Iran with a youth group to live in Israel when she was thirteen. She was married at seventeen, had children, and now supplements her husband's income by taking care of infants in her home during the day. Her husband is stubborn and highly critical, and the only man in her life with whom she has a good relationship and from whom she gets love and respect is her son, who lives, for her, on the other side of the world.

Esther has terrible pains in her arms and sometimes can hardly do her housework or cook. If she does not have his meal ready, her husband gets angry, and if he is angry, his heart bothers him, and he blames his heart problems on her. Esther has been to the doctors at the clinic across the street for the pains in her arms numerous times. They x-rayed her, did other tests, found nothing wrong, and sent her to physical therapy. She went to the physical therapy sessions for several weeks, but it did not help her and she stopped going. Yet, she kept on complaining about the pains in her arms.

Rheumatism and pains in the limbs provide an idiom to articulate various social and personal problems. Esther's case illustrates a middle-age woman in a marriage situation that is far from satisfactory, whose "uterine family" as Wolf (1972) puts it, is breaking up. Amir's rheumatism, which he attributes to dampness and winds, is also a way of gaining attention from others in spite of his making them and himself nārāhat by closing the windows. Articulation of distress in limb pain, however, is related to something else in Iranian culture. In the Persian politeness code, ta'ārof, there is a phrase to thank a person who does something with the hands for others, whether preparing a meal, sewing a piece of clothing, or fixing something broken: *dast-i shomā dard nakoneh*—"May your hand never hurt (you)." These women and men with pains in their arms are people who work for others, who seem to not be getting the kind of appreciation for their work or for themselves that they want. Not working because of the pains relieves them of some of their role responsibilities and is a culturally legitimated way to gain attention for psychosocial problems in the family or in the society that they cannot express, or of which they may not even be cognizant. Limb pains enable them to articulate distress in relationships with family members or to express the frustration, anger, or nārāhati that they cannot verbalize. The behavioral aspects of the presentation of pain permit the ailing individual to manipulate others to care for him or her.

Whereas emotional nārāhati shows one is powerless and not in control of self, and sometimes enables one to control others who work to ameliorate the person's nārāhati, physical nārāhati, as the manifestation of powerlessness (when sick or somatizing), enables one to be in control of others. Thus, women who feel powerless in their social situation of being mothers and housewives whose work never ends and who have no recourse but to work, have pains of rheumatism in their arms which thwart their working. For some, it is a physical manifestation of the nārāhati that they cannot verbalize. But for most, it is a bād, wind in the joints, rheumatism, caused by working with cold water, sleeping in cool places, and being exposed to climate considered unfavorable for the body.

The Body and the Spiritual: Supernatural Conceptions of Sickness

Another possible agent in the etiology of sickness, besides the natural forces of diet and climate, is the supernatural, mostly in the form of the evil eye (*cheshm-i bad*). Not everyone among the Iranian Jewish community believes in the evil eye. However, those who do take precautions to avoid its detrimental effects: they use talismans given by holy men, or wear talismans made of certain natural or manmade materials which are known to have some sort of efficacious value, and at other times they use methods of divining to discover the person who gave the evil eye, thus abolishing its effects.

The kinds of ailments which are attributed to the evil eye are sudden afflictions which have no other known cause, such as sudden crying spells, sudden childhood sicknesses, an unexpected fall, a miscarriage. These may be attributed to the evil eye by the person afflicted or by someone in the person's family. The evil eye is given to someone willingly through jealousy, or more often, unwillingly. In other words, the person who is accused of giving the evil eye is not responsible for it. To counteract the influence of the evil eye, one could burn wild rue (*esfand*) and encircle the smoke around the afflicted person's head, thus ridding the influence of the evil eye. Another method is to wash off a child's face upon entering the house, thus washing off the jealous glance that some stranger or known person gave. Or one may have family members break an egg, divining the name of the person who gave the evil eye by calling out people known and pressing the egg at each name, and when the egg breaks, that person whose name was mentioned is considered to have given the evil eye, and its influence will then disappear. The following examples depict afflictions attributed to the evil eye:

> When she was in Iran, separated from her financé for two months preparing for the wedding while he was working in Israel, Tamar went through fits of crying spells and, she said, nervousness. She attributed her behavior to wanting to be near her fiancé. Her grandmother, however, thought it was due to the saying of *mobārak* (congratulations, Persian) by a woman in their synagogue whose daughter was older than Tamar and not yet engaged. So the grandmother burned esfand (wild rue) over Tamar's head, opened all the windows and doors so the smell and smoke would go outside and everyone would know that they are getting after the evil eye. In trying to determine if the esfand helped, Tamar said that there is just so much one can cry and she stopped crying after they did that. So her grandmother attributed it to the esfand, but she said she cried a few days later anyway.
>
> Maurice, now a physician, said that when he was a child he was once very sick and the family attributed it to the evil eye. He does not believe in it, he said, but the treatment worked. Someone holds an egg and people in the family call out names and with each name, the person holding the egg presses the shell, and if it breaks, the name called out as it breaks is the person who gave the evil eye. Then they go to the person's house, gather up some dust from the door or gate, come back, mix the dust with the broken egg, and put a dot of it with the right forefinger on the child's forehead, between the eyes, and/or on the palate. They then throw out the rest in front of the house of the person who gave the evil eye. Other ways of ameliorating the situation with the person who gave the evil eye are also practiced: when the egg breaks on a name, one goes to that person and gets something from his or her hand to eat or drink, or money to put in water which one then drinks; or one puts the broken egg in the middle of a crossroad so it will be stepped on and taken away. And one does not tell the person who gave the evil eye that he or she gave it, as the person was not responsible.
>
> Shahnaz tried to get pregnant for several years, and when she finally did, she had a miscarriage in her fourth month. Her husband attributed it to the evil eye: a young woman he was dating before he married Shahnaz lives upstairs with her mother, and the mother once said *mazal tov* (congratulations, Hebrew) to Shahnaz when she heard of the pregnancy, and it was an envious look that she gave, the evil eye which caused the miscarriage.
>
> Gila, the young thin woman who suffered from kam khuni, had a miscarriage a few days after I had asked her father, who owed me five dollars, to return the money that he had kept from me for three months. He always denied he owed me anything, and kept brushing off my request. However, one day as I was walking by their house, he called me to come in, that he has the money for me. Upon entering, I saw the family very disconcerted. The father gave me the five dollars and when I asked how they were, I

was told of Gila's miscarriage. Although on every other occasion when I had entered the house, I was warmly greeted, this time I wasn't. A cold politeness hung over the house and molded our conversation. I attributed the father's giving me the five dollars when I did not ask for it as a way of ameliorating the evil eye which they thought I gave to their daughter, causing her miscarriage.

Mrs. K., a wealthy grandmother in her late sixties, suddenly fell one day as she was walking across her salon in Tehran, breaking her leg for which she came to Israel for treatment. She attributed her fall to the evil eye and wears a turquoise ring and an agate pendant to ward off any other effects of the evil eye.

The above examples of sickness attributed to the evil eye indicate both an attempt to give meaning to an occurrence of illness that came suddenly or whose cause is unknown, rare, or anomalous, and a social situation in which responsibility for the sickness is blamed on another. Blaming another exemplifies social distance, fear of the unknown, and attempts at retribution where the person blamed for casting the evil eye, unlike a witch, is not accused of having done so: the person is either unaware of having the evil eye or, if jealous, may not have intentionally committed any act of ill will, and an accusation could only create discomfort and antagonism between families.

In order to prevent an attack of the evil eye, talismans are worn or are put up in or around the house to guard it from evil forces. These are made from natural and man-made materials which have some sort of supernatural powers derived from the substances of which they are composed (metal, stones, vegetal material), from designs or inscriptions written or engraved on them, or from their relationships to the astrological and alchemical properties which influence their production. Congruence between the different layers of cosmogenic reality involves amulets and talismans in relation to the supernatural, stars, planets and life on earth (see Nasr 1968:223–24). Al-Suyuti, the famous fifteenth-century physician, wrote, "The recitation of charms and the wearing of amulets are a form of taking refuge with God for the purpose of securing health, just as is done in the case of medicine" (1962:221). Thus, the talisman and amulet are not simply static materials but are active forces as therapeutic agents mediating the power of the supernatural with the person, in which each level of reality is ruled by another which surpasses it, the supreme reality being God.

Among Iranian Jews, as among Iranian Muslims, prevention against the evil eye consists of amulets composed of materials considered supernatural by their relationship to other elements in the cosmos, by virtue of their location, such as near a shrine, or by being blessed by a holy man. In addition, written and spoken prayers of holy men are deterrents against the evil eye.

The two main stones used for protection against the evil eye are turquoise and agate, both of which have a long usage in Islamic magico-religious tradition.

Turquoise is believed to bring good luck and happiness. Perhaps its value is also attributed to the location of the turquoise mines near Mashhad, the second holiest city of Iran, the seat of the Shrine of Imam Reza. Donaldson (1938:152–53) wrote that people look at turquoise to rest their eyes and recondition their eyesight. Agate is valued as protection from all evil, accident and poverty, and it can be used to cure diseases of the eye. According to Iranian Shi'ite tradition, "Ali asked the Prophet what agate was, and he received the reply that it was a mountain in Yemen which gives witness to the unity of God, proclaims the apostleship of Mohammad, witnesses to the Imamite of Ali and his heirs, and promises Paradise for the Shi'ites and hell for their enemies" (Donaldson 1938:152).

Iranian Jews were also part of a mystic tradition based upon the congruence of the various forces of cosmogonic reality as perpetrated in the Kabbalah, which was influenced by Islamic and Christian mystical traditions. They, too, adhered to the supernatural properties of such amulets as influential and legitimate operators, compelling the subservience of the supernatural for the procurement of health. Just as the Iranian Jews adhered to the Iranian health beliefs concerning diet and climate, so did they concur on the beliefs regarding such supernatural forces as the evil eye. And as the Iranian Muslims go to a prayer writer (*du'ā nevis*) for talismans, prayers, and other forms of religious cures, Iranian Jews visit their holy men, called mullas in Iran and *hakhamim* in Israel.

The hakhamim are considered to be wise, learned men, schooled in Torah, Talmud, and the Kabbalah. Because of their knowledge of the religious texts and their ability to forecast, predict, divine, and then devise ways of rectifying someone's troubles, they are seen as powerful and as having a special relationship with God. They utilize the religious texts of Judaism along with traditions based upon Islamic conventions, astrology, letter-magic, and divination in order to treat people who come to them with a wide variety of problems: inability to sleep at night; crying spells; barrenness; help in finding a spouse; protection against the evil eye; divination of causes of economic troubles. Therapy comes through prayers invoked orally by the hakham or written on paper, the latter concerning various procedures of what to do with the prayer depending on what the trouble is.

One neighbor of mine had difficulty sleeping. He went to a hakham who was originally from Baghdad and is reknown in Jerusalem for his clairvoyancy. He gave my neighbor a number of long slips of paper on which the names of groupings of angels were written several times. These strips of paper were photocopies (how modern technology enters into traditional sacred treatment!) of an original typed list. He was to cut each grouping and every night before going to sleep, put the paper with the angels' names in a glass of water and drink the water, the names being imparted to the water. This neighbor's wife was suffering from crying spells induced by the sudden stabbing death of her brother in Tehran, and her husband took her to the hakham who had them come back the following day with three apples onto which he wrote a prayer for her to eat three times that day.

The relationship between the client and the hakham is secretive, although other's may be in proximity of the transaction, such as another learned man who apprentices himself to the hakham, and members of the hakham's family who live in the house in which he works. Most people are reticent to tell others what the prayer on the talisman says, as its supernatural value is not to be tampered with. In horror a young Israeli friend of mine, whose parents immigrated from Iran, said she would not read a talisman I had gotten because it was private, and, besides, she said, it was in Rashi script, which she said she did not read (Rashi was an eleventh-century Talmudist from Provence, France). To one man I mentioned that an American friend gave me an Iranian Islamic talisman in a silver container which was inscribed with phrases from the Quoran, and that I had opened and took out half of the parchment to see what was written. He looked at me in surprise and was quite upset, saying that I ruined it. When I tried protesting I didn't, because I am Jewish and this is an Islamic prayer, he said that it does not matter, that God is the same God (P., *khodā hamin khodāst*), and that in Iran Muslims often see Jewish mullas for prayers and Jews visit *sayyid*s (holy men considered to be descendants of the Prophet) for prayers and talismans. The more obscure the prayer, the more powerful, as it is the mystery of the word, whether understood or not by those who wear the talisman or who utilize its formula, that possesses the promising power of well-being (cf. Tambiah 1968).

The hakhamim in Israel are visited by people from all over the country, primarily by Middle Eastern Jews. One, a Yemeni in Jerusalem, is famous for having founded a yeshiva. His method of helping those who come to him is telling them to improve themselves and pray, said an informant, and by praying for the person himself. Another, located in Beersheva, divines personal problems from *mezuzot* (talismans posted on each door of a religious Jew's house, containing a prayer from Deuteronomy) which clients bring to him. One man described his experience with this particular hakham: "I took my *mezuzah* and he looked at and said I have problems in my house. He said what happened. After, I read psalms that he gave me to read each day. He said what my wife did and I have to make reparations for it. He said my wife did an abortion. I didn't know and after I asked my wife and she said she did it. I saw him six months ago. Usually you have to make an appointment. I went alone. I thought maybe he will or won't receive me. Usually you make appointments by phone. I got his address from a friend. I phoned from Tel Aviv to see if he was home."

People hear about hakhamim from friends or family who have had beneficial experiences with them. Although appointments are usually made months in advance, protectzia (Hebrew, pull, influence) can get one an earlier appointment. Hakhamim gain their fame by word of mouth. There are those besides the two mentioned above who have special methods of dealing with the supernatural and their clients. One gives a bottle of water to drink which he blesses, and he blesses the client. Another gives only a blessing to the client. Some lesser known hakhamim will bless objects, such as *matzah shmura,* the unleavened bread eaten on Passover made from the first harvested wheat of the spring, telling their clients that they should carry this piece of *matzah* with them at all times to protect them from the evil eye. And others bless their clients by touching the top of the heads of men or laying their hands above the heads of women, the latter perhaps menstruating, consequently impure and taboo to the touch of men.

In sum, the hakhamim are religious men who practice a form of religio-magic healing in addition to divining the cause of personal problems, writing therapeutic prayers for an individual's health or misfortunes, and giving blessings for those who ask for their religious touch. Another form of sacred curing for one's ills, both physical and spiritual, are pilgrimages to shrines and holy places. Several Jewish shrines in Iran, such as the tomb of Esther and Mordechai in Hamadan and the shrine of Serah bat Asher near Isfahan, and in Israel, such as the Wailing Wall in Jerusalem, the Tomb of the Patriarchs in Hebron, and Rachel's tomb in Bethlehem, are the most frequently visited sites. Then there are those tombs of men who are considered to be holy, such as that of Shimon bar Yohai in Meron, to whom the mystical text, the *Zohar,* is attributed, and Yonatan ben Uziel, a medieval rabbi to whom people pray for a spouse. At these pilgrimage sites, individuals pray for their own health and well-being as well as that of their families. During the upheavals of the Islamic Revolution, people also prayed for Iran's future.

The supernatural causes and cures of ill health and distress form a part of the popular system of health care and maintenance among Iranian Jews. Combined with religious traditions, which are an amalgamation of Jewish and Islamic mystical thoughts and practices, this form of treating sickness or misfortune attributed to supernatural powers is added to that of diet, climate, and Western medicine as an all-inclusive way of viewing the individual in the world—a person subject to various forces, all of which must be taken into consideration in order to maintain one's health and vitality.

Body Language or Language of the Body: Expressing Emotions and Pain

The body enters into the discourse of human interaction in both verbal expressions and nonverbal presentations. Not only is the body symbolic of the individual's relations to others, but it is a biological entity that is socially and culturally delineated. The way people look at the body and feel about the physiological conditions of the self vary cross-culturally, and linguistically. Expressions of the body depict cultural conceptions of the body as a biosocial entity. In the English language we have cold-blooded and hot-blooded people, people with gall, and people who are heartless. No doubt these terms are related to a historical tradition based upon Hippocratic-Galenic views of the body, many of which come to us as "survivals," without our knowing the origin of the terms and phrases we use. The same may be said about the phrases frequently used in Iran in which the body is the idiom of verbal interaction, forming ways of communicating about relationships, emotions, and feelings. The ta′ārof "May your hand never hurt (you)" is but one of a number of idiomatic expressions. People reply to the previous phrase with another expression, "*Sar-i shomā dard nakoneh*," "May your head never hurt (you)." These phrases, utilized in interaction, exemplify the concern of the body as being subject to illness, to hurting. Although not really taken literally in terms of an individual's potential ills, there is the realization within the culture, as the previous section portrays, that the individual biological body is subject to both natural and supernatural agents which could cause it to be sick. In addition, sickness was and is part of life in a culture which not only had developed a way of dealing with the perpetual regard of the body and its relationship to the foods ingested and climate surrounding it, but also had experienced other afflictions: trachoma, famine, influenza, leishmaniasis, smallpox, typhoid.

Body terms are used in contemporary Iranian conversation and in classical Persian poetry, where the body is used as a metaphor for emotions in human interaction. This body terminology has been derived from the classical tradition of Ibn Sina's physiology and is now used in idioms which reflect the classical theory of the body as a physiological and spiritual entity. Before exemplifying how body terminology is metaphoric of emotion, a review of Ibn Sina's theories of the body will be delineated; then, examples of phrases and emotional expressions in poetry and in contemporary language will show how the body is used metaphorically for emotional expression.

According to Ibn Sina, the physical, psychic, and spiritual worlds are linked by the "breath." The breath unites with blood to serve the rational soul. It is sent out through the nerves, enabling them to provide sensation to all parts of the body. The blood itself is the prime agent of nutrition and is manufactured from food in the liver. From the liver it goes to all parts of the body, part of it combining with breath in the heart.

The body has three vital organs, in which the primary faculties arise. These are the heart, the source of vital breath, innate heat and seat of emotions of fear, joy, and delight; the liver ("concentrated blood," Ibn Sina 1930:66), the seat of reproduction, and the human passions; and the brain, the source of sensation and movement. The animal or vital faculty resides in the heart; the vegetative or natural faculty resides in the liver; and the rational faculty resides in the brain. These faculties are activated as the breath goes through and takes something from the center of the organs.

According to Ibn Sina, the liver and blood together correspond with the special sense of smell and the mental states of anger and vexation, and with weeping.[5] This correspondence enables us to better understand the use of the word *jegar*, liver, in phrases used in everyday language and in classical Persian poetry. The liver, as the seat of the baser passions, connotes one's relationship or feelings to another, especially in terms of emotional involvement. A few examples taken from the Persian poem *Layli and Majnun* by Nizami, a poem of unrequited love in which the young heroine, Layli, is married off to an older man while her beloved, Qays, runs away to the desert where he becomes crazy from love and is thus called Majnun, Arabic for "crazy," demonstrate the use of the term "liver" to signify relationships between two people emotionally involved with one another:

Chandān jegar nahafteh khordam.
I ate so much liver in secret.

Atr-am 'z shamimeh-yi jegar kon.
Make perfume from the scent of my liver.

Sanduq-i jegar ham az jegar bast.
She locked her liver outside the liver box.

In the lines of poetry, Layli and Majnun express their feelings toward one another by using the liver as a metaphor for their emotions. The first sentence pertains to pining away for one's love. The second connotes an opening up toward one's love, and expressing one's love. The third refers to Layli's death, closing off her emotions not only to her husband for whom she had no feelings of love whatsoever, but also to others who loved her and whom she loved.

In contemporary discourse the liver is also used to denote attachment or feelings toward another person. Four expressions denote the burning or cooking of the liver, connoting the powerlessness of the speaker:

Jegaram misuzad ("My liver burns."—said when one feels sorry for someone and does not know what to do)

Jegar suz ("burning liver"—painful, heart-rending)

Jegaram kebāb shod ("My liver became a kebab."—said when someone feels sorry for another person).

Jegar-i to bekhoram ("I could eat your liver."—expression of emotion of caring to someone one loves)

By understanding the relationship between the liver and its product, blood, which when mixed with breath gives sensation to the body, we can surmise that the use of the terms "blood" (*khun*) and "bloody" (*khuni*) in Persian poetry has to do with being vexed, irritated, angered, and troubled (the mental states corresponding with liver and blood, according to classical medical theory) and the lack of equilibrium thus found in the breath. The metaphors of blood-stained cheeks or pouring blood (*khun rikhtan*) are often used to signify the act of crying in mourning someone who has died or when death is likely, such as when someone goes off to war. In the poem *Layli and Majnun* (the first two excerpts below) and in Ferdowsi's epic work, the *Shahnameh* (the third and fourth excerpts) both men and women cry bloody tears:

Khun rikht bar āb-i zendagānish.
She poured blood [shed tears] upon the water [tears] of her life.

Chandān 'z sereshkash khun rost,
kān cheshme-yi āb rā bekhun shost.
Several of her tears grew bloody,
that washed away that watery eye in blood.

Bezad na'areh va khunesh āmad bejush.
Hami kard muyeh va hamizad khorush.
He cried and blood came out in a tumult.
He kept tearing out his hair and he kept crying.

Cho barkhast āvāz-i kus az daram
Biāmad por az khun do rukh mādaram.
When the sound of the battledrum rose from outside my door
My mother came full of bloody cheeks.

Regarding mourners, which several of the examples above illustrate, the customs of weeping, tearing hair, and scratching cheeks typify the lamentations:

> All the persons present [at the funeral] then rip their clothing from the neck to the waist, tear out their hair, scratch their faces and strike themselves on the chest. (Chardin 1811:481)
>
> The men open their clothing as if to tear it and put dust on their heads. Sometimes a woman will scratch herself, tear out her hair, expose herself bareheaded to the sun and sigh. (Wilson 1921:210)

The Moharram ritual, depicting mourning for Hussein, is also replete with blood as men slash themselves with chains or swords in the ceremonial procession. The red bloody tears in the poems are probably a consequence of tears running down bloody cheeks, cheeks scratched as an act of mourning. When the cheeks are scratched and the blood pours out, the person indicates the nārāhati—the ghoseh (sorrow)—of mourning. However, blood is not only part of the rituals of mourning, of being a woman (cf. M. Good 1980), and of eating (both the Jewish and Islamic dietary laws forbid the consumption of blood), but it is also the humor which carries the breath in traditional medical theory. The breath and blood unite, in classical medical theory, to serve the rational soul. In popular discourse, the term "blood" is used idiomatically to indicate vexation, suffering, or conflict in relations with others, an overcoming of the rational soul (see Haim 1958:283–84):

Khun-i ou az khun-i man rangintar nist. (literally, "his blood isn't more colorful than mine"; figuratively, "he is no better than I am; we should both suffer equally")

Khun-i jegar (del) khordan. (literally, "to eat the blood of one's liver (heart)"; figuratively, "to eat one's heart out; to suffer very much (in silence)")

Khunkhar. (literally, "bloodeating"; figuratively, "bloodthirsty; cruel")

Khunsard. (literally, "coldblooded": figuratively, "coldblooded; calm, indifferent, lenient, easy-going")

Khunsard budan. (literally, "to be coldblooded"; figuratively, "to be calm, keep one's head")

Khungarm. (literally, "warmblooded"; figuratively, "warmblooded, warm-hearted")

Khun rikhtan. (literally, "to pour blood"; figuratively, "to commit murder")

There is a difference in usage of the word "blood" poetically and colloquially. In poetic language, blood is used as an idiom to denote grief and sorrow in the permanent severance of relationships due to actual or potential death, and in popular language the use of the term "blood" in phrases indicates, as in English, relationships of conflict or, in the sense of "warm-blooded," closeness with others. Conversely, the liver is used as an idiom, poetically as well as colloquially, to denote connection and emotional relationships between two people both alive.

Other emotional terms in contemporary Persian are sometimes composed of words connoting body parts. Among these are the following:

Persian word	English meaning	Etymological construction
deltang	lonely, homesick, nostalgic	*del* = heart; *tang* = tight "tight heart"
delvāpasi	anxiety, concerned, uncertain	*del* = heart; *vā* = back; *pas* = back; "the heart going back on itself"
sarkhordagi	disillusionmennt	*sar* = head; *khordagi* = eating, corroding, wearing away, hitting; "being hit on the head, worn away on the head"

The three words listed above are part of a lexicon of emotional expression in the Persian language. In the previous chapters, several terms were noted which dealt with the expression of dysphoric affects. These words were Persian transformations of Arabic terms, such as nārāhati, ghamgin (sad) and ghȯseh (sorrow), and asabāni (angry). The three words above are derived from Persian only, and the interesting thing about them is that they are compound words composed of bodily parts to which something has happened. These terms exemplify emotional states which are explained in terms of the body, used in contemporary conversation to explain one's feelings, but are not as commonly used as is the term nārāhat. Here, then, we see a number of terms and phrases in which parts of the body are used to express negative affects. However, these poetic and differentiated terms for negative emotions in Persian, many of which are derived from body parts, and in Persianized Arabic, are subsumed under the idiom nārāhat.

Concerning phrases about the body and sickness rather than the body and emotions, Persian is replete with poetic and somewhat figurative phrases to describe types of pain, some of which could be translated into similar concepts in English, others of which are rather lyrical and require a different conceptual translation of terms. For instance, what we would call, in English, a gnawing pain, is described in Persian as "they are eating me from inside" (*az tu marā mikhorand*), and a "shooting pain" or "sharp pain" is the term *tir mikesheh*, where *tir* means "arrow" and *mikesheh* is an auxiliary verb meaning "dragging, pulling, carrying." A more vivid image of pain is the concept of a snake twisting within one: "biting like a snake" (*mesl-e mār migzareh*) and "I have a snake twisting in my stomach" (*man dar delam mārpich dāram*, where *mārpich* is actually a compound word meaning "spiral," derived from *mār*, meaning "snake," and *pich*, meaning "twist").

Phrases for pain, bodily descriptive terms for emotions, concepts of how the body works and what causes sickness are all part of cultural explanations of illness, and form the basis of illness behavior. People learn how to be sick. What symptoms they have and how they express them are culturally influenced, as are treatments for sicknesses and transactions with curers. The body is thus a biosocial entity in which feelings, both physical and emotional, are expressed. And in a culture like Iran's, in which certain negative emotions are socially disruptive and certain positive emotions, such as love, are powerful and dangerous, especially in a society in which marriages traditionally were arranged, the body is used metaphorically and behaviorally to express one's feelings.

Somatization and Nārāhati: Body as Metaphor

A further question remains: how does culture affect somatization? Somatization, as stated previously, is the expression of social and personal problems in bodily reactions and in bodily complaints rather than in personal or social terms. The body, then, becomes a metaphor for expression of personal and/or social problems, emotional or otherwise. The particular symptoms which different people focus on while somatizing are most likely influenced by their culture. For Iranians, in this case, symptoms of somatization may include problems of the digestive tract, headaches, pains in the limbs—these due to cultural conceptions of illness relating to hot/cold foods and to the influence of climate on the health of a person.

By considering somatization metaphorically, bodily complaints may be understood as "experiencing one kind of thing in terms of another" (Lakoff and Johnson 1980:5). This is not to say that people consciously somatize and therefore realize that their bodily complaints mean something else. Rather, as metaphor, bodily complaints indicative of somatization incorporate communication of something to someone, an English metaphor being the communication of feeling "ill at ease" (or even "dis-ease") to self and others. Why communication is carried on through the body rather than through other means is also culturally influenced: there may be social stigmas attached to showing certain kinds of emotions or problems, as in the expression of personal, emotional nārāhati; there may be psychological suppression of certain problems which are denied from consciousness and redirected as physiological expression; there may be conceptions of being more attuned to one's physical presence, focusing on one's body as an entity of sensitivity in the world, to the physical elements around it and in it, as in the Iranian context. To paraphrase Levi-Strauss, then, bodies are "good to think."

Many of our conceptions of the world in which we live have to do with our bodily orientation to it, with such basic metaphors as up, down, in, out (see Lakoff and Johnson 1980). Interaction with the physical environment, other people, and bodily functions form human experience, which is then modified by culture. Culture influences our defining abstract concepts in terms of more concrete entities, such as defining emotions in terms of bodily concepts, in which the body is the metaphor for emotions, or for social or personal problems. The understanding of abstract and hard-to-define conceptions such as nārāhati in terms of the body may be explained by Lakoff and Johnson (1980:177) as follows:

> many aspects of our experience cannot be clearly delineated in terms of the naturally emergent dimensions of our experience. This is typically the case for human emotions, abstract concepts, mental activity, time, work, human institutions, and social practices, etc., and even for physical objects that have no inherent boundaries or orientations. Though most of these can be *experienced* directly, none of them can be fully comprehended on their own terms. Instead, we must understand them in terms of other entities and experiences, typically other *kinds* of entities and experiences.

The body is not symbolic in terms of standing *for* something else, but in terms of comprehending one thing in terms of another. Take the term nārāhat, for instance. This one word denotes two metaphorical notions that partially explain emotional states and physical states. Neither the emotional state nor the physical state, in Iranian culture, may be related to one another. The experiences of these states may be equally disrupting, creating basic experiences which are in one way similar, that is, in terms of being in an uncomfortable state, but the conceptions of the physical and emotional may not be similar. The emotional concerns relations with other human beings, whereas the physical concerns interaction with the external environment which influences the internal workings of the body. Although different, both pertain to the concepts of the individual as sensitive (hassās) in relation to others and to surrounding physical conditions. This alludes to the notion of individual temperament, as conceived by Ibn Sina and still extant today. There are those individuals who are more sensitive than others, some more sensitive emotionally, some more sensitive physically. Such individuals are more prone to being nārāhat, either in an emotional sense or in a physical sense. Nārāhati in an emotional sense has repercussions which could be detrimental to one's social situation in terms of showing one's personal weakness or in causing others to become nārāhat, whereas physical nārāhati, also showing weakness, but physical weakness, is not considered socially disruptive, but is seen as a result of physiological malfunctioning, for which one musters social support in order to help rid one of the bodily troubles.

Because of the unwillingness to express emotional nārāhati, physical nārāhati may be metaphoric of personal problems. Not all physical illness, however, can we say is somatization among Iranians. That would be a dangerous statement to make and a hazardous course to follow. What is of concern here is the experiencing of one thing—dysphoric affect—in terms of the other—the body. Because of the cultural proscriptions against expressing certain kinds of negative emotions, because of continuous daily focusing on the body in terms of diet and climate and how these two elements influence health, because of the lack of colloquial vocabulary for negative emotions and a preponderance of phrases for pain, because of the use of body symbolism to reveal emotions toward others and to express certain kinds of negative emotions, the body becomes a vehicle to communicate the negative affects that cannot be shown or conveyed verbally.

Nārāhati is a state of being, emotional and/or physical. Although the emotional expression of nārāhati may be culturally disapproved of, physical sensitivity and expression of physical illness are not. Consequently, it may be possible to say that there is a tendency toward somatization in Iranian culture which is grounded in cultural conceptions of the body and illness. But what causes somatization are social situations, personal problems, and interpersonal transactions. As is often the case of immigrants and refugees who are uprooted from their culture of origin, Iranians in Israel suffer from a variety of illnesses. The problem of accommodation to Israeli society and the frequent nārāhati resulting from it, as expressed verbally within the community and nonverbally in terms of illness, have already been addressed. The question now becomes: what happens when Iranians, who may or may not be somatizing, encounter Israeli doctors in their quest for treatment?

Chapter 7
Israeli Doctors and Iranian Patients: The Dilemmas of Diagnosis

Because of the reticence of vocalizing nārāhati and because of problems of life in Israel—the sociocultural dissonance of immigrants, insecurity due to the continuous state of war and the consequent economic situation (high taxes, high inflation rate, high tariffs), familial difficulties (children not obeying, wife working, husband expecting too much)—the body, for some people, becomes a metaphor to express the social, cultural, and familial difficulties which are inconvenient, inconceivable, or imperceptible to manifest verbally. Consequently, not feeling well physically frequently signifies not feeling well culturally, socially, or personally. This is apt to be the case when patients return to clinics with vague aches and pains after physicians, using various physical examinations, are unable to locate any organic pathology. The problem of what to do with the symptoms is one for both patients who are concerned about their feelings and physicians who are concerned about their profession.

When Iranians in Israel feel ill, whether with stomach aches, sore throats, heart palpitations, or pains of rheumatism, they either rely on home remedies, such as foods or herbal medicines, or go to a doctor, or both. Like most people who do not feel well, they frequent doctors to find answers for what bothers them, seeking a name for their physical feelings, a diagnostic label, a verification for their illness. However, when patients somatize, present strange symptomalogy, or vocalize their complaints in a style that is foreign and unfamiliar to the physicians, doctors have difficulties with diagnosis. They want to rule out biological or physical abnormalities, and to do so they order series of paraclinical tests. When these tests come out negative, the doctors are in a dilemma: what is wrong? what should they do?

The dilemma of doctoring and diagnosis, of Israeli doctors and Iranian patients, is a problem of medical understanding: the effects of patient somatization on the physicians creates doubts about professional knowledge and ability.

Iranian patients come into primary care and hospital clinics with complaints that are difficult to diagnose and treat. The physicians are baffled at and annoyed with their Iranian patients, and ultimately, as doctors, they are impotent, unable to diagnose. The physicians' discourse on their problems with Iranian patients reveals something about the doctors themselves, about their frustrations and fears. Somatizing patients put physicians in an interpretive dilemma regarding diagnosis and a personal (and interpersonal) dilemma concerning professional efficacy. The dilemma is resolved by shifting the blame onto the patients and mark them as problematic with the label "Parsitis."

Kupat Holim and the Israeli Medical System

Nearly 80 percent of Israel's population belong to Kupat Holim Histadrut, the Sick Fund (Kupat Holim) of the General Federation of Labor (Histadrut), the country's oldest and largest system of primary care medicine. The sick funds insure 95.4 percent of Israel's population: Kupat Holim Histadrut covers 83 percent of the insured population, with the rest covered by the smaller sick funds, such as Kupat Holim Leumit, Kupat Holim Amamit, and Kupat Holim Maccabi (Central Bureau of Statistics 1982:687).

The sick funds in Israel are affiliated with political parties. Kupat Holim Histadrut is linked to the Labor Party via Histadrut, whose members are obligated to join Kupat Holim. Because of the ideological differences of various Zionist organizations at the time of the Yishuv, the pre-state settlement, other sick funds were established by people who opposed the socialist orientations of the Labor movement. Kupat Holim Leumit was established in 1933 by people who were politically unable to secure medical care from the Histadrut; it is now affiliated with the conservative Herut party that is part of the Likud coalition. Kupat Holim Amamit was founded in 1930 by the former General Zionists, who are now also part of Likud, to provide medical coverage for the self-employed in rural and urban areas; its present membership is primarily from the self-employed urban middle class, and its political association is tenuous. Kupat Holim Maccabi, not affiliated with a political party, was organized in 1940 by unemployed doctors who immigrated from Central Europe, and serves professional and affluent urban inhabitants. The physicians employed by the smaller sick funds work in private clinics, whereas those employed by Kupat Holim Histadrut work at one of the 1,225 Kupat Holim clinics throughout the country which provide ambulatory services (Kupat Holim Histadrut is the sole provider of biomedical health services in development towns, rural areas, and outlying urban neighborhoods), or in one of the fifteen hospitals where one-third of the hospital beds (3,931) are maintained by Kupat Holim (Yishai 1982:286).

Although Israel does not have national medical insurance, Kupat Holim Histadrut (from here on, referred to as Kupat Holim), as the prominent health care organization in Israel, provides coverage for the majority of wage-earners, salaried employees, and self-employed who pay monthly dues to Histadrut. When people talk about going to Kupat Holim, they mean the clinics affiliated with the Histadrut, the Federation of Labor.

Kupat Holim evolved as an outgrowth of the colonization of Palestine by Jewish settlers from Eastern Europe and Russia. While establishing the kibbutzim as a way to return to the land, ideologically as well as physically, and while developing new urban enclaves, the workers confronted and oftentimes were overcome by endemic and epidemic diseases. Notable were outbreaks of malaria transmitted by mosquitos breeding in swampy land throughout the valleys and plains. This was the case in the Jezreel Valley in which the first kibbutzim were constructed, and in the plain north of Tel Aviv, where towns like Hadera were established. Many workers were dying from malaria, typhus, and other diseases.

Without families to care for them when they were sick, the immigrants, mostly single and young, were in need of a health care system. Kupat Holim was thus developed in 1912 by agricultural workers, doctors, and nurses who ascribed to the Socialist Zionist ideology, to provide health care for the settlers. By 1921, with the founding of Histadrut, the different Kupat Holim in various areas of the country were united under Histadrut's umbrella to become a bureaucratic network of health services. These services included hospitals (the first to be established was at Kibbutz Ein Harod in the Jezreel Valley, later to be moved to the nearby town of Afula), primary care clinics in settlements and urban neighborhoods, pharmacies affiliated with the clinics, convalescent homes, maternity and child-care clinics, medical benefits in case of accident or disability, rehabilitation therapy, laboratory tests and medical technology, preventive and environmental public health programs (clearing swamps, certifying potability of water, giving innoculations).

Since the Socialist Zionists were the largest and most powerful of the settlers in Palestine, Kupat Holim became its medical arm. When new settlers came to the country, Kupat Holim provided them with medical services. Their goal was to furnish comprehensive health care for an immigrant population confronting a different climate and different health hazards than those they were used to. In order to pursue the ideological target of creating a Jewish homeland, the workers of Kupat Holim worked, so to speak, for the workers of the land. Such was their socialist framework, publicized in various pamphlets geared to potential immigrants and benefactors:

> [The staff is] wholly devoted to its medical and public duties. Many Kupat Holim doctors believe in public medical service for ideological reasons as Socialists and active members in the Labour Federation. . . . They regard their functions administering medical care not only as a profession but as a public and social mission. (Kanievsky 1947:8)

> It is worth mentioning that all *Kupat Holim* hospitals (except the one in Haifa) are surrounded by orange groves or other plantations. The Central Hospital [in Afula] has been completely surrounded by a suburban housing development for employees. It is also worth noting that physicians and their families reside at the hospitals, giving full time to their duties. The Kupat Holim staff is engaged, body and soul, in the services of the sick and the wounded. (Israel Histadrut Campaign 1948, pamphlet, no page).

> Convalescence provision is of particular importance for pioneer workers and settlers unaccustomed to manual occupations and a tropical climate. Kupat Holim was the first organization to establish such institutions in the country. (Generation Federation of Jewish Labour in Palestine, 1948, pamphlet, no page)

By the time of the mass immigration in the 1950s, the supposedly idealistic doctors and Kupat Holim had become a segment of the national bureaucracy dealing not only with the sick, but also with the integration of immigrants into the society. Immigrants are given three months of free medical insurance at Kupat Holim and nine months at reduced rates. The poor are given free care paid for by the Ministry of Social Welfare.

Both the immigrants and the poor frequent Kupat Holim and have become the subject of studies by Israeli medical sociologists, who attribute the high utilization rates of Kupat Holim to its providing latent needs to the population through connections with other bureaucratic chains in the society: a note from Kupat Holim facilitates acquiring sick leave, permission to move to a larger apartment when there is a housing shortage, or privileges in buying certain luxuries.[1] Although these studies show that the differences in utilization rates are a way to integrate into the society and obtain latent needs, the more complex problem of somatization as a consequence of sociocultural dissonance—which contributes to the problem of high clinic utilization rates—is disregarded. Most of the immigrants who repeatedly utilize Kupat Holim are those whose indigenous cultural orientation is at odds with that of Israel, or they are people who encounter and amplify the major stressors of the society (economic difficulties, wars and deaths of loved ones, crowded housing) due to their own disrupted social support systems and/or personal vulnerability: their personal, social, and emotional predicaments are culturally transformed into the sicknesses that the doctors see.

The doctors who work at Kupat Holim, unlike the ideal image portrayed by the propaganda pamphlets issued in the 1940s, are not devoted "body and soul" to the sick. They are dedicated to their profession as most physicians are. Yet, in spite of their orientation to the service of the sick and to the upholding of scientific standards, many physicians, according to Ben-David (1958), dislike the lack of independence that working for a bureaucratic organization implies: feeling subjected by the organization; having difficulties maintaining authority as an individual physician within the institution; being unable to be at the forefront of the development and implementation of advanced medical technology and knowledge. Doctors blame Kupat Holim for the high utilization rates: because patients feel they do not have to pay every time they see the doctor, they come to Kupat Holim for every problem. Although that may be the case—and indeed I heard patients mention that they go to the doctor because they might as well use what they pay for with monthly dues—there is also the feeling among patients that doctors really do not care so much about them because they are not getting financially rewarded.

Nevertheless, private practice, which would create a doctor-patient relationship mediated by fee-for-service, is still not commonplace in Israel. Since the majority of Israel's physicians are not self-employed, they receive similar salaries based on a nationwide scale. However, unlike Kupat Holim doctors, hospital-based physicians who have private patients, especially those who are uninsured in Israel—primarily tourists and foreigners—can reap the benefits of extra compensation by charging higher fees than they would normally receive from insured patients. The extra pay accrued by some of the hospital-based doctors, in addition to their positions working at the forefront of scientific medicine, give them a higher status than the Kupat Holim doctors. Although physicians and medical students deem the scientific specialized segments of medicine affiliated with hospitals of higher status than community-based family medicine, they feel that community medicine must and should exist, and value the care for the population that Kupat Holim provides.[2]

However, the frustrations for Kupat Holim doctors, more than dealing with the bureaucratic organization itself, have to do with treating problems of "real" and "illusory" sicknesses. "Real" sicknesses, as noted by several Israeli physicians, are those with organic pathology, complaints which can be substantiated by the doctors through physical examinations and/or paraclinical tests. "Illusory" sicknesses, on the other hand, are functional problems that disturb the patients who present them and the doctors who treat them.[3] "Illusory" here pertains to an erroneous perception of somatic functioning. It concerns the doctor's and patient's interpretations of the patient's feelings and the presentation of symptoms. Dealing with "illusory" sicknesses is difficult and frustrating for physicians who use various scientific tests to decipher the problem: doctors do not want to be mistaken about the existence of underlying pathology, nor deceived by the illusive qualities of nonorganic sicknesses. Accordingly, because patients who frequent Kupat Holim clinics oftentimes present minor, nonorganic, or "illusory" sicknesses, many Israeli physicians at Kupat Holim feel as if they are doing band-aid work. They prefer the challenge of interesting cases in the hospitals, and frequently are frustrated with patients who repeatedly visit the clinic.

What Kupat Holim-based and hospital-based physicians have in common is a professional medical language which overrides their various immigrant backgrounds and crystallizes their cultural diversities into a common denominator of medical discourse, through which they camouflage their individual differences and clarify the cultural differences in problematic patients. Although physicians in Israel recognize the social and cultural influences on patients' presentation of symptoms and problems, they do not know how to delve into the various aspects of an individual's sociocultural background to help treat the patient. In Israel, as in most countries in which (biologically oriented) Western biomedicine is the norm for professional medical standards and practice, the psychosocial aspects of sickness are given a low priority in medical studies (although there are a number of medical anthropologists, sociologists, and psychiatrists who are hired by clinics and hospitals in Israel). If social sciences are studied, they are usually geared to those aspects of the behavioral sciences which would enable the physician to have patients comply with the physician's orders. Therefore, the medical establishment, not understanding the social and cultural influences on sickness causation and illness behavior, and confronted with problematic patients who overutilize the health services, blame the institution and the patients.

As a result, patients who display certain similar symptoms and problems are perplexing, especially if the patients come from a particular ethnic group, and the medical establishment then singles them out. Such problematic patients are frequently those whose cultures contrast with that of the doctors and nurses. Accordingly, with the emphasis on Israelization and modernization, physicians and nurses denigrate traditional forms of healing as superstitious, such as hakhamim's prayers and amulets, while promoting the presumably rational and scientific Western biomedicine. Shuval et al. (1970:137) even see physicians in Kupat Holim as carrying on the function of helping immigrants acculturate to predominant Israeli norms by their emphasis on biomedicine: "overt attempts by the physicians to pressure patients to give up traditional, ethnically-oriented customs and behavior patterns represents *support* for those immigrants who desire to move out of the traditional ethnic environment and into the wider range of Israeli society." Thus, Kupat Holim, as seen by some Israeli sociologists, performs the latent function of integration of immigrants. Yet, it is ironic that some of the reasons for which patients probably somatize and present various physical and psychological symptoms to Kupat Holim doctors have to do with the precise problems of integration and cultural degradation in the society that are fostered latently, and sometimes conspicuously, in the clinics.

Immigrants, Clinic Utilization, and Israeli Sociology

Many of the earlier epidemiological studies of clinic utilization and hospitalization in Israel focused on which population groups used which services for which problems. The overriding assumption, born out of the powerful sociopolitical Zionist ideology, was that the longer the immigrants were in the country, the more "Israeli" they became, the less they would be prone to various kinds of psychological problems.[4] Most of these studies compared immigrant groups and psychiatric morbidity through compilations of statistics, indicating that distinctive psychiatric problems varied with country of origin. However, most of the studies lacked sociological or cultural explanations for the variations in medical and psychological problems that patients from different immigrant groups were experiencing.

Several investigators sought to understand who was sick and why. Hes (1958) writes that hypochondriasis among hospitalized Oriental Jewish immigrants was a way of expressing schizophrenia: "we felt a difficulty diagnosing schizophrenia in Oriental patients. . . . often we saw patients with no signs of withdrawal and complaining only about bodily symptoms. It was our impression that these hypochondriacal complaints were in many cases a manifestation of a schizophrenic syndrome" (p. 18). Hes was trying to fit patients' behavior and symptoms into previously conceived (Western culturally defined) categories in order to define, label, and hopefully understand. Others followed Hes in their research, differentiating Orientals from Westerners.

Halevi (1963) categorizes patients who were hospitalized in psychiatric institutions during 1958 into illnesses coordinated with country of origin. The data show how many of which country were admitted for which problems. However, in spite of the higher number of Eastern European manic-depressives, which the author attributed to the Holocaust experience, and of Iranian neurotics, the problem is made more complex and interesting by the absence of information pertinent to anthropologists: what in the cultural background of these hospitalized immigrants caused them to express their symptoms in the ways they did, and how did their expression of symptoms induce the psychiatric staff to label them the ways they did? Both the expression of symptoms and the labeling of sickness are culturally prompted. Halevi's article, examined in more detail below, is interesting for the statistics, but does not answer such questions.

Neither are such questions answered in other articles. Maoz et al. (1966)

conducted an epidemiological study of a development town in northern Israel, showing that the North African–Middle Eastern population suffers from more personality disorders and psychophysiological complaints than other patients, that most of the patients are women from Poland, and that the Europeans have more psychoneuroses. Social stereotypes enter into descriptions of North African patients (remember, Moroccans were stereotyped as "carrying knives"), who are depicted as exhibiting "personality disorders . . . of antisocial violence or of unsuitable aggressive type" (p. 282). Immigrants from Near Eastern Asian countries, on the other hand, were seen as having a "relatively high rate of psychoneurotic and psychotic reactions. . . . Women from Iran and Iraq showed a typical syndrome which was defined by the authors as an unclassified neurotic reaction, of hypochondric introvert character, with psychophysiological manifestations 'all over the body' " (p. 282). The authors, and the psychiatric staff, were looking for characteristics which would differentiate their patients along immigrant, and therefore cultural, lines, but they did not examine the cultural delineation or the social development of the illness that the immigrants manifested.

By the late 1960s, the classifications of Oriental and Western were beginning to be blurred as socioeconomic class and education took over as categorizing variables: if Orientals would successfully become absorbed into the society, become educated, Israeli, and less traditional, such psychophysiological problems would lessen. In this framework, Lerner and Noy (1968) studied patients at the outpatient psychiatric clinic at Hadassah Hospital in Jerusalem, claiming that "the connection found between somatization and ethnic origin seems to stem from the fact that among patients of oriental origin the majority have had little schooling only, and that it is indeed the low level of education that effects the high degree of somatization in the oriental groups" (p. 147). Although further on in the article they contradict themselves by stating that the European immigrants in Israel did not have such high levels of education either, the implication behind their argument was that as soon as the Oriental Jews were educated in Western civilization, they would stop somatizing.

Shuval et al. (1970:87), carried out this line of argument by focusing on lower class, "traditional" peoples rather than on Orientals per se, noting that those patients who are the most problematic are the "lower-class, less acculturated, less sophisticated subgroups of the population." Antonovsky (1972) takes Shuval one step further to say that Israelis turn to physicians to satisfy nonmedical needs (meaning no "real" sickness) because they focus on ambiguous symptoms which must be clarified by physicians and because of "an inherent value on health" of "Jewish culture" (p. 452). However, Antonovsky's argument is weakened by the omission of examples of "ambiguity," the fact that there is no such thing as a universal Jewish culture, and the total disregard of sociocultural stressors in Israeli society.

Ben-Sira et al. (1978) try to formulate an understanding of patient utilization of health services by looking at somatization as an effort to mobilize support by those people who lack resources in the society and who are under stress. They assume the problem is one of "faking"—that people pretend they are ill in order to utilize the latent functions of Kupat Holim (sick leave, welfare, and so forth), only later to feel the real pains for which they see the doctors. Finally, Honig-Parness (1982) replicates Shuval's 1970 study but shows that immigrants with high levels of "need deprivation" utilize Kupat Holim only if they have symptoms, and that lower classes and the elderly use the medical services more than do other groups in the society.

What can we abstract from this brief synopsis of studies? Although Israeli sociologists have been among the first to study systematically the relationship between immigration and health, we can question their assumptions and their goals regarding immigration, illness, and clinic utilization. Is their functionalist orientation (influenced by Eisenstadt's early work on the absorption of immigrants [1954] and by Parson's studies [1951, 1953] of the sick role and medical professionals) able to shed light on the problematic of somatization, interpretation, and diagnosis? Considering that many Israeli sociologists and social psychologists ignore the significance of culture, I would say not, as their studies reproduce the conventional knowledge that "absorption" of immigrants would eliminate social and cultural problems.

Those carrying out the studies, like other members of the society, are ensconced within Israel's ideological framework, which holds that "mixing of the exiles" should eliminate cultural differences as immigrants become absorbed in the state's social and economic organization. Although few would want to change the socialist underpinnings of Kupat Holim, they assume that overutilization of clinics falls within the structure of the medical system itself and is supplemented by the economic and educational problems of the Oriental communities. But they ignore, as do many medical sociologists, the more complex problems of sociocultural dissonance, social and cultural powerlessness of immigrants, and the cultural formation of illness. The belief in Israel was and is that cultural differences should be subordinated and eventually eliminated as immigrants become Israeli. The fact that many of the Oriental immigrants somatize is seen to be a result of their "primitive" culture, and education and Israelization are expected to eliminate somatization. Now that the immigrants have become more or less Israeli-ized, but many people continue to somatize, class rather than national background has become the variable used for comparison. However, it is a sly euphemism, since the majority of the poor are Oriental Jews.

Rather than pitting epidemiological rates against one another to note differences of illness among ethnic groups, we should decipher, if possible, the ways people express distress—physical, emotional, or what have you—in the clinical setting: people who are labeled as neurotic or psychotic might be complaining in a manner legitimate and intelligible in their cultures of origin which, when in contact with Western-trained physicians, seems bizarre. This, I believe, happens to be the case concerning Iranian patients and Israeli physicians. Where do the patients and physicians see each other? What are the clinical settings? What do the physicians think about the Iranians and why? These questions will be answered by focusing on the professional health care delivery system in Jerusalem and its use by Iranian patients, and on the communication difficulties that the clinicians have with their Iranian patients.

Kupat Holim and Psychiatric Health Care in Jerusalem

The major facility for primary care in Jerusalem is Kupat Holim. Between 1979 and 1981, when I was doing research, there were thirty-eight clinics in various neighborhoods throughout the city. The clinics themselves vary in specialized services (such as physical therapy and x-ray), and at times patients are referred to other clinics than their own for these services. Of lesser importance in Jerusalem are two other types of primary care sick funds, Maccabi (three addresses) and Meuchedet (two addresses): they have no general clinics; doctors see patients in their offices or houses; they have no official connections with mental health clinics but do have part-time psychiatric consultants. Kupat Holim, however, is affiliated with mental health clinics throughout the city.

Because of the psychosocial problems that immigrants experience, mental health is a salient and important aspect of health care in Israel. In 1976 the Ministry of Health divided the city of Jerusalem into four zones, each affiliated with a quarter of the city to serve a population of 150,000 or less. Each zone included one psychiatric hospital and one or more outpatient mental health clinics for adults, youths, and children.[5] People are referred to the hospitals or mental health clinics by their physicians at Kupat Holim, by their families, or by themselves. The doctors of Kupat Holim clinics know about the mental health facilities and the staff of the mental health clinics consult at different neighborhood Kupat Holim clinics. However, referral and use of the various facilities available depend on the different physicians' attitudes toward psychiatric services, relationships with patients, and understanding of problems which have psychosocial or psychobiological components.

Other psychiatric facilities in Jerusalem include a hospital for emotionally disturbed children, a drug clinic, and an alcohol clinic. In addition to the Kupat

Holim system and psychiatric facilities, there are a number of major and minor hospitals which serve different areas of the city, minister to different populations, and are recognized for specific medical or public services.[6]

Mental health services are free for Israeli residents and citizens. Influenced by Israeli ideology, which stresses social and economic support for immigrants, the mental health personnel help settlers and sabras contend with the emotional, social, economic, political, and familial problems facing them in the present and which they faced in the past (persecution, Holocaust, uprootedness, war). There is an awareness that sociocultural stressors within the society are oftentimes extreme, and that immigrants and sabras have numerous difficulties and problems with which to cope. The staff in the clinics and the hospitals are involved in community outreach programs, and are linked with other social services in the society, such as the welfare system, schools, youth organizations, and geriatric agencies. Psychiatrists, psychologists, and social workers practice primary prevention, crisis intervention, short-term therapy, long-term therapy, and consultation.

This provides the context in which the visit to the doctor can be described. If someone does not feel well, the person goes to the local Kupat Holim clinic in the morning or in the afternoon, whichever is more convenient (there is a three-hour break in the middle of the afternoon, from one to four). At the main desk in the entrance of the clinic, the person picks up a ticket from a clerk to see the physician with whom the person is registered. Each physician is allocated between four and six patients an hour. Although the wait could be long, patients have the possibility of seeing neighbors and friends who also drop by for consultation with the doctor. The waiting room thus becomes a neighborhood rallying point where people discuss their physical problems, their treatment, evaluate the physicians and nurses, give advice to others about their ills, and comment on various social and economic problems of the country. The consultation with the physician is often brief, and patients frequently leave the physician's office with slips of paper to take to the laboratory for tests, to the x-ray department, to other clinics for different services, or to the pharmacy for medication. Sometimes there are referrals to hospitals if the physician feels that further tests are necessary. Occasionally, patients are directed to one of the local mental health centers if the doctor detects psychosocial problems. That, however, is rare, and many physicians, hurried, couched within the biomedical framework, are often reluctant to take time out to explore the relationship between their patients' symptoms and their underlying personal or social problems.

People referred (by self or others) to mental health clinics are examined for the first time on one of the days when the staff screens potential patients. At staff meetings, the psychiatrists, psychologists, and social workers go over their interviews. As a group they decide whom they will take on as patients and for what kind of therapy, short-term or long-term. Next, an appointment is made with the client for intake, in which family and personal history is noted as well as various problems that the person is troubled by and would like to have help managing.

The psychiatric staff, unlike the biomedical practitioners, often become involved in the lives of the patients. They do home visits for the elderly and ill, have transportation to the clinic for those who are too disoriented to make it on their own, and provide an informal group therapy "clubhouse" open every day for patients who need daily doses of medication. Although there are always the problematic patients—those who are not psychotic but who have difficulties talking about the problems bothering them and for whom "talk therapy" does little good, those who want medicine and nothing else, those who habitually miss their appointments, or those who refuse to come to the clinic—the psychiatric staff attend to the social, cultural, and psychological concerns of a wide range of patients from various socioeconomic, cultural, and educational backgrounds. At times they try to understand how the cultural differences affect their patients, and at other times they give up, baffled, unable to comprehend the patients or the problem, and are frustrated with the therapeutic encounter. Such is the issue to be explored in the following chapter. Here, however, we will see that the problems of misunderstanding and frustration between the clinicians and patients begin in the clinics of Kupat Holim and the hospitals where patients seek biomedical treatment.

"They Can't Deliver a Real Message and They Make an Elephant Out of a Piece of Grain."

The statement above was expressed by an Israeli professor of neurology, trying to make sense of the differences between Iranian patients and those of other nationalities, and to explain the difficulties that he, as a physician, has in understanding them. His difficulties are shared by numerous physicians, some of whom characterize Iranians as no different from other Middle Eastern Jews in their behavior and concepts about illness, whereas others consider Iranians as among the most problematic patients. Why do the doctors differentiate between Iranians and other patients? Why are Iranians considered problem patients?

In the epidemiological studies carried out by Halevi (1963) and Maoz et al. (1966), Iranians rank higher than other immigrants with certain psychiatric problems. In fact, according to the data reported by Halevi (see table 7.1), Iranians ranked highest in the categories of "unspecified psychoses," "total psychoses," and "neuroses," making them the immigrant group with the highest number of first admissions to psychiatric hospitals in 1958. What is of interest here are two points: the substantial number of Iranians who received treatment in

Table 7.1: First Admissions per 100,000 Jews Aged 15 and Over by Country of Origin, 1958

	Schizo-phrenia	Manic Dep.	Unspec. Psych.	Total Psych.	Neurosis	Person Disord.	Total Cases
Israel	80.8	23.4	19.5	138.7	24.1	49.5	223.4
E. Europe	34.2	51.1	9.2	124.3	21.5	14.1	160.2
Balkan	50.1	42.4	14.5	144.6	17.0	16.0	180.8
Cent. Europe	44.3	54.9	6.7	137.7	25.0	24.1	191.6
Iraq	74.0	19.9	15.2	140.4	43.6	41.8	235.3
Yemen	56.8	19.6	15.7	123.3	58.7	37.2	221.2
North Africa	71.7	26.0	18.9	140.2	56.7	50.4	254.5
Turkey	80.4	32.7	29.8	184.5	47.6	47.6	279.8
Iran	72.5	24.2	52.3	197.3	80.5	36.2	318.1
All origins	60.4	37.1	15.4	143.3	33.3	32.0	213.2

Source: Halevi, H. S., 1963, Frequency of Mental Illness among Jews in Israel, *International Journal of Social Psychiatry* 9:276.

psychiatric hospitals, and the considerable number of Iranians in comparison to other immigrant populations with "unspecified psychoses." What are these "unspecified psychoses"? Halevi does not describe the symptoms, but the careful inquisitive reader will discern that the variations in data among those with "unspecified psychoses" delineate cultural differences and reveal a problem of understanding of symptom presentation and communication. The fact that so few Eastern Europeans (9.2 out of 100,000) and Central Europeans (6.7 out of 100,000) are categorized under this classification while Iranians compose the major group (52.3 out of 100,000) indicates an understanding of the Europeans by the (European) classifiers and a miscomprehension of the Iranians. The symptoms of the Iranians for the medical and psychiatric staff must have been so foreign and bewildering that they were unable to fit them into any of the established categories of psychiatric morbidity. Thus, "unspecified psychoses" became an instrumental label, symbolizing the differences and difficulties that Iranians posed for the medical and psychiatric workers, and signifying the complexities of culture and the convenience of labeling in medical interaction.

Still today, Iranians generate problems for the Israeli medical establishment. According to physicians, Iranians are "hypochondriacs" who complain of multiple aches and pains, have strange complaints, show aggravation of real symptoms, worry unnecessarily about minor things, visit doctors frequently, have few verifiable organic problems, are unable to recognize social or psychological influences on their health, go from doctor to doctor in search for an illness label, and—for those who are not Israeli residents or citizens or who do not have Kupat Holim insurance—bargain with the doctors over their fees for treatment. In the latter category are those Iranians who came to Israel especially for medical treatment, notably with well-known physicians at Hadassah Hospital in Jerusalem, or who came for tourism but, while there, went for check-ups. Many of the Iranian tourists had family in Israel, and while visiting them, made appointments with various specialists for examinations. Entire families would come in, and they were labeled by the hospital workers as having "check-up disease." The feeling among the Iranian tourists was that Israel's doctors are better than those of Iran, so they might as well take time out to make sure they are healthy. The feeling among the doctors who saw them was that Iranians worry unnecessarily about everything.

Israeli physicians have seen three different types of Iranian patients. First were the immigrants, such as those whom Halevi and others labeled as having "unspecified psychoses." The immigrants, settled in various communities, frequented their local Kupat Holim clinics and, if dissatisfied with their treatment or if needing further specific assistance, visited specialists at hospitals. Among the immigrants have been those who suffered from "real" diseases and "illusory" sicknesses. Another category of Iranian patients were the tourists, now few if any, who made numerous appointments with physicians in hospitals for "check-up disease." The third category were those who had come from Iran specifically for medical treatment for a variety of problems for which they were unable to obtain sufficient care in Iran or for which they trusted Israeli physicians more than Iranian. Among this group were upper-, middle-, and lower-class Iranians of all religious faiths, the poor often receiving aid in the form of contributions from family and neighbors for their travels and medical expenses. Many who came from this group had "real" physiological disorders: lupus, Hodgkin's disease, infertility, genetic conditions, eye disease, tumors, osteomyelitis, paralysis, neurological and orthopedic problems. But others presented symptoms similar to those Iranians who resort to visiting Kupat Holim, symptoms which lacked pathological findings. Among these symptoms have been pains in the arms and legs, back pain (oftentimes, according to several physicians, associated with an underlying problem of impotence), heart complaints, weakness, pain all over the body.

By the time of the Islamic Revolution, Iranians were the largest population of foreign patients at Hadassah Hospital—880 Iranians in 1978 compared to the second largest foreign population group, 78 Americans (see table 7.2). The increase of foreign Iranian patients commenced after the Six Day War of 1967, continued to rise until 1974, when fewer came, showing the after-effects of the

Table 7.2: Patients from Abroad Discharged, by Country of Residence, 1962–79

Countries	1962	1963	1964	1965	1966	1967	1968	1969	1970	1971	1972	1973	1974	1975	1976	1977	1978	1979
African Countries	2	7	2	1	—	5	3	—	5	5	8	6	1	2	10	4	2	4
Argentina	—	1	1	—	1	3	1	4	—	2	—	—	—	—	—	—	—	—
Austria	2	2	2	—	—	2	1	2	1	1	—	3	1	5	—	—	—	—
Belgium	1	3	2	—	1	—	2	2	—	1	—	—	—	1	3	—	2	—
Brazil	—	—	—	—	—	1	—	—	1	3	—	1	—	—	3	—	—	—
Canada	2	2	—	—	—	3	3	2	4	—	—	2	11	9	7	11	9	3
Cyprus	6	21	17	18	33	26	25	52	44	46	45	32	27	14	14	23	13	17
Ethiopia	10	3	12	1	5	—	3	19	25	40	33	33	3	3	1	4	1	—
France	6	5	1	1	1	1	1	5	3	4	8	14	4	5	5	1	3	5
Germany	1	—	3	1	5	3	4	1	2	—	13	8	11	3	5	4	2	8
Great Britain	4	5	1	1	5	—	3	8	6	4	2	5	2	6	4	4	2	16
Greece	2	1	2	1	2	1	3	3	—	2	—	4	3	2	4	6	3	—
Holland	3	1	1	—	—	—	4	2	—	1	4	—	1	3	4	3	—	1
Iran	10	17	57	34	46	50	102	135	172	213	378	352	286	437	741	926	880	184
Italy	3	2	1	1	—	1	4	—	3	2	8	6	3	2	13	2	5	7
Poland	1	2	—	—	6	6	13	4	1	1	2	1	—	—	—	—	—	—
Roumania	—	—	—	3	1	1	—	2	3	2	2	1	5	—	—	—	6	3
South Africa	2	5	—	2	1	—	2	2	—	1	2	2	3	2	12	3	4	2
Switzerland	2	1	1	—	—	—	3	—	2	2	2	2	4	6	3	1	2	1
Turkey	—	—	—	3	1	1	—	—	10	8	2	1	—	—	4	7	4	15
U.S.A.	21	25	12	17	11	11	35	41	44	77	79	62	43	43	43	50	78	59
U.S.S.R.	2	2	3	3	1	5	5	1	1	1	—	—	—	—	—	—	—	—
Others	20	19	19	16	25	16	9	17	74	20	47	45	23	21	39	28	50	41
TOTAL	100	126	137	102	144	138	225	302	401	436	635	580	432	559	915	1077	1066	366

Source: compiled from the charts which appeared annually between 1965 and 1980 in Hadassah Medical Organization, Statistical Report,

1973 Yom Kippur War, and reached a maximum of 926 in 1977, a year before the political upheavals began in Iran.

Because of the large influx of patients from Iran, several Iranian-Israeli entrepreneurs developed businesses to assist them: a small hotel owned by a family from Yazd became a meeting place and residence for patients and families; Hebrew-Persian translators appeared at the hotel and at the hospitals; one translator bought a minibus which he used to transport patients to and from the airport and Jerusalem, sometimes using it to give tours for those people who wanted to see more of Israel than the hospitals of Jerusalem. In addition, some hospital-based physicians gained financially from the transactions with their Iranian patients: aside from earning higher fees paid by private patients who had no Israeli medical insurance, several doctors developed distinguished reputations among Iranians which gained them invitations to Iran to perform surgery or to help establish clinics.

Most of the specialists that Iranians saw at hospitals were cardiologists, neurologists, and orthopedic surgeons. Since conventional Iranian conceptions of illness focus on the heart and on pains of rheumatism, especially of the arms and legs, it is understandable that such specialists were sought. Many Iranians were somatizers, presenting a problem that hospital-based specialists were not accustomed to treating. The reactions of these physicians, frustrated by their encounters with Iranian patients, illustrate the significance of culture and the complexities of ethnicity in clinical interaction:

> They are all neurotic about illness. Iranians have no conceptions of Western medicine. Medicine to them is like voodoo. It costs X amount of dollars but they like to sacrifice to foreign gods. There is no logic in it. No understanding of medicine. They can't understand what is told to them. . . . They worry unnecessarily about minor things, things that they wouldn't worry about if they understood illness. They don't know the basis of the body workings, such as what the heart does and what the kidneys do.

> Iranians have a hypochondriac personality. They are too aware of their organs. . . . They ask what and how to eat and are surprised to find out there are no major influences of food on the eye. [This was said by an ophthalmologist].

> Iranians are more *nudnik* than other ethnic groups. Like glue, they adhere to you asking questions.

> They will go to other countries to see physicians if they are told nothing is wrong. . . . They think of feelings differently from the way we do. We may ignore things, and they feel pain. Pains of Iranians aren't because they are primitive, but they hear such ways of talking from their parents.

> Iranians are primitive. They take small things and maximize them.

> Their attitude is strange to us. They have a different mentality. . . . Iranians, like anyone else in Jewish or Arab or American society, have among them those with slight hypochondriac tendencies.

> Patients, especially Iranians, come with the same aches and pains all over the body. . . . Iranians show aggravation of real symptoms. They have terrible reactions to trauma. A minor head injury shatters the personality. They have a personality problem. It's not that they just become hysterical about something, but they totally break down and are not able to function. . . . The Iranian feels he has to impress you. He has pains everywhere. It is hard to feel what is important or what is not. Regarding pains all over, many are convinced they feel pains. They have a hysterical reaction to pain.

> Iranians are different. Their electric circuits are wrong.

> It's not the sickness that's different with the Iranians, but the presentation of symptoms. They have neurotic and bizarre complaints. There is always a pattern. They are perfectly healthy until one day when suddenly something happened and they are sick. They relate that onset to something around the environment and there are things that are bizarre that start it—like a color. . . . They say such things that their hair is burning, that they have a sense of heat in their thigh. The doctors find nothing.

> They have no different pathology than the regular population. . . . They may be more sensitive. That is, they always have the feeling that when they get colds, they get all kinds of aches and pains and other diseases.

> Many patients we saw were from villages who couldn't afford medical services in Iran. . . . Many were uprooted from their villages and went to cities where people weren't so religious, where life was new. They were under stress which led them to be ill in nonphysical ways. . . . The doctors in Iran were cheating them, so it was cheaper to come to Israel. . . . Iranians look for purely physical answers to their complaints. They are nagging, and few are really sick. They want several consultations. . . . I like Iranians. They are lovely people. They have such a close family life that nowhere else in the world can you see it.

The physicians, from Europe and South America in addition to Israel, related in their various complaints about Iranians' symptomatology a basic problem of perception, communication, and efficacy. In spite of the doctors' contradicting one another's opinions, they all indicated the intricacies of clinical communication. The Iranians present one symptom or several at once, the doctors find nothing, they explain to the patients that there is nothing wrong, the patients ask similar questions repeatedly which annoys the physicians, who think the patients pay no attention to them, and the patients, dissatisfied, search for other doctors to find what disturbs them while the physicians, dissatisfied, grumble about what difficult patients the Iranians are. Among the symptoms that Iranians complained about, which seem nonsensical to the physicians, were questions and problems that are important in Iranian culture. For example, those who asked about the impact of certain foods on the health of the eyes are posing legitimate questions since, in Iranian culture, the hot-cold food categorization limits what is good and what is bad to eat for certain ailments; colds and their influence on other aches, pains, and diseases concern the influence of climate on the body and the development of rheumatism; aggravation of symptomatology, such as a head injury, relates to the physical and emotional sensitivity of the individual. Israeli physicians do not know about these aspects of the cultural patterning and presentation of illness. Iranian physicians, however, see no differences between Iranian patients and those of other nationalities, and understand Iranian behavior in the clinical setting as a manifestation of Iranian cultural patterns and of traditional medical concepts of sickness:

> Nothing is wrong with Iranians. It's just that Iranians have no patience, that's all. Maybe the doctors here don't understand them because they are lazier in Hebrew and have accents. They ask a lot about the diseases they have, if they are not dangerous, if there are things they can buy privately for it.
>
> Iranian patients don't like being sick. If the doctor tells him not to work, he will work. Iranians can't stand to stay at home. If he is a man and feels he is a man, he must never be sick. Also, Iranians won't care about the medicines you give them. They will find a way that's best for them—not taking everything when they are told to take it, but relying on their own judgment.
>
> Iranians have pains in their arms or legs—rheumatism—because the climate in Iran is cold.

The physicians at the hospitals examine patients with whom they have no long-term relationship. As specialists, they expect to find pathological problems and to use their scientific training, as physicians, researchers, and professors, to treat and cure the patients. Somatizers and chronic complainers present a very real challenge to their professional background as practitioners of biomedicine.

Those physicians who work at Kupat Holim are also challenged by patients who somatize. However, the relationship between the Kupat Holim practitioners and their patients differs from that of the hospital doctors and their patients. The doctors at Kupat Holim have the same patients, often several members of one nuclear family, whom they see regularly. They work (although they might not reside) in a neighborhood and are familiar with what goes on in the local surroundings. And because they see patients with minor complaints most of the time, they are accustomed to dealing with people whom they consider as having no "real" disease, except for such problems as influenza, the common cold, stomach ailments, or sore throats. Many have little patience with those patients who keep presenting the same symptoms for which they find no cause. Some physicians will refer such patients to mental health services, whereas others ignore their complaints and keep saying that the patients are healthy. In the latter case, both the patient and the doctor leave the clinical encounter discontented, as did Esther the metapelet (child-carer) in the previous chapter. The patients feel pain, aches, something wrong, whereas the physician, having sent the patient for a battery of tests, deduces "it's all in the nerves." The patient returns to the doctor. The doctor still finds nothing organically or physically the matter. The battle continues until one gives up. Sometimes the physician gives up in frustration and recommends that the patient see another doctor, or go to psychiatric services. The patient may or may not take the physician's advice. Many, however, refuse to go to a mental health clinic. There is a stigma attached to seeing a psychiatrist on the one hand, and, on the other, many believe that their physical pains have nothing to do with anything for which a psychiatrist could help.

Such is the problem Kupat Holim doctors have with Iranian patients: somatization coupled with particular styles of clinical communication. Iranian patients differ from those of other ethnic groups in that they present chronic bodily pains in particular complaining styles. Most other patients consult Kupat Holim physicians primarily for acute self-limiting diseases or somatic malfunctioning of some part of the body (thyroid trouble, hemorrhoids, asthma, ulcers). Chronic bodily pains often are not visible to physicians but can be felt by the patients. Acute self-limiting problems are "visible" either through clinical examinations or through laboratory tests. Somatic malfunctioning of some part of the body can also be verified by clinical or paraclinical examinations. Therefore, those who come to the clinic without "real" diseases that can be verified by physicians' examinations, such as those who come with the "illusory" problems of pain which cannot be verified by tests, or those who come to the clinic for the rewards it gives them in terms of employment benefits or welfare, create difficulties for doctors.[7] For the non-Iranian physicians of Kupat Holim, Iranian patients are the difficult ones.

In order to confirm, or disconfirm, Israeli doctors' opinions of Iranian patients, I handed out a questionnaire at a Kupat Holim clinic in the neighborhood where I had lived, which had a middle-class Iranian population that expanded with refugees from the Islamic Revolution. The questionnaires, which were translated into five languages (Hebrew, Persian, Yiddish, French, English), were designed to determine which ethnic groups utilize the clinic for what kinds of problems. I distributed the questionnaires in the waiting area of three doctors' offices. During the times when I distributed the questionnaires there seemed to be so few Iranians that I assumed the doctors' discourse on Iranian patients was influenced by their ideas of Iranians from outside the clinical setting—of Iranians being stupid, stingy, and suspicious. However, when I tabulated the questionnaires, I saw the situation of the Iranians in a different light.

Two hundred eighty-five completed questionnaires were returned.[8] Of these, 123 were abstracted for comparative analysis, since they comprised the five largest ethnic groups utilizing the clinic. Of the remaining 162, the variety of backgrounds of the people using the clinic were so vast that comparison among groups would have been inefficacious: among the 162 were immigrants and Israeli-born children of immigrants from twenty-six countries numbering one to twelve people per group. Therefore, I extracted from the aggregate the five largest immigrant groups, including within these groups Israeli-born children of parents who both immigrated from the same country. The inclusion of Israeli-born children takes into consideration the doctors' categorization of people on medical files which includes parents' country of origin, thereby classifying patients according to ethnic origin. Thus, the 123 comprised the following five groups: 35 Iranians; 15 Iraqis; 25 Moroccans; 24 Poles, 24 sabras. Those I consider sabras are those whose parents were also born in Israel (or Palestine).

Breakdown of the reasons patients noted for their coming to the clinic yields four categories of medical problems: somatic malfunctioning, medical notes (such as excuses for work or school,) or tests, chronic pains or troubles, acute self-limiting situations.[9] These categories are derived from the answers patients wrote to the question, "Reason for seeing doctor." A comparison of the five largest ethnic groups' utilization of the clinic for the four categories is tabulated below (table 7.3). The rows designate which percentage of each group utilizes

Table 7.3: Categories of Medical Problems of Patients at a Kupat Holim Clinic, Jerusalem, 1980

Immigrant Group	Somatic Malfunc.	Notes/ Tests	Chronic pains or Troubles	Acute/ Self-lmtg.	Total
Iranians	11%	3%	49%	37%	100%
	(4)	(1)	(17)	(13)	(35)
Iraqis	7%	20%	20%	53%	100%
	(1)	(3)	(3)	(8)	(15)
Moroccans	24%	8%	16%	52%	100%
	(6)	(2)	(4)	(13)	(25)
Poles	12.5%	37.5%	17%	33%	100%
	(3)	(9)	(4)	(8)	(24)
Sabras	12.5%	12.5%	12.5%	62.5%	100%
	(3)	(3)	(3)	(15)	(24)
					123

the clinic for the four categories, and the number in parenthesis under each percentage indicates how many people of each ethnic group come for the different problems.

The chart indicates that 49 percent of all Iranians who filled out the questionnaires see their doctors for chronic pains or other chronic bodily troubles. The differences between Iranians and patients from other immigrant groups presenting with chronic pains, using a χ^2 test, is statistically significant at $p<.001$. This signifies that Iranians do tend to utilize the clinic for chronic pains more than do people from other ethnic groups. Although doctors' conceptions about Iranian patients may be influenced by the stereotypes of Iranians outside the clinic, these data validate the doctors' opinions that Iranian patients present chronic pains more than other people.

Not only do Iranian patients exhibit chronic pains more than other patients, but the ways they present their problems also differ from other patients. This, however, is not usually mentioned by most of the physicians, who are often unaware of differing verbal and nonverbal styles of communication. Verbally, many Iranians in pain raise their voices in pitch while complaining about the troublesome part (or parts) of the body. Sometimes the patient complains of several problems at once, presenting multiple symptoms which have nothing to do with one another according to the physicians' repertoire of medical knowledge. Symptom presentation verbally gives the doctors a list of clues as to what the actual problem may be, and multi-complainers skew the clues. Along with the verbal presentation comes the nonverbal indication of distress: displaying a painful look on the face; giving the impression of weakness by seeming to lose balance and groping for something for support; rolling the eyes up in distress. In addition, some traditional Iranian patients show respect for the physician by exhibiting ta'ārof behavior to someone of a higher status: the patient sits quietly with the head slightly lowered, speaks softly to the doctor, uses qualifying phrases to apologize for disturbing the doctor, sometimes puts the right hand over the heart to request a service (the gesture often used among Iranians when saying "*qorbān-e shomā*"—"[I'm] your sacrifice"—indicating the vying for lower status in social transaction, oftentimes used to request a favor), and leaves the office thanking the doctor profusely.

The presentation of symptoms combined with Iranians' conceptions of the body and cultural notions of sickness etiology creates not only certain syndromes which the doctors see in the clinical setting, but also reinforces the ethnic stereotypes that are associated with Iranians outside the clinical setting. Iranian conceptions of sickness causation, as presented in the previous chapter, concern such theories as the climatic influences of moisture and cold provoking rheumatism, hot and cold food consumption influencing health, and the evil eye causing acute disorders. Patients visit doctors for ailments associated with the above etiologies and for other problems whose cause they do not know, in search for relief and for validation of their sick role. When Iranian patients question physicians about their bodies, especially when issues of cultural conceptions of illness and health are implicated, such as the people who asked the ophthalmologist if there are any foods they should eat or avoid for the health of the eye, the concerns are logical for the Iranians, but appear ridiculous for the Israeli biomedically trained practitioners. The doctors do not know about Iranians' medical beliefs and practices and react to the questions of their Iranian patients by blaming the patients' lack of knowledge about the physiology of the human body.

In addition, certain ways that Iranians present pain are seen as strange by the medical establishment. One physician mentioned that she had a patient who kept saying he had a snake twisting in his stomach. She thought he was hallucinating, but realized he was not, as he was lucid except for his utterances about the snake. She later concluded that he was translating literally a phrase from Persian (*mārpich*) into Hebrew. Since there are immigrants who do have difficulties with the language, direct translations from one language to another of idiomatic expressions engender miscommunication. Such a problem was parodied by the Isfahani-Israeli playwright who had written about Mulla Davut: in another play he ridiculed the Israeli doctor-Iranian tourist patient interaction at a hospital clinic where another Iranian acts as a translator for the Iranian tourist. The tourist tells the translator, upon the doctor's questioning him about his problem, that he fell down and hurt his leg. The Persian phrase for "to fall down"—*zamin khordan*—literally means "to eat earth." The translator tells the doctor, in Hebrew, that the man "ate earth and hurt his leg."

Mistranslations of idiomatic expressions, traditional beliefs, the presentation of organic complaints for which the physicians, with laboratory tests, find nothing wrong, and the repeated visits of Iranians to clinics or to different doctors in search for an illness label exemplify miscommunication and differences in explanatory models (cf. Kleinman 1980). Iranian notions about sickness, its presentation, and its treatment do not necessarily coincide with those of the Israeli physicians, and at times seem quite absurd to the medical personnel. Doctors at Kupat Holim clinics have to contend with such issues on a daily basis with all their patients, not only with Iranians. However, Iranians represent special difficulties to Kupat Holim physicians. These Kupat Holim internists, many of whom immigrated from different (usually Western) countries themselves and who work at various Kupat Holim clinics in Jerusalem which serve neighborhoods where Iranians live, expressed their views of their Iranian, and other patients:

> There is something about Iranians we can't figure out. They are primitivim—hypochondriacs. They're like children, running to doctors whenever they feel a pain. . . . The problem is communication.

Some symptoms—pain, nervousness—are seen in Iranians, but I'm not aware of who is Iranian. . . . There are no differences between Iranians and other Easterners but there is a difference between Easterners and Westerners.

Doctors can't understand Iranians who like to be sick. . . . Persians honor doctors very much, and doctors have to honor them back. Honor plays a big part in relations among Persians.

I don't know. . . . I think the ethnic group with the most hypochondria is the Yemenites.

Iranians always complain about pains in their arms and they always call it rheumatism.

All immigrants complain. It is a procedure of being immigrants. Rumanians and Iraqis who came in the early 1950s had the same complaints.

Iranians come in all the time asking for notes not to work. In Iran they were rich and here they start from the beginning. They are more hypochondriacal than other *edot* [ethnic groups]. Most Iranians have no organic problems, but speak about their heart and stomach. What makes them different from other edot is that they are multi-complainers. They come in with alot of bodily problems and only later will talk about social problems. They have funny ideas about their bodies. And they go to other doctors rather than psychiatrists. They want more tests. . . . I see children of Persians more than the children of other edot.

The problem with Iranians is that they are a closed people. They don't reveal alot in psychiatric intakes. They're not aware of functional problems and have only organic complaints, especially chest pains, palpitations, and weakness. They are multi-complainers. But the problems of culture and illness and somatization are not just among Persians. It's similar among other edot—Moroccans, Yemenites, Cochini, Kurds. . . . Iranians are committed to their families and are dedicated to the hospitalized patient—they will even sleep under the bed.

Several variables are involved in the doctors' reflective discourse on Iranian patients: the way Iranians present their symptoms; Iranians' conceptions of the body; ethnic stereotypes; differences in explanatory models between doctor and patient; problems of physician efficacy. The first two variables represent the cultural patterning of symptom presentation. The third is a silent factor mediating doctor-patient relationships, fueling physicians' interpretations of patients' symptoms. Differences in explanatory models, often tacit, unfathomed, misconstrued, engender questions about the doctors' own efficacy. Ultimately, some doctors come to doubt their patients and, sometimes, themselves.

Doctoring, Diagnosis, and the Double Bind

For the physicians, the Iranian patient is annoying and problematic. The doctors interviewed indicated that basic problems of communication and understanding were at the heart of the matter. Most of them attributed the problems to Iranians' lack of both Western education and biomedical knowledge, and to their presenting organic problems that have no pathological bases. The latter problem, that of somatization, is recognized by many physicians as being characteristic of other peoples—some say of all immigrants, others say of Orientals, and most concur that it is prevalent among Iranians.

Somatization presents a predicament to biomedical practitioners: at once there is the patient suffering, yet the suffering is contradicted by laboratory tests, x-rays, and other means of penetrating the body to secure biochemical underpinnings of the complaints. When the tests provide no answers to the symptoms presented, and when the patient returns with the same or similar problems, the patient is labeled as hypochondriacal, hysterical, or with an analogous term. The illness is not considered "real." And the major consequence of the doctor-patient negotiation is ignored: the divorce of the psychosocial from the biological in biomedicine's interpretation of presenting symptoms creates a distinction between "real" and "illusory" sicknesses which, ultimately, places physicians in a double-bind.

Physicians understand the workings of the human body by reducing them to basic biochemical principles with which they interpret somatic dysfunction. Interpretation begins by translating the verbal messages and nonverbal cues of the patient who describes his or her symptoms (see Good and Good 1981a). Because the biomedical paradigm of sickness is essentially reductionistic and empiricist, problems of communication in the clinical settings complicate the process of interpretation and diagnosis. If the patient does not express symptoms in a language which can be easily deciphered by the physician, the work of diagnosis becomes more complex as the doctor wades through a variety of messages. Physicians, trained in a cultural milieu of biomedicine and socialized in a cultural setting which shapes their own ideas of how people should behave when sick, expect certain basic behavior from their patients. When doctors and patients are from the same cultural background, communication in the clinical setting is more likely to proceed smoothly in comparison to when doctors and patients come from different cultural backgrounds. Thus, the Iranian physicians distinguish no differences between their Iranian patients and other patients, or, to look at it another way, they do not see Iranians as problematic when compared to people of other ethnic groups: they can discern the messages their Iranian patients convey. However, the Israeli physicians distinguish Iranian patients as different.

The Iranian patients place the Israeli doctors in a quandary by persistently presenting symptoms for which the doctors find nothing pathologically wrong. Consequently, the Iranians are labeled by the physicians as "hypochondriacs"—as if they are simulating sickness as opposed to those patients whose symptoms can be verified by laboratory tests, and therefore have "real" diseases. If the sickness that the patient exhibits is not "real" and does not conform to somatic referents, or to the biomedical paradigm, it (the patient and the symptoms) challenges the physicians' role, knowledge, and power, creating a crisis of inaction, and therefore, failure of therapy. The doctors, themselves, are aware of the predicament that somatizing patients such as Iranians put them in and voice their opinions about the interpretative dilemma:

> The first rule in medicine is to see if there is an awareness of a nonorganic problem. The Iranian patient doesn't comply. He regards it as organic, and the physician fails to diagnose something organic.
>
> They come in with so many complaints and they can't figure out what is important and not important, and it mixes up the doctor.
>
> I don't like hypochondriacs. I can't treat them and that makes me uncomfortable, especially since their opinions will be that I'm a bad doctor. I also fear what will happen if the hypochondriac is really ill.
>
> You can't tell an Iranian he's healthy. You must say what he has is not serious and he will be okay. Then he blesses you and is happy.
>
> I don't refer patients to psychiatrists. If doctors can't find anything wrong with patients, it might not be psychosomatic illness, but it may be the stupidity of the doctors. There are many unknown things in medicine.
>
> The doctor's alertness must be high in order not to overlook something real. . . . With Iranians, organic complaints are colored with other complaints and it is difficult to pick out the real problem.
>
> Doing medicine on Iranians is like veterinary medicine, not human medicine. They can't relate to their bodies and tell the doctor what is going on. They tell all kinds of bizarre things which don't tie in, and it becomes guesswork of the doctor to form a diagnosis. . . . Because it is so difficult to figure out what is wrong with the Iranian patient, it is difficult to decide what tests to do, let alone the expense of doing all the tests. . . . Doctors don't like to operate on Iranians because when they complain of pain you don't know what they mean, if it's a lot or a little, especially since pain is so subjective and Iranians complain so much.
>
> There is no connection between what the complaints are and what the doctor finds.
>
> I see people with real problems. If the neurological exam is negative, I send them back to the doctor who referred them.
>
> Doctors have a problem telling such patients that nothing is wrong. Many doctors feel they have to give the patient something, such as vitamins. If the patient leaves the doctor with pills in hand, they get a fixation with their disease. And so the idea of being sick, and getting pills to confirm it, perpetuates itself. If I see a patient that I find nothing wrong with, I tell him or her there is nothing the matter. . . . If I find nothing wrong with their heart, that they should see a psychiatrist? It's not my style.

What is getting defined in the doctors' discourse on doctoring and the Iranian patient is the failure of diagnosis. Why the failure, and what does it do to the doctors? Because physicians learn to read the body as a text, the presenting symptoms should signify some fundamental physiological reality. When the symptoms are diffuse or confused, either by the messages disclosed by the patient or by the negative results of paraclinical examinations (blood tests, x-rays, urinalyses), the physician's deciphering of the meanings of the distressed patient frequently indicates not a biological dysfunction, but nonorganic conditions. Because of the melange of messages that some of their Iranian patients deliver, the physicians are confused. These patients are difficult to diagnose: physicians cannot diagnose the nonorganic problems which do not fall into their previously known and accepted disease categories, and thus they fail (are unable) to name, label, locate, or figure out what the problem is. The failure to diagnose symptoms which are nonorganic is interpreted to mean that the patient's problems are not "real." People who present "illusory" problems therefore cannot be treated, as biomedicine has no cure for the nonorganic complaints. This is where the doctor's predicament comes in.

If the physicians tell the patients that nothing is the matter with them, the doctors are afraid that the patients might think they are incompetent physicians, and will thus question their efficacy. Efficacy cannot be questioned if professional power is to be maintained. The doctor is the professional with knowledge of sickness and curing and through this knowledge and license to give treatment, the physician is in a powerful role—one of life and death, eventually—concerning the patient. The patient is the focus onto which the physician can demonstrate professional and personal power, and knowledge. However, with patients who present nonorganic problems, and expect treatment which the doctors are incapable of providing, there is a failure of power, and a failure of knowledge. Therefore, such patients put physicians in a double-bind by rendering them powerless at the same time that they are powerful.

The powerful-powerless doctors search for a resolution to their plight by blaming the patients for being so problematic. Yet, since they must interact with the patients, they can choose one of several alternatives: they can involve themselves as curers by giving the patients placebos, vitamins, or tonics, thus masquerading as powerful; they can tell the patient that the feelings of pain, weakness, or insomnia are in the "nerves," thus discrediting the patient from his or her perception of physical self, presenting the patient with a label of the problem, and avoiding the furtherance of interaction; they can admit they are not sure what the problem is and refer the patient to a specialist, thus relieving themselves of the responsibility of decision making while maintaining a professional stance and indicating that others are more knowledgeable; or they can refer the patient to a psychiatrist, risking the patient's trust in his or her own biomedical perspective with the possibility that the patient would label the doctor inadequate, not knowledgeable, and thus, powerless. Many times such encounters result in patients' going doctor-shopping in search for a diagnostic label for their ailments.

Consequently, problems of physician powerlessness and efficacy are made all the more problematic with patients such as those from Iran whose symptoms they find bizarre, whom they see as hypochrondriacs who abuse the health care system, and who are stereotyped by the society at large with negative attributes that influence and are reified by their own clinical perceptions of them. Rather than looking at the sociocultural concomitants of communication with Iranian patients, those issues and problems that induce the patients' somatization in the first place, they dismiss such patients as having sicknesses that are not "real." Rather than looking at their knowledge base of biomedicine as being inadequate to answer or help solve the predicament of communication, they blame the patients for their problematic symptoms. Some physicians apologize for not knowing enough, acknowledging that in the future doctors will know more about the workings of the body than they do now, and that not finding any biological disorder does not mean that nothing is wrong, but that medical knowledge is not so advanced. The Cartesian dualism which separates mind and body in two disparate but related domains forms part of the foundation of biomedical practice, even though the majority of Israeli physicians recognize and give credence to the influence of culture on illness. This acknowledgement, tacit and not quite elaborated or understood, is admitted through recognition of behavioral and symptomatic differences among different ethnic groups of patients. But beyond this recognition the physicians do not know what to do. The domain of biomedicine, focusing on the "real," disregarding the "illusory," ultimately disregards culture as a variable in the clinical setting when the body becomes the locus of attention. When the messages and meanings presented by the patient are indecipherable by the physician, the culture of the patient is held responsible for the physician's inability to diagnose organic pathology, rather than looked toward as the background for understanding the patient.

The physiological—tangible, real—is the jurisdiction of those physicians of Kupat Holim and the various hospitals in Israel. The cultural, social, and psychological, admitted as being part of the illness experience and presentation, is tenuous, hazy, imprecise. When challenged by the unknowable or unknown, such as the somatizing patients, the physicians are at a cul-de-sac, unable to be effective, afraid to seem ignorant, involved in the double bind of being simultaneously powerful and powerless. Unable to successfully heal, they retreat further into the domain of orthodox biomedicine or cautiously step out into the domain of mental health by referring their patients to psychiatric services. Both doctor and patient are then defeated by aborted treatment. Overpowered by the unknowable, the pains of the patient for whom they can do nothing, some physicians capitulate into biochemical reductionism, whereas others solicit the support of social and psychological services. Therefore, in Israel, when general physicians fail in therapy for the somatizing patient, the mental health practitioners take over.

Chapter 8
"Parsitis"

Melancholy persons with confused breath keep sad after agencies producing a sense of desolation and sadness—such as the following: (1) reflecting that one's fatherland is distant; (2) pondering over many injuries past and done with; (3) hate and rancour; (4) bad health; (5) difficult circumstances of life; (6) thinking terrible things are going to happen in the future; (7) thinking of the necessity for death, which natural judgment ignores because of the obvious fact that we must die; (8) thinking about something that is disturbing to meditate upon; (9) being away from an agreeable occupation; (11) distraction from that which is desired and wished for; (12) many other similar things, and others which are beyond comprehension. Things of this sort easily sadden a mind which is disposed to become sad.

Ibn Sina, *Canon of Medicine*, page 545.

The problem of sadness, according to Ibn Sina, concerns an individual's nature or temperament (tabi'at): certain people with minds that are "disposed to become sad" will do so when provoked by one or more of the precipitating factors he lists. Many of these factors induce nārāhati among Iranians in Israel. Noticeably absent from Ibn Sina's list, however, is the influence of human relationships on a person's sadness. Here we can speculate that the importance and power of human relationships and the family supersede reflection about or admission of their influence on a person's sadness. These kinds of social influences and other nārāhati-producing problems, some similar to the ones Ibn Sina notes, induce a number of Iranians to seek care at mental health clinics in Israel.

When Iranians, as patients, express in very Iranian ways bodily problems to Israeli clinicians who cannot discover any pathological bases for their complaints, the predicament of the clinical transaction arises, culminating in the label "Parsitis." The label—given informally to Iranian patients by Israeli therapists and physicians—is a culturally laden appellation that has several significations: reflecting the role of culture in the patient's expression and the therapist's interpretation of the problem; signifying the relationship between the therapist and patient; connoting frustration in the clinical transaction; and occasionally suggesting the failure of therapy. The patients want a name for what ails them and the physicians are unable to diagnose a cause or produce a name. We have seen how somatizing patients create a double-bind for physicians, making them powerless to act while they are sanctioned to act. To resolve their problem when they find nothing to diagnose, many physicians refer their somatizing patients to mental health services. At the mental health services a diagnostic label is given to the patients.

There are, however, problems with diagnoses in psychiatry, as there are in biomedicine. Biomedicine searches for an underlying biochemical or dysfunctional cause for the person's physical symptoms, whereas psychiatry searches for an underlying psychosocial or biochemical reason for an individual's thoughts and behavior. If the former cannot find a cause, a diagnosis cannot be given, and the patient receives no official label for the problem. However, psychiatry does label patients, and when the behavior of both the patients and the therapists is molded by culture, labeling frequently becomes problematic.

The Problem of Diagnosis

Biomedical diagnosis is complicated by the uncertainties of medical knowledge as well as by communication between patient and physician, which is mediated by culture, social structure, stereotypes, ethnicity, concepts of the body, human relationships, and emotional states. All of the above are also involved in psychiatric diagnosis as the therapist translates the presenting symptoms of the patients, whether physical or psychosocial, into psychiatric nosology. The problem of naming or labeling physiological and psychosocial symptoms is a problem of classification, of creating order out of disorder, of making sense out of information which is often nebulous, of the quest for understanding. Classification is key to medical and psychiatric practice, and by studying how healers classify sickness and related disorders we can understand how society and culture influence medical practice. In the cases studied here, we will see how the labeling of Iranian patients by Israeli medical personnel is influenced by the social and cultural aspects of Israeli and Iranian society outside the clinical setting. Consequently, clinical interaction must be interpreted, not as an entity unto itself, but in terms of its position within a sociocultural system, as it mirrors the sociocultural situation outside the clinical setting in which various ideas, beliefs, relationships and experiences impinge on the clinical encounter and engender the labeling of phenomena which are sociocultural products as well as medical problems.

The process of labeling, of classifying the symptomatology, is a major issue for the practitioner, who needs a label as a sanction for action, and for the patient, who needs a name for his or his discomfort. We see this phenomenon among primary care and hospital physicians in Israel, who were frequently baffled by the bizarre complaints of their Iranian patients. Since Iranian patients' syndromes evade previously conceived medical categories, they are considered to be hypochondriacs, fakes, or, at best, problematic. Because there is no officially sanctioned label, no category into which these patients' symptoms fit, the doctors are at a loss to treat them. Without the name, there is no treatment, except, perhaps, with placebos.

Where the biomedical practitioners leave off, the psychiatric staff takes over. At the the psychiatric clinic, a label is given to the patients. The problem of the patient—or with the patient—is named. With the name, derived partially by transactions between patient and therapist in the clinical setting, partially by transactions and stereotypes within the society as a whole, partially by current psychiatric nosology, and partially by the therapists' particular orientations, therapy can begin.

Social and cultural factors determine the labeling process more than practitioners are aware of or would like to admit. The division of psychiatric nosology into subcategories in a kind of "scientific taxonomy" of disorders and diseases as seen in the American Psychiatric Association's *Diagnostic and Statistical Manual III* (*DSM III*) lulls mental health practitioners into believing that more exact terms, which have evolved and have been classified in the past decade, capture concrete and real psychiatric problems. What is missing from the classification of individuals into more complex and supposedly precise psychiatric appellations is culture.

Labeling a symptom makes it a cultural phenomenon which sanctions action by the practitioners, and culture enters into the labeling process by influencing the practitioners' perceptions and interpretation of the patients' symptoms. The classification of patients' behavior and speech into presumably discrete psychiatric categories is also influenced by such social factors as ethnicity (for example, Fernandez-Marina 1961 and Mehlman 1961 on the "Puerto Rican syndrome"), gender (women often are labeled as "hysterical" whereas men are dubbed "hypochondriacal"), or relative age (geriatric patients are frequently designated as victims of Alzheimer's disease, whereas their symptoms could be those of depression, stroke, Huntington's disease, Jakob-Creutzfeldt syndrome, subdural hematoma, tumor, or a reaction to medication). In addition, preconceived conceptions of societal roles that a person of a certain age and gender should carry out influence psychiatric classification. For instance, many young mothers who seek therapy when suffering from depression receive reinforcement from their therapists to continue in the role which brought on their depression in the first place (Weissman and Klerman 1977). Social class, likewise, prejudices labeling: similar behavior may be classified as mental illness among lower-class people and as personal peculiarities among those of the upper class (Hollingshead and Redlich 1958).

Although some psychiatrists claim that labeling people as mentally ill is a social phenomenon regarding behavioral norms and differences in power relationships, others are concerned with the development of proper psychiatric nosology for diagnosis of mental illness.[1] However, a different kind of labeling problem entangles the transactions between Iranian patients and Israeli practitioners, where Iranian patients seek a label and Israeli therapists make one up informally and are obligated to designate another formally. Many of the Iranian patients in outpatient mental health clinics in Israel are somatizers, the very people who visit psychiatrists, most of the time unwillingly, without exhibiting aberrant behavior commonly believed to be that of mental illness. These are the problem patients that primary care practitioners fail to diagnose. In this case of somatizers in outpatient mental health clinics, what happens with labeling and diagnosis?

Culture, as an element of communication mediating the symptoms presented by the patient and the interpretation of them by the therapist, underlies the dilemmas of diagnosis of Iranian patients by Israeli practitioners. This includes therapists' and patients' evaluations of the clinical encounter, problems in understanding resulting from previously conceived expectations, and how social and cultural factors outside the clinic influence transactions within the clinical setting and diagnosis. Ultimately, the diagnostic label will be revealed as a culturally fabricated factor of classification related to the social need to create order out of disorder. The diagnostic label, rather than bridging the therapist-patient relationship, often obfuscates the clear understanding of the patient by the therapist—especially when culture influences the interpretation and possible misunderstanding of the behavior and speech of others.

In the Mental Health Clinic

The problems of diagnosis and treatment of Iranian patients in Israel begin in the primary care clinics and continue in the mental health clinics. Most of the latter's patients are referred by primary care practitioners. However, since some physicians do not acknowledge somatization as signifying underlying psychosocial distress, some people who could benefit from psychiatric services are not referred. Others, fearful of the stigma that going to a psychiatrist implies, shun the psychiatric clinic. Those who do appear at the mental health clinics, therefore, are those searching for therapy, a label for their symptoms, a sanctioning of their condition. A few approach the clinic for the social services it provides its clients, such as letters to receive welfare, to take to the courts if the need exists, to have a child in the army stationed closer to home.

In the clinic where I worked, the patients comprised a varied population: they were immigrants and sabras, secular and religious, poor and middle-class, Ashkenazi and Oriental, ultra-Orthodox Hassidim and atheists, adults, adolescents, and children. Many of the Oriental immigrants were from Iran, Bukhara, Iraq, and Afghanistan, fewer from North Africa. The Ashkenazi immigrants were from Eastern and Central Europe, the United States, Russia, and South America. The staff, however, was primarily middle-class and Ashkenazi. They came from Western Europe, South America, Russia, the United States, Israel, and Morocco.

Iranians who were patients at this clinic came from a variety of socioeconomic backgrounds, from various regions in Iran, had immigrated to Israel between the late 1940s to 1978–79, varied in their religious practices from nonpracticing to observant, and differed in levels of education and fluency in Hebrew. In spite of all their social differences, they came to the clinic with remarkably similar symptomatology, primarily complaining of physical ailments with few psychosocial grievances. Of the thirty-four charts I read, twenty-nine, or 85 percent, were of patients who came to the clinic presenting predominantly physical symptoms.[2] Of these, twenty were referred to the clinic by their primary care practitioner at Kupat Holim; three women were referred by Tipat Halav (mother-infant neonatal clinics affiliated with Kupat Holim and located in various areas of the city); four were referred by physicians affiliated with hospitals or places of employment; one woman was referred by a social worker and another woman came by herself. The remaining five patients presented primarily psychological symptomatology when starting therapy at the clinic: one woman was brought to the clinic by her husband; one came by herself; two were referred by psychiatric hospitals where they had received treatment, having been brought there by family members who found their behavior strange; and one man, whose chart did not note physical symptomatology, was referred to the clinic by Kupat Holim.

What kinds of symptoms did the Iranian patients present at the mental health clinic? The preponderance of symptomatology, since the patients were referred by biomedical physicians, were physical problems. Among the most common were (in no particular order) headaches, weakness, backaches, whole body hurting, heart palpitations, lack of appetite, dizziness, insomnia, stomach aches, digestive problems, arm or leg pains, and rheumatism. Secondary problems tended to be existential, psychosocial, or interpersonal, often elicited by the therapist within the context of the screening interview rather than being problems that the patients voluntarily admitted: nervousness-anger;[3] sexual problems (lack of desire for sexual relations, fear of sex, or impotence, the latter frequently considered a physical problem); screaming at and hitting children; fear; inability to tolerate noise. Through therapists' questioning, additional problems emerged: keeping anger inside; bad relationships with spouses; inability to function in the familial or work role; poor relations with other family members or friends. Furthermore, some patients presented physical symptomatology that was peculiar and outlandish to the therapists, such as one woman's receiving "an injection for blood deficiency" or another woman's complaining of her liver burning.

The majority of Iranian patients, however, exhibited a series of physical symptoms from which they sought relief. This is exemplified by four people who were under treatment in the clinic. Gabi is a forty-seven-year-old man who has sleep difficulties, headaches, burning in the stomach, weakness, digestive problems, dizziness, and backaches. He attributes his sickness to hepatitis, from which he suffered ten months before he started treatment at the clinic. In addition, he lacks desire for sexual relations, is afraid of getting angry at his children, and has difficulties functioning at work. Shlomo is a sixty-year-old man who was referred to the mental health clinic for "neurasthenia" by a Russian immigrant practitioner at Kupat Holim for his symptoms of insomnia, pains in the neck, and general bodily aches (back, arms, legs, chest) for which there were no pathological findings. At the mental health clinic he talked about impotence, people and noise bothering him and making him nervous (*atzbani,* H., or he could have meant the similar-sounding Persian term, *asabāni,* "angry"), worrying about his sons in the army, and his inability to work. Mira is a forty-one-year-old woman who works three days a week as a cleaning lady and suffers from headaches, heart palpitations, pains all over her body, insomnia, and dizziness. Upon being questioned, she says that she feels poisoned, cannot speak with people, hits her children, cries, and is slowly getting angry at her husband, who studies in a yeshiva and does not help in the house. Nomi is a forty-four-year-old woman who speaks little Hebrew and suffers from continuous headaches, pains all over her body, lack of sleep and appetite, and has difficulties in her marital relationship.

In each case, the problem facing the psychiatric staff is to make sense of the symptoms presented in order to determine what is wrong so that they can treat the patients. How do they translate the physical symptomatology and presenting behavior that the Iranians exemplify into psychiatric lexicon? What are the issues involved in determining the underlying psychosocial or biological problems of the patients? What is the procedure for determining the psychiatric terminology used by the staff about the patients, and how does this vary from a formal, albeit not so standardized, system of nosology in the written form to informal discourse when clinicians talk among themselves? Foremost, how do the stereotypes about Iranians in the society at large influence, primarily latently, the perceptions of the staff toward them?

The four patients whose symptoms are presented above were all diagnosed as depressed. In fact, twenty out of the thirty-four received this diagnosis, which was further subdivided into depression (14), masked depression (2), slight depression (1), severe depression (1), neurotic depression (1), and post-traumatic depression (1). The decision as to why someone is labeled depressed, and further, what kind of depression, appears dependent on the background and experience of the therapist (the therapists at the clinic were psychiatrists, psychologists, social workers, and students of psychology and social work doing their internship, all of whom shared in the responsibilities of screening, intake, and therapy), and on the ability to recognize certain symptoms as expressive of some type of depression.[4] The designation of depression for the four cases I have reviewed centers on the complaints of bodily aches and pains, insomnia, and either difficulties functioning at work and/or problems relating to family members or others. These symptoms, vegetative and psychosocial, are the signifiers of depression for the psychiatric staff. However, what happens when patients express symptoms which are difficult to "read," that is, symptoms which fall into several or none of the psychiatric categories?

Because Iranian patients enter the psychiatric consultation with bodily symptoms, it is through elicitation and questioning by the therapist that they talk about social and personal problems. However, few speak about psychological feelings and emotions. That is not part of their style of articulation of their problems. The Iranians do not come into the clinic with complaints of depression, sadness, or anxiety. These are the labels which, in negotiation with the therapist, they take on if they understand the problem as a psychosocial one. Frequently, the process of accepting a psychosocial label as opposed to a biological-physical one for their problem takes patients several sessions with therapists. Often patients never accept it. One who did accept the therapist's naming of his problem was Amir, the jeweler who sold his shop and store. He came to the clinic with various bodily complaints which the therapist labeled as depression. While the therapist sees Amir's bodily complaints as a result of depression, Amir sees his depression as a result of his bodily complaints. In spite of his accepting the label of depression, he views its etiology differently from his therapist.

For the therapists, the problem is not so much convincing the patient to accept their label as it is to treat the patient. The label is often an expedient device for the therapist to understand and then treat the people who come to the clinic. With the Iranian patients, the label is problematic because the symptoms presented are problematic: physical complaints; sometimes personal, social, work, and familial problems; rarely existential or psychological problems. The therapists make sense out of the Iranian's symptomatology by looking at the common denominators of their complaints, seeing whether any of the problems fit psychiatric diagnostic labels (for example, major depressive disorder), speaking to them in order to elicit more than what the patient is willing to tell, writing summaries of presenting symptoms in the file along with a psychiatric label, and, perhaps, including a description of the patient's character or personality.

The common denominator of Iranians' complaints, according to the psychiatric staff, is the problem of somatization, coming to the clinic with a variety of bodily pains, some quite peculiar for the non-Iranian therapists. Iranians do not stress, as the purpose of entering therapy, their inner feelings, except, perhaps for being nervous (atzbani, H.—"angry" could be a gloss for Iranians). This differentiates them from other patients. Nor do they usually come to the clinic for situations of psychosocial distress. When they do, they often expect the clinicians to solve their problems for them, an expectation which the clinicians do not consider their psychotherapeutic function. When patients complain about sleep difficulties and lack of appetite in addition to physical complaints, and if they also mention problems at work or with the family, the therapist concludes that the patient is suffering from some type of depression, because these are symptoms associated with depressive disorder in the psychiatric nomenclature. However, when patients present physical symptoms (headaches, whole body hurting, heart palpitations, backaches, arm and leg pains) different from those classically defined as the somatic concomitants of major depressive disorder, and do not, upon questioning by the therapist, express difficulties functioning in their work or familial duties, or reveal problems in relationships with spouses, or, if expressing problematic relationships, couch them in terminology which is not seen as significant by the therapist, patients are classified under a different psychiatric label than depression. Part of this labeling process involves the fit between the patients' presentation of symptoms and psychiatric nosology. Another part involves the stereotypes that Iranians have in the society at large and, therefore, in the medical-psychiatric establishment as a subset of the society.

Categorization of the Iranian patient occurs before the psychiatric interview begins. From cultural stereotypes of Iranians in Israel, many therapists are cognizant of the conception that Iranians are stupid, stingy, and suspicious. From the biomedical physicians and other personnel at Kupat Holim and the hospitals, they hear about the strange complexity of symptoms without pathological findings that Iranians tend to show. And from their own interaction with Iranians at the mental health clinic, they see the presentation of physical symptomatology with little outward self-reflection concerning psychosocial problems. With the social and cultural background and the psychiatric interview come the classification and labeling of the Iranian patient.

Interaction between therapist and patient occurs in a private room in the clinic. The staff member, educated, Westernized, often not a native-born Israeli, either greets the patient in the waiting room and leads him or her to the interview room, or has the patient sent to the appropriate room by the secretary. The therapist and the patient sit opposite each other on chairs with no object (desk, table) intervening. The questioning proceeds with the therapist asking the patient why he or she came to the clinic at that particular time. According to what the patient says, further questions elicit psychosocial problems and current happenings in the patient's life. The therapist often initiates each question in the imperative, with the phrase "tell me" preceeding the question. The imperative method of questioning is inadvertently indicative of the nonreciprocal relationship that prevails in clinical settings. By focusing on the imperative, the therapist develops and maintains a position of control in interaction with the patient. Rather than asking, for instance, "Do you have any problems in your relationship with your husband?", the therapist is able, by the way the sentence is formulated, to draw out answers that the patients do not express freely: "Tell me, do you have any problems in your relationship with your husband?" The answers received depend on the therapist's ability to interview and maneuver the interrogation, on the patient's readiness to respond, and on the insight that the patient has concerning the questions that the therapist poses.

Out of this clinical encounter between patient and therapist come the perception and evaluation of the presenting symptomatology, both physiological and psychological (see Basker et al. 1982). The conversation between the two is later translated into written form by the therapist in the patient's file to serve as a reference for other staff members who may interact with the patient. Because of memory lapses and the impracticality of recording the entire conversation, the therapist abstracts from the conversation what he or she considers significant for the diagnosis. The resulting abstractions in the files I read range from long, detailed accounts permeated with the patient's ideas and stories about self and other as reflected through the lens of the therapist, to brief notes having little to do with what the patient has said, concerning primarily the therapist's evaluation of the interaction with the patient and notations of medications prescribed. Each patient's file, then, contains statements by therapists about the patient concerning his or her symptoms, problems, vocalizations, and ideas—all filtered through what the therapist views as important or appropriate for inclusion.

Furthermore, the psychiatric diagnosis is recorded in the files. The diagnosis is important in order to treat the patient, to help the patient in the future concerning problems that he or she may be suffering from, and to communicate about the patient with other therapists who might take up the case. As the file is a text and must be read as one (or more) person's evaluations and conceptions of a conversation or series of conversations, the reader must recognize that a variety of sociocultural factors enter into the translation of the clinical conversation into a written file.

In addition to the written text is the oral discourse among therapists about patients in which patients' problems are made sense of and evaluated. During discussions among clinicians, topics which do not appear in the file, such as jokes about the patients and comments on the patients' ethnic background, form part of the way in which the clinicians distinguish themselves, as professionals and healthy, from the patients, who are laymen and not well. Such joking also functions to release tension and control angry and frustrated feelings. In addition, oral discourse is an informal means of making sense out of the problematic patients. However, what occurs in oral discourse reflects sociocultural transactions between therapists and patients, especially when patients hail from a specific group.

Israeli clinicians speak about the similarities of Iranian patients as opposed to other patients, seeing them as somatizers with strange bodily complaints who cannot function in their work or familial roles, sometimes fear anger and feel like exploding, and are unable to tolerate noise. These clinical manifestations are translated by the clinicians into a peculiar syndrome particular to people from Iran, labeled informally in clinical discourse as "Parsitis" or "the Persian syndrome" (see Basker et al. 1982 and Minuchin-Itzigsohn et al. 1984). For clinicians faced with a conglomeration of symptoms which they find strange, and about which they must make sense in order to treat the patient, the label "Parsitis" or "the Persian syndrome" is an instrumental means of locating the problem in the patient's background without attempting to understand what in the background could be indicative of or precipitating the symptomatology. The label also becomes an informal diagnostic entity, indicative of the problem that clinicians have in trying to interpret the equivocal. However, the label's danger in informal discourse is that it tends to affect the impartiality of the clinician in the cross-cultural encounter: the Persian patient is seen as a symbol of "Parsitis," and sometimes is misdiagnosed.

Even though the informal appellations concerning Iranian patients do not appear in the formal language of the files, they do enter into the original negotiation which determines what the official diagnosis will be. In addition, part of labeling Iranians as having a particular syndrome reflects the particular characteristics that they have in the society at large, since patients from other ethnic groups who come into the clinic with bizarre physical complaints and who do not recognize any underlying psychosocial etiology are not usually diagnosed as having any distinctive syndrome particular to their ethnic groups.[5] The latter problem may be related to the relatively lower incidence of somatization without psychosocial cognition among patients from other immigrant backgrounds.

The danger in stereotyping Iranians as somatizers with peculiar behavior concerns misdiagnosis from both biomedical and psychiatric standpoints. Two cases illustrate this danger. One pertains to an Iranian university student who, having ringing in his ear, went to a primary care practitioner who found nothing wrong and sent him to a psychiatrist. The psychiatric examination revealed no particular psychological or personality problems, and the student was told that there was nothing the matter with him, that the ringing was probably a reaction to the pressures of being a student. Several months went by and finally the student went to a different practitioner who, after resorting to various tests, discovered a malignant tumor as the cause of the symptom. Such medical horror stories are not particular to Israeli practitioners and Iranian patients, as people everywhere have favorite anti-doctor tales. The problem with this story, however, was misdiagnosis based upon ethnic stereotyping.

Another case pertains to psychiatric diagnosis. A young Israeli-born man of Iranian parentage had been on and off care at the clinic in which I worked, and one day he suddenly appeared. One of the psychologists expressed, in a staff meeting, that he has "the Persian syndrome": a carpenter who stopped working after an accident in which part of his thumb was cut, he has bodily complaints, insomnia, and all he wants from the clinic is sleeping pills. The psychologist thought he was malingering and asked for a psychiatric evaluation. During the psychiatric interview, which I witnessed, the young man sat down, shrinking his body into himself, his shoulders hunched, his chin down on his chest, his hands placed between his thighs. He looked at the psychiatrist only once, when she said she heard he had cut his thumb. When he showed her his thumb, she asked him why he didn't look at her, and he replied, "What does it matter? It's not important." His answers to her questions revealed that many of his problems were related to his army experience. He felt that his wife was repelled by his behavior, and she had asked him to see a doctor for his nightmares. He had gone to Kupat Holim a few years before, and they had referred him to the mental health clinic. In his nightmares he dreamt that people were after him, and sometimes he thinks people on the street talk about him. When the psychiatrist asked him if he hears voices, he said yes, that they tell him to go to work and to sleep better. All his problems are because of lack of sleep, he said. Because he doesn't sleep, he is weak. At work he gets dizzy or gets headaches, and his legs are weak and he can't stand up. It starts an hour after he starts to work, and he has to sit down. If he rests for a few minutes or half an hour and then resumes work, he has to sit down from weakness after ten minutes. When the psychiatrist asked how he supports himself, he replied that a friend of the family gives them money. Concerning his army experience, he said that he had fought in the Yom Kippur War. He said that before and during his army experience, he had a number of good friends. But many of his friends were killed during the war, and now he doesn't have alot of friends. He also stated that he had run away from being killed. All he wants to do now is kill Arabs. But the last time he was called up for *miluim* (annual army reserve duty), they didn't want him and he felt embarrassed and hurt. When he left the interview, the psychiatrist said to me that she did not think that he was malingering, as the psychologist had indicated. She said he had real problems, and was neurotic and depressed. The young man, however, did not attribute his problems to depression but, rather, to his lack of sleep.

This case exemplifies cultural differences in explanatory models of the psychologist, psychiatrist, and patient regarding the patient's complaints and symptomatology. The psychologist based her analysis on the patient's symptoms *and* on his ethnicity, whereas the psychiatrist's diagnosis was based primarily on the patient's statements and behavior. The patient's self-diagnosis was a somatopsychic one, founded on cultural conceptions of the body and the mind.

The transformation of the colloquial "Parsitis" or "Persian syndrome" into conventional psychiatric terminology is influenced by the patient's symptoms, how they are presented, and the interaction between the patient and the therapist. The above case is indicative of how two different clinicians interpret one man's symptomatology. When interpreting files of patients, then, one must read the notations as the outcome of particular symptoms, particular conversations, and particular negotiations in particular settings, with a particular therapist. When Iranian patients exhibit strange complaints to Western-trained clinicians who have no ideas about cultural influences on illness, sickness beliefs, or presentations of symptoms, and when the clinicians must fit the patients into a previously conceived rubric of terms, a problem is created: are the Iranian patients expressing their feelings, personal problems, or physical symptoms in the same "language," whether verbal or nonverbal, that the Western-based psychiatric epistomology understands, and if not, how does the clinician make sense of what is happening?

The problem, therefore, becomes one of translation of verbal and nonverbal signifiers into categories understandable to clinicians. These categories are not only part of a professional lexicon, but they are also culture-bound. They are divided in such a way that certain symptoms fit into certain diagnostic entities, while other symptoms either fall out of the psychiatric rubric altogether or are grouped into such obscure categories as "unspecified psychoses," various neuroses, or personality disorders. Certain personality disorders, as will be seen in the following section, represent aberrations from supposedly normal psychosocial functioning. However, culture, socioeconomic class, social problems, and problems of sociocultural dissonance which produce the psychological "disorders" are not deemed etiologically important by the therapists who work primarily within a psychological idiom.

When patients from one cultural background have symptoms that are similar to one another but different from those of other ethnic or regional backgrounds, it is assumed that culture has an influence in presentation of symptoms, as in the case of the Iranians. Often these differences are not quite understood by therapists whose values contrast with those of their patients. This kind of cultural misunderstanding engenders the label "Parsitis" and other psychiatric labels for Iranian patients: since there are only a finite number of categories into which the symptoms fit, the clinician adjusts the patient's symptoms as suitable for one of the models of psychiatric diagnosis. The problem here then becomes how therapists diagnose, and how misunderstanding of symptomatology leads to misdiagnosis, and, sometimes, to failure of therapy.

Symptoms and Diagnosis: Interviews and Inference

Therapists' knowledge, understanding, and diagnoses of their patients' psychological and psychiatric problems are based on the theoretical and empirical knowledge of their profession, on an underlying (culturally-shaped) conventional knowledge which molds both their understanding of their patients and their professional knowledge, and on the patients' verbal and nonverbal communication of symptomatology. Israeli therapists' misunderstanding and misdiagnoses of Iranians' symptomatology occur because the patients' symptoms do not always fit the definitions of the diagnostic categories that make up therapists' theoretical and empirical repertoire, and because the stereotypes about Iranians in Israeli society influence clinical transactions. The therapists' misdiagnoses are "misreadings" of the patients' presenting symptomatology, which is culturally patterned and expressed. Because of the misdiagnoses, and because of the difficulties of communication in the clinical setting, therapy fails.

Problems of cultural misunderstanding, unbeknown to many clinicians, can generate erroneous or inaccurate diagnoses, such as "personality disorders" in some cases or the failure to diagnose depression in others. How can clinicians tell when an individual from a completely different culture is exhibiting behavior which is at odds with the values of the patient's culture or subculture? How do clinicians from one culture make sense out of the behavior of people from another cultural group who may seem peculiar in comparison to the clinicians' standards and norms, but who may fit in with those of the culture in which they were socialized? These, indeed, are the problems posed for therapists working in cross-cultural situations. Determination of who is exhibiting strange behavior can be intricate when subtleties of cultural differences are blurred in the clinical setting, especially when clinicians are not cognizant of the fact that their own cultural biases becloud their analyses of patients. This happened in the case of Amir, the jewler who sold his shop and his apartment.

The varied diagnoses for Amir were derived from examinations with several clinicians, some assuming he was depressed, others analyzing him with qualifying statements about his character or personality: "neurotic depression"; "depressive personality who suffers from severe depression on an erotic background"; "obsessive personality"; "schizoid personality"; "infantile personality"; "anaclitic personality". It appears that the types of "personality disorders" describing Amir pertain to the difficulties of understanding that the clinicians had while communicating with him. However, in comparison to many other men of his background, the "personality disorders" which were attributed to him are not valid. Many Iranian males of his generation have similar values and behavior. The difference is that he sought care in both Kupat Holim and in the mental health clinic for numerous bodily and personal complaints. The interaction between Amir and the therapists—between an Iranian man with traditional values concerning husband-wife and parent-child relationships, not working and depressed, and the Western, highly educated and motivated men and women of the clinic—engendered a suitable diagnosis of depression on the one hand, and a series of qualifiers, seemingly resulting from cultural misunderstandings couched in psychiatric terminology, on the other.

The diagnosis of depression for Amir is suitable because his symptomatology fits in with the therapists' understanding of depression, which is based upon vegetative, affective, and cognitive elements.[6] The vegetative symptoms include severe sleep disturbances, fatigue, lack of energy, abulia, appetite disturbance, and attention and memory problems. The affective signifies the expression of dysphoria, and the cognitive pertains to the individual's description of self regarding self and others. Amir's symptomatology fell into the vegetative aspect of depression (fatigue, "rheumatism" in all parts of his body, sleep difficulties), the affective (sadness about his failing business transactions), and the cognitive (inability to function at work and problems with familial relationships). His expression of the affective and cognitive components, such as his complaints of being "nervous," are culturally determined, as are some aspects of the vegetative symptoms (rheumatism). What happens, however, when Iranians present vegetative, affective, and cognitive symptoms which differ from those recognized as depression by the therapists? How does culture color expression of psychological problems such as depression?

Iranians express depression in culturally determined idioms. Among these are somatization and anger, both of which are correlated with nārāhati.[7] Because many Iranians tend not to reveal personal nārāhati since it signifies weakness, vulnerability, and powerlessness in relations with others, they ostensibly somatize psychosocial problems. There are cases in which somatization takes on seemingly bizarre symptoms for the clinicians, such as lack of blood (kam khuni) or pains in the arms. Therapists usually do not consider such aches and pains without pathological bases as denoting any underlying affective state, such as depression, particularly when no other recognizable signs (sleep and appetite disturbances or sadness) are manifested. Sadness, as we have seen in chapter three, is a differentiated nārāhati, an emotion which is culturally respected, whereas anger is not. Since anger is a dangerous and antisocial emotion in Iranian culture connoting lack of self-control, uncontrollable anger is distressful. When Iranians complain to Israeli therapists about being angry, they confuse its meaning in Persian (asabāni) with the similar-sounding Hebrew term (atzbani) that means "nervous." To the therapists, the articulation of nervousness does not represent an affective or cognitive symptom of depression. To the Iranians, however, anger is a dysphoric, socially disruptive, sometimes alienating emotion, and some of those who seek help at the mental health clinic want help overcoming their anger, whereas others enter the clinic seeking care for their somatic complaints.

When Iranian patients see psychotherapists and complain about physical ailments rather than discussing deep personal feelings, or when Iranians complain about certain personal difficulties and do not respond to the clinicians' questions the way the clinicians expect, classification of the patient becomes complicated and troublesome. Difficulties in the communication process between therapist and patient are magnified by Iranian patients' physical symptoms of recurrent and peculiar pains combined with complaints about certain personal difficulties (relations with children and spouse, not working, fear of showing anger), their reluctance to express deep personal feelings to strangers, and their not responding to the clinicians' questions or stubbornly concentrating on their own physical ailments. The clinicians resolve the communicative difficulties, which are in actuality based on cultural misunderstandings, by resorting to psychiatric labels on the patients' charts and to informal labeling about the patients among themselves.

The effects of cultural misunderstanding on the diagnosis of patients' presenting symptoms can be examined by contrasting the therapists' analyses of four patients with my own anthropological investigation, in that understanding the cultural background of the patients facilitates the deciphering of symptoms that clinicians have trouble interpreting. One patient is Menasheh, a forty-five-year-old married man who immigrated to Israel in 1959, has four children, and is in a relatively poor economic situation. Another is Monir (whose expression of nārāhati is conveyed in chapter three), a twenty-nine-year-old married woman who immigrated to Israel as a single woman in 1974, married a year after her immigration, and within a period of four years gave birth to three children; she lives in a middle-class neighborhood and works at home as a housewife, mother, and metapelet (child-carer). The last two are a couple, Shira and Habib, who have eight children and a poor marital relationship.

Case 1: Menasheh

Menasheh was referred to the mental health clinic by a doctor at one of the major hospitals in Jerusalem. The letter from the physician stated that Menasheh was injured with minor bruises in a traffic accident two years before, was examined at a hospital and sent home. At the time of the accident he reported pains in the chest and back. Although the chest pains went away, he continued to complain about pains in the back and knees. He returned to work but after nine months was in another accident and has not worked regularly since, saying that the pains became worse and prevent him from working. He has pains in the back, knees, head, and forearms. Although he has slight spondylosis, it is not considered to be the cause of his pains.

At the mental health clinic screening, he complained of back and chest pain and, according to the interviewer, "he considers himself in a dangerous condition." The interviewer also noted that Menasheh is of "middle intelligence" and diagnosed him as exhibiting "post-traumatic neurosis" and that he is "*psychi,*" the Greek-Hebrew slang for "nuts," a term indicating that he does things and says things which are somewhat peculiar, but not indicative of psychosis. Unfortunately, he came to the clinic only a couple of times. My interview with Menasheh indicates why he did not continue with care, and what he sees as his major problems.

I met Menasheh in the lobby of the clinic and led him to the interview office. He followed me up the stairs, having gotten up from the chair slowly with both hands holding his back in pain. He ascended the stairs behind me, slowly, in the same way, in pain, hands on back. Our conversation lasted a short thirty-five minutes. Menasheh did not want to talk or answer my questions, replying many times, "Don't know." His silence and gloominess were broken when he spoke about being nārāhat and about his expectations from the clinic.

Menasheh left his home in Isfahan at the age of twelve, following an older brother to Tehran where he began working as a peddler, buying and selling socks. He worked as a peddler and at other odd jobs until he immigrated to Israel. For three years he was a laborer in Beersheva, employed by Keren Kayemet, the Jewish National Fund; then he moved to Jerusalem, where he was a driver for a large construction firm. He said that since the accident he has been out of work. What he wants from the clinic, because he cannot work, is help getting *parnasa* (H.)—maintenance, support, livelihood. Since he has been out of work, he says he goes to the employment offices searching for parnasa, but no one wants to give it to him. So why go for treatment in the clinic? "Parnasa is more important, because without it, what do you feed your children, how do you get Kupat Holim?" Since the doctors in the clinic do not help him obtain employment, why come see them?

It was during the discussion about his not working that we talked about being nārāhat. I asked him what causes it and he replied, "Nervousness (H., *atzbanut*). Someone angers him" (H., *Mishehu margiz oto*). Here, at first, he uses the Hebrew word, the noun *atzbanut* which is similar to the Arabic-Persian *asabāniyat*. As already noted, the Hebrew word means "nervousness" whereas the Persian means "anger." However, Menasheh's next sentence uses the Hebrew word which means "anger, provoke"—*margiz* (conjugated in third person singular, present tense). This term implies that his anger is caused by external circumstances of someone angering him, causing the anger to happen. He refused to illustrate what he meant. When I asked what could be done to prevent someone from being nārāhat, he replied, "Find out what bothers him. Calm him." The answer implies that the other should be sensitive to one's plight and take an active role in assuaging one's nārāhati. However, when I asked him what his family does to appease his nārāhati, he replied, almost hopelessly as if to indicate that his situation is futile, "What can they do?" Again, he would not elaborate. So I decided to discuss with him the differences among nārāhati, atzbani, and *dikaon*, the Hebrew term for "depression." His perceptions indicated a general unfamiliarity with the term dikaon, its similarities with nārāhati, and the use of atzbani to mean both "angry" and "nervous":

> I don't know the difference between dikaon and nārāhati. The are almost the same. Everyone has a different nature. Some people are more atzbani than others. Someone gets atzbani quickly, others don't. . . . Everyone's nārāhati becomes atzbani. Someone angers him (margiz oto), and the person becomes nārāhat or in dikaon. . . . If someone has no problems with someone, he has no nārāhati. People who should give work and don't give work make someone atzbani.

Menasheh's perception of the terms presented to him indicate that one's nature—the physical-emotional being that one was born with in the sense to which Ibn Sina refers—influences whether or not the person will become angry, nervous, depressed or nārāhat, and contributing to these emotions are the various external problems which he feels the individual has no control over, such as someone not giving him work. Since that is a problem which was distressing him, I pursued the issue, asking him what happened when he went to find work. His reply signifies differences in understanding between the clinicians, employers, and himself, where he suddenly finds himself in a predicament that he considers not of his own making: "The doctor wrote a letter that I was in dikaon [depression] and then I didn't get a job. I didn't know what dikaon was and I thought I was just atzbani. To me they are the same thing."

Menasheh's difficulties were then compounded by the psychiatric label of depression which, he said, was on the letter, although not in his chart at the clinic. Because of this letter and its label, the meaning of which he did not quite comprehend, he found more difficulties obtaining employment. He was thus involved in a vicious circle: car accident, pains, can't work, sees doctors, gets letter, searches for work, can't work. Because of his economic situation, he felt it was worthless to continue with treatment at the clinic since he expected the staff to provide him with help obtaining parnasa. Instead, the letter he showed employers prevented his employment, according to him. Finally, he spoke about the uselessness of doctors and psychiatrists: "They don't help. They don't give work, parnasa. They are all the same. They want you to talk about your problems which make you more depressed instead of being happy. They should make you try to forget your problems. I went from place to place the past four years—no work, no parnasa. It makes my head spin." Then he said that my questions make him more depressed and didn't help him. He walked out of the interview with his hands on his back, saying he has pains in his back, legs, and kidneys.

Menasheh attributes all his problems to the accident and his inability to find work. However, rather than expressing his feelings and thoughts about his psychosocial situation to the clinicians, he comes with problems of pain, and his bodily presentation, his way of walking with hands on back, amplifies his symptomatology. In addition, his expectation that the clinicians, with their connections to other offices in various bureaucracies in the country, would help him find employment was thwarted by the letter they gave him indicating that he was depressed. Furthermore, he believes that talking about his psychosocial problems makes him more depressed, and feels that the clinic's responsibility is to make him happy, the opposite of what was happening to him the few times he came for therapy sessions. Therefore, he severed his connection with the clinic.

Menasheh's psychosocial problems are deeper than his not finding work since his accident. Since he is reticent to speak about his personal nārāhati, he inadvertently creates an impasse for the clinicians. The clinicians see a man, sullen, complaining of various bodily pains that could not be verified medically, and talking about wanting parnasa. His expectations of the clinic could not be met by the staff. They found him difficult to deal with, a patient who has no insight, who persistently focuses on his body, who does not exhibit the vegetative signs of major depressive disorder. Thus, the clinicians do not label him as depressed, but as "psychi" and exhibiting "post-traumatic neurosis." Had the clinicians understood the problems of nārāḥati, anger, asabāni-atzbani, sensitivity, and somatization of psychosocial problems, they might have diagnosed Menasheh as "depressed" instead, and treated him for depression, a disorder from which he seems quite likely to be suffering.

Case 2: Monir

Monir was referred to the mental health clinic by a social worker. She came to the clinic asking for help and advice so she would not scream at and hit her children, complaining also that she is nervous (H., atzbani) and lacks strength. She is afraid of losing control. Through questions posed by the therapist, she spoke about working as a metapelet (child-carer) because of economic pressure. Her husband "buys too many expensive things—colored television—and so I have to work to pay the debts." She told the therapist that her childhood in her family was not good, that her father left the home and ran after other women, forcing the mother to leave the children during the day in order to work and provide for the family. The therapist noted that Monir "fears that she herself will return to this state with her children." She came to Israel alone at the age of twenty-two and was married a year later. She feels pressure that the house be orderly and that her husband be satisfied. She worries about her brother who is sick with cancer in Iran. Furthermore, she mentioned at a later interview that she occasionally has a problem with paralysis of her right arm which inhibits her from working and caring for her children. The diagnosis for Monir was "immature personality, conversive [sic] symptoms, sociopathic personality." Conversations I had with the psychiatrist who treated her revealed more about her and, also, more about the person making the diagnosis.

He spoke about the paralysis of her arm, that it occurred for the first time one week after the wedding, and she attributed it to her husband's family joking about one of her feet being too short. She was afraid her husband would divorce her and that his family would think she wasn't a virgin. One time during an attack of arm paralysis she tried to commit suicide with valium but realized that the drug helped her condition. She then imputed the occasional paralysis on her right arm to "nerves." Once when her one-year-old child asked for food, her arm became paralyzed as she started to feed him. The psychiatrist mentioned that Monir has "some spondylosis" which would, if anything, produce pain, not paralysis. He said that her paralysis is hysterical and from it she acquires the secondary gain of not working or relating to her children. When I asked him what he meant by the diagnosis he gave her, he defined the terms: "immature personality": "she's impulsive, and if she wants something, she wants it immediately. . . . We know from her behavior in conversation"; "sociopathic personality": "Someone wants only to receive, thinks they deserve something, that others have to give me. She says she needs money for her teeth, someone to help her at home, that she needs help."

My interview with Monir revealed a different woman from the "hysterical, immature, sociopathic personality" that the psychiatrist saw. I interviewed her in her apartment in one of the Jerusalem suburbs. Monir was on the phone when I arrived, and when she hung up, she walked around the room, ignoring me. My impression from her behavior was that she was either on tranquilizers or suffering from depression: her physical movements and responses were slow; she spoke softly with little affect; she did not respond to her children's behavior as they played around with the volume of the television and climbed all over the furniture, screaming and screeching; her facial expression was distant, with the "omega sign" between her eyes—a characteristic furrowing of the brow seen in severely depressed people.

After what seemed to me to be an incredibly long time, I started talking to her. We sat down together on the couch, going over a questionnaire, which she read along with me. She spoke about her background in Iran, that her family was very poor, that her father peddled cloth, that her parents argued frequently, that they moved from Isfahan to the Jewish ghetto (mahalleh) of Tehran, where her father left the family and took a second wife, returning to them when she died (this differs from the account the psychiatrist noted). While in the mahalleh, Monir completed her high school education, receiving a diploma from Alliance Israélite. Because she was a good student, the principal hired her to teach first grade. When she came to Israel, she asked her parents to send her diploma, but it was lost. This upsets Monir because she would like to study to be a physical therapist: since she has been helped by physical therapy for her back problem, she would like to help others.

When she came to Israel, she studied in an ulpan, lived with a sister for a month, moved out, rented a room by herself, and found a job as a seamstress and laundress. She met her husband's family at a bar mitzvah, and they introduced her to her husband. He works in the warehouse of a hospital in Jerusalem, but his hours had been reduced to part-time. When he works overtime, all the money goes to taxes. She said that his family is not good to her. No one ever calls up to inquire how she is doing, to ask if she needs help or to find out how the children are. She does not see her own family very much because they live in the Tel Aviv area. She also mentioned that she has very few friends in Jerusalem, and it is difficult for her.

Our discussion about nārāhati, dikaon, and atzbani revealed a different understanding of the terms than that of Menasheh. Monir was able to express her ideas more readily, and her thoughts were more similar to those of the medical establishment than were Menasheh's. She describes nārāhati as "sadness," saying that it is caused by "problems in life," similar to what Ibn Sina wrote. To repeat Monir's evaluation of her own expression of nārāhati, which was indicated in chapter three, she said that she does not show when she is nārāhat: "I hide my nārāhati inside. Or I would make others also nārāhat. Why should others know what problems I've got? But if someone is very nārāhat I can feel it from his face." She spoke about her nārāhati in Iran deriving from poverty, arguments in the house, and her father marrying twice, and in Israel, from loneliness. I asked Monir if being nārāhat could make someone sick. "Yes," she replied, "the worse illness is that of not being in a good mood. Nothing is worse than nārāhati." On discussing if pains could be caused by nārāhati, she said, "I have back pains and I think it is from atzabim" (H, nerves; it is unclear whether she derived this concept from the physicians at Kupat Holim, from friends or family, or from media). I pursued this term, which differs from atzbani, in that the Persian term for "nerves" is asāb and closer in meaning to the Hebrew atzabim. I asked which comes first, nārāhati or atzabim, and then she said—similarly to Menasheh who spoke about atzbani (nervous, "angry")—that nārāhati comes first, then atzabim, and that atzabim is mental, not physical. Her explanatory model of her own problem, then, follows that of the biomedical model, that her "nerves" are caused by psychological problems rather than physical ones, and the "nerves" give her pains. Concerning the distinction between nārāhati and dikaon, she said that they are the same thing, in other words, that nārāhati is depression.

Monir expressed her dissatisfaction with the physicians she saw:

> They are not good. They know only about a runny nose and not other things. They can't distinguish between different illnesses. When I was nursing my second child, he suddenly didn't want the milk. In Iran they say that if the child doesn't want the milk, it is bitter and it means you are pregnant. I went to Kupat Holim and they said it is impossible for me to be pregnant so quickly and they didn't do any tests. Then two months later, when my stomach was so big, they finally did the test and I was pregnant. I even didn't feed the baby one whole day to test him that if he is hungry he will drink my milk, but he didn't and I knew I was pregnant. How can the doctors work there and not know such things? Also, I had problems with my back. It hurt and I couldn't do anything and one leg was shorter than the other. They kept telling me it was nerves but finally they took x-rays and found that one of the discs isn't right. So I've been going to physical therapy and that is helping me. Also once a month my neck can't move and

my arm can't move. They took x-rays and said maybe the same thing is wrong with my neck. In a few days I get their results back.

Monir also verbalized her disappointment with the treatment she received at the mental health clinic. She said it is similar to my asking her questions and her answering, that she gets nothing from them. She sighed, mentioning she is very nervous and very tired from having three children so close in age and all she does is wash diapers. She doesn't understand how religious women, who practice no form of birth control and therefore have large families, can do it. She does not know how to handle the situation and is upset at herself for yelling at the children. A friend of hers told her about the social worker who referred her to the clinic. She does not like the clinic because she does not obtain from them what she wants: to tell her how to manage with her life, how to behave with her children, how to work in the house and not be angry with the children. They did nothing for her but ask questions. Then every time she went to the clinic she had to find a babysitter and it had cost too much. Therefore, it was not worth her time and money to continue with treatment. Therapy thus failed due to the differences in expectations and opinions that Monir and the therapist had of one another.

From my conversations with and observation of Monir, I would classify her as depressed. However, since she did not express any of the symptoms of depressive disorder according to the therapists' nosology, which was based on the *Diagnostic and Statistical Manual II* in use at the time, she was not diagnosed as depressed. The diagnosis that she did receive from the psychiatrist indicates a basic misunderstanding by the psychiatrist of Monir's background, in addition to a stereotypic evaluation of both Iranians and women: because the concerns she expressed to the psychiatrist indicated her dissatisfaction with her role as a mother, he evaluated her as an "immature" and "sociopathic" woman who circumvents her responsibilities, and he recommended as treatment "guidance and support in function as a mother." This appears to be an inherent misconception of her condition since, according to my interpretation, her being a mother of three children so close in age prevents her from working outside the house, taking courses, and visiting her family.[8] Because of her separation from her siblings and parents, the lack of close relations with her husband's family, and her relative isolation in the home, she is lonely, tired, and finds child-raising difficult. It was not mentioned by Monir, but in Iran there were family members within the neighborhood who often helped take care of the children. Therefore, had the clinician considered Monir's cultural background and present social situation, perhaps he would have diagnosed her as depressed and treated her accordingly, rather than labeling her with negative attributes cloaked in psychiatric semantics which had created a communicative impasse in therapy.

Accordingly, many of the diagnoses and interpretations of patients' problems and presenting symptomatology may be erroneous due to the lack of understanding of the cultural background of the patient which influences the expression of dysphoric affect and bodily symptomatology, as in the cases of Menasheh and Monir. Such lack of cultural understanding on the part of the therapists ostensibly influenced the diagnoses and treatment of a married couple, Shira and Habib, whom I did not have a chance to meet. Both Shira and Habib were in treatment at the clinic but did not comply with appointment times and were difficult for the staff to communicate with and, apparently, to diagnose.

Case 3: Shira and Habib

Shira was married at the age of fourteen to a man eleven years her senior, whom her parents chose. In 1970, at the age of nineteen, she and her husband and children immigrated to Israel. Now, twenty-nine-years-old and the mother of eight children, she works as a cleaning lady several times a week. She was referred to the mental health clinic by Tipat Halav, the mother-infant neonatal clinic. Shira has had a number of physical complaints: "fire in the stomach"; her heart troubles her; from her last pregnancy she suffered from nausea, loss of blood, and fainting; she received "an injection for blood deficiency"; since her last birth she has suffered from weakness. During the interview, she spoke about her personal and social problems: she fears death; her husband does not help in the house or with the children; it is difficult to do the housework with all the children; she feels nervous; she has no patience for the new baby and fears she will hit him. She was diagnosed as having a "neurotic reaction to the last birth" and a "psycho-physiological reaction," and was described as "nice, quiet, a little passive," "middle intelligence," and having a "passive dependent personality."

Habib works in a warehouse and was injured at work four years before he began treatment at the mental health clinic. He saw doctors at Kupat Holim in the interim for problems of headaches, weakness, and heart palpitations, which he attributes to the accident at work. His physician at Kupat Holim referred him to the mental health clinic where he complained of weakness (for which he wanted pills), headaches, back pains, heart palpitations, the necessity to eat every four hours, sleep disturbances, and sensations of burning all over his body. He also noted that the injury at work made him confused and that he has difficulty working. His job is inferior to what he was doing in Iran and he feels tension at work. He mentioned having had a heavy foreign accent in the past. He also spoke about chronic fears, sexual problems, and being angry that his wife works and doesn't have his meals on time. He gets angry at work and that influences his memory. He is upset that his son doesn't listen to him and he wants his wife to stop working. Habib wanted a letter from the clinic to take to the court where he had to go for creating disturbances in the electric company when he went to dispute his bill. He said that he "eats himself from the inside and doesn't shout." The diagnosis given to Habib was "nervousness," "exaggerated anger," "conversive [sic] symptoms," "passive-aggressive husband and obsessive with problems of authority."

In addition to the problems of the diagnoses of husband and wife, who seem to me to be suffering from the consequences of sociocultural dissonance and resultant nārāhati and depression, they do not appear at their fixed appointments with therapists in the clinic, which is disturbing to the staff. I was not able to interview this couple, singly or together. The husband spoke to me curtly on the phone in the clinic, saying that neither he nor his wife wanted to talk to me. Obviously, they are a problematic couple for the staff, as they have their own expectations of what the staff could do for them, yet they do not comply with the staff's expectations. In addition, their strange bodily complaints and requests, such as an "injection for blood deficiency," could be seen as deriving from cultural notions of sickness in which kam khuni, as blood deficiency, causes weakness. The clinic staff, however, consider the complaints as typically Iranian. Although Shira and Habib exhibit some of the complaints of major depressive disorder, such as Habib's sleep disturbances, the rest of their symptomatology, their psychosocial problems, and their expectations from the clinic engender frustration in the staff. This frustration results in diagnoses involving personality labels and qualities of character more in line with the stereotypes of Iranians than with the particular problems from which the couple is suffering.

What has been expressed in the clinical setting of the mental health center with Iranian patients and non-Iranian, Western-trained therapists is a misunderstanding based upon previously conceived cultural stereotypes: for the therapists, the Iranians being the problem patients par excellence, and for the Iranian patients, the clinic being a place which could alleviate them of their physical and/or personal problems. These conceptions enter into the diagnosis of patients and the consequent interaction between therapist and patient. For instance, the therapist who examined Monir commented on her intelligence, as had the clinician who interviewed Menasheh: "Intelligence is average, even though she has no level of formal education." Such comments on the intelligence of patients, when the patient comes from a different culture than the therapist and the therapist maintains stereotypic impressions of that culture, indicate problems of communication between therapist and patient. The characterization of Iranians as "stupid" in Israeli society thus appears in psychiatric evaluations under the guise of "intelligence." Several phrases exemplify the usage of the term to characterize Iranians:

> Since they [a man and his wife] are not very intelligent, there is no close relationship between them.
>
> If you don't pay attention to the [injured and partially blind] eye, she has a pretty and intelligent face.
>
> From the words of the family the patient studied twelve years. They didn't show even a certificate of finishing school. It's difficult to understand how she learned in school in a small village in Persia and also doesn't know any other language but Persian.[9]

The psychiatric staff envisage Iranians as fitting one of two molds, that of the "stupid, stingy, suspicious" stereotype, or that of the average Israeli with similar backgrounds in terms of education, values, and norms. The therapists expect all their patients to comply with appointment times, to participate in the therapeutic discourse, and to take medication if prescribed. Whereas other patients easily speak about their social, economic, and familial problems, Iranians do not; their focus on the physical and their resistance to vocalize psychosocial difficulties or early life experience (which the therapists see as influencing symptomatology), produce difficulties for the clinicians. Moreover, Iranian patients expect the therapists to help them solve their daily troubles: to ease their problems, not to bring up all the things bothering them which make them more nārāhat, and not to make them think of what they consider to be irrelevant situations with regard to their present condition, such as speaking about one's childhood. Therefore, in addition to the lack of cultural understanding on the part of both the therapist who gives help and the patient who receives help, expectations of the obligations of the other confound communication and therapy. Consequently, the reciprocity that both therapists and patients expect from the clinical encounter becomes thwarted, jeopardizing treatment. Expectations that the staff has toward Iranian patients, molded by preconceived sociocultural stereotypes about Iranians intermeshed with clinical transactions, lead to another set of clinically held stereotypes, "Parsitis." The danger of cultural stereotyping in a clinical setting appears in diagnosis, and then in treatment, resulting in unsuccessful therapy if the diagnosis is erroneous and if expectations of therapist and patient differ.

Homa: Bodily Distress Misunderstood

One major problem of the mental health clinic where I worked is (as is true of most clinics) its artificial setting, its separation from daily transactions of the patient. On the one hand, the physical separation of the clinical encounter from the patient's home life is convenient for the therapists and reinforces therapists' autonomy. One could contend that, if therapy were to occur in the patient's home, the pressures of home life and familiar surroundings could prevent the patient's distanciation from his or her problems and thus preclude disclosure of them. On the other hand, the conversations which occur in the clinical setting omit relevant personal and social information, as in the case of Monir. How do therapists obtain and evaluate the information that is nebulous and missing but important? Would the diagnoses of Monir, Menasheh, Shira and Habib have been any different if the therapists had seen them in their own environments? One would hope so. However, the interaction in home visits is often colored by prejudgments about the patients and about the patients' cultural background. We can see the influence of such sociocultural and psychiatric stereotypes on interaction in the home setting in the case of a sixty-five-year-old Iranian woman named Homa who was visited by a young immigrant psychiatrist from Latin America and a North African-born nurse who came to Israel as an adolescent in the early 1950s.

Homa is a problematic patient for the clinic staff. According to a psychiatrist who was treating her, she "suffers from a depressed condition with hypochondriac pains and signs of fear." Apparently, twenty years ago she had been hospitalized for a psychotic episode. While in the hospital, Homa's husband entered the room and climbed into her bed to sleep with her. When Homa tried to push him out, he started hitting her, and she screamed. Her husband never was in treatment at the clinic or at the psychiatric hospital, whereas Homa seeks treatment at various medical facilities.

Homa and her husband live in a two-room apartment in an area of Jerusalem that was on the border before the Six Day War and is now surrounded by modern apartment buildings. They have five children, the youngest an unmarried daughter of thirty, their only child in Jerusalem. She rents an apartment in a different area of the city. The children visit her between once a week and once a month. Other than that, Homa is alone with her husband.

Because the daughter who lives in Jerusalem feared that her mother would go into a psychotic state as a result of depression, she brought her mother to the mental health clinic after a lapse of six years, during which time she was treated once by a therapist who noted that she was a "difficult, stubborn, obstinate" woman who had "no interruption of thoughts except for the primitive mentality." At the clinic Homa complained about problems of functioning of her digestive system, problems with her liver, rheumatism in her legs, and bad relations with her husband.

Three months after she recommenced treatment at the clinic, she was admitted to the hospital for apparently having tried to commit suicide. However, it remained questionable what actually occurred. Her daughter found her unconscious in the apartment, and, after hearing her mother complain about not wanting to live, assumed her mother took an overdose of drugs and rushed to have her stomach pumped. Homa denies suicidal intent. At the hospital they found no pathology and were not sure if she took any pills.

After the alleged suicide attempt, the clinic sent a psychiatrist and/or a psychiatric nurse to visit her at her home. I went on three home visits. The psychiatrist briefed me before the home visit that Homa is an anxious, confused, and depressed woman who has all kinds of pains and complains about poor relations with her husband and that her children don't visit her. He also said that her orientation is alright, that she has no paranoid or suicidal thoughts or hallucinations, that her memory is slightly impaired, that she is very hypochondriacal, and that food and drink linked with the digestive system are central in her complaints. In addition, the psychiatrist remarked that Homa's husband is in a bad psychological state and walks from room to room. His diagnosis of Homa is that she "suffers from mild depressive state with organic mental syndrome (arteriosclerotic basis, loss of memory and concentration) with arteriosclerosis and in the past a suicidal attempt."

We entered Homa's apartment. It was clean and decorated with modern furniture; framed family photographs and reproductions of famous paintings (such as Gustav Klimt's "The Kiss") hung on the wall. Homa, who welcomed us, is short and plump. Her gray hair was covered by a kerchief tied under her chin and her body was covered with layers of clothing—pants, skirt, several sweaters, apron. When we walked in the apartment, Homa kept repeating, "*Kappara*, Doctor," over and over, touching the doctor's head with her right hand, signifying her gratitude to the psychiatrist for his doing the favor of visiting her, showing her mercy. As we sat down she complained about pains in her liver, that it is burning, and that she has to drink lemon juice and eat lemons and that her daughter can't understand why she eats so many lemons. The doctor and nurse exchanged glances, as if to say that here is another weird thing and where did she think that one up. They looked at me and asked if I now understood how strange she is. I told them I understood what she was talking about, and when Homa left the room for a few minutes, I briefly mentioned that Iranian foodstuffs are divided into hot and cold categories, and that in Iranian poetic language there are a multitude of phrases concerning the liver as the seat of human passions, to express feelings of closeness for someone. Subsequently, on our way back to the clinic, I suggested that since Homa has a poor relationship with her husband and does not see her children as frequently as she would like, perhaps her sensations of burning liver signify her feelings of loneliness and powerlessness, and her desire for lemons, the coldest of fruits, works as a palliative for her burning liver.

The fact that her daughter does not understand Homa's need for lemons is indicative of a cultural and generational gap between Homa and the daughter with whom she is the closest.

When Homa returned to the living room, she asked the doctor for something cold. He asked her to show him the pills she takes. She brought them out, handed them to the doctor, sat down on a chair, complained about her liver again, and then suddenly said she couldn't breathe, and began to pant, with her mouth forming an "O" shape, "Hoooo, hoooo, hoooo, hoooo, hooo, . . ." The doctor smiled, said that what she was doing is great, but told her to stop it. She continued for another minute, and suddenly stopped. Again, she asked for a cold medicine, for penicillin.[10] The doctor said he could not give it to her. Then he and the nurse discussed giving her an injection and changing her medication. The nurse said she would give her an injection of something cold that would help her pains in the liver, and she administered the injection in the bedroom. Afterward, the doctor took some pills out of his bag and told her to take them at night to help her fall asleep, that they were cold and would help her liver. However, the bag of pills was the same bag that Homa had given him previously when he asked which medication she was taking. Homa was smarter and more aware than he had expected. She told him those were the pills she had just given him. The doctor and nurse exchanged glances again, and then he said she was right, and explained how to take them.

My explication of hot-cold foods and Homa's focus on her liver showed the psychiatrist and nurse that the bodily disorders about which Homa complains have a cultural basis. They seemed to enjoy playing with the hot-cold terminology regarding Homa's medication, while sustaining her ailments by giving her placebos, thus creating the pretence that they have the power to control her condition. However, Homa still asked for more medication.

The second visit to Homa's house occurred two weeks after the first. When we entered, the nurse noticed a gooey-looking liquid containing some seeds in a pan on a chair in the hall and, making a face of disgust, commented to me that this must be garbage that Homa did not throw away. She asked Homa what it is. Homa replied that it is *sohān*, an Iranian sweet made of sugar, shortening, and nuts (a speciality of the city of Qom, and very "hot" in the categorization of Iranian foodstuffs). But Homa also described it as "something like medicine." The nurse shrugged her shoulders, shook her head, and started to walk into the living room when I mentioned that sohān, when hardened, is a delicious and distinctive sweet.

When we sat down in the living room, the doctor asked Homa how she is and she replied, "Not good. What is this life—a week, two weeks, a month, two months . . ." Then she asked for cold medicine again, for penicillin. At one point she spoke about her husband, whom she dislikes. She said he had seven wives and she is the eighth, that he promised her gold and carpets, that his father had a lot of land in Kurdistan, Iran, where he was from, but he beats her. The doctor asked if she wants a divorce. "Who will pay for gas and electricity and food?" she replied.

To check her memory, the doctor asked about her hospitalization twenty years before. She denied it, then later said her husband beat her there. The doctor asked her if the treatment at that time was good. Homa said no, because there was an Ashkenazi doctor who didn't speak a word of Hebrew. The nurse, who had been working at the hospital at that time, nodded, and said he was a Russian. The doctor did not understand: "His name was Ashkenazi?" Homa corrected him—his ethnic affiliation was Ashkenazi.

Homa asked for an injection as we got up to leave. She again had complained about her liver and had panted with the "hoooo, hoooo, hoooo." The doctor said he would bring her strong, very cold, and expensive pills the following day. But Homa insisted on getting an injection, although earlier in the visit she said the injection from the last time helped her only one day. The doctor reminded her of this one-day effect, but then she said it helped for three days. So he and the nurse agreed she should be given a placebo (unknown to Homa), which the nurse administered.

As we were leaving, the doctor, wishing to joke with Homa, whom he liked even though he found her requests for medication troublesome and her bodily complaints peculiar, decided to tease her and test her awareness. The living room clock had stopped at 5:30, and it was 10:30 A.M. He asked her the time. She said it is around 10, but both of her clocks are broken. The doctor asked if it is ten in the evening or in the morning. Homa smiled, and said evening. The doctor grabbed her hand, smiled, said shalom, and that he would return the following day with the medicine.

The doctor did not return to Homa's house the following day. Three weeks after that visit, I went to see her with a new nurse. When we entered the apartment, Homa immediately asked me where the doctor was, that he was supposed to come two weeks ago to give her the medicine and didn't, and that she waited and waited for him because she wanted the medicine.

We sat in the living room and Homa complained about her liver burning. I asked her where the liver is and she smiled, replying, "I'm not a doctor, how should I know? You tell me." I said that if it hurts she has to know where it is. She said in the stomach, and put her hand on her diaphragm above the navel. Then again she said she wants to die, and began to pant the "hoooo, hoooo, hoooo." She stopped and said her soul (*nafs*, P., *nefesh*, H.) entered her here, pointing to the same place where she located her liver. The new nurse, listening to the conversation, was amused and curious, but changed the subject. She asked Homa if she works around the house, if she cooks and what foods she prepares. Homa took us to the kitchen to show the different meals she makes for her husband and for herself, as she cannot eat fat and sugar.

When we were about to depart, I noticed that the paper lamp hanging from the ceiling over the living room coffee table was torn. Homa explained that a few days ago her husband was angry at her and wanted to hit her, but he hit the lamp instead, and broke it. While leaving, the nurse told her she would return with medicine for her pains.

On our way back to the clinic, I presented my symbolic interpretation of Homa's pains to the nurse, explaining why she focuses on the liver. Homa's complaints can be construed by their connection to Ibn Sina's theories of medicine. The liver, according to Ibn Sina, houses the vegetative or natural faculty whose function is reproduction and nutrition. The liver's function of digestion is aided by innate heat which is provided by the heart. The innate heat varies along with the "breath," and both are related to the physical feelings of the emotions. According to Ibn Sina, the "breath" links the physical, psychic, and spiritual world, and combines with the blood to serve the rational soul. The blood, however, is the principal instrument of nutrition and is manufactured from food in the liver. From the liver it goes to all parts of the body, part of it combining with breath in the heart. The liver and blood together correspond with the mental states of anger, vexation, and with weeping. The liver, in popular nonmedical discourse, as the seat of the baser passions, connotes one's relationships or feelings to another.

Because of Homa's hapless relationship with her husband and distance from her children, the burning liver can be seen as signifying her powerlessness (as do the phrases utilizing the liver—jegar—in chapter six). In fact, one of these phrases, jegaram misuzad—"My liver burns"—is said when one feels sorry for someone and does not know what to do. Homa feels sorry for herself, and does not know what to do. She has burning sensations in the liver, difficulties with digestion, and complains about her "soul" (nefesh, H.; nafs, P.) entering her liver and not being able to breathe. Her symptoms, symbolizing the social, personal, and familial predicaments that have befallen her and which she is powerless to change, signify a contemporary, perhaps idiosyncratic, version of Ibn Sina's theories of medicine.

The nurse found the information I told her (less detailed than what has been delineated above) interesting, but that did not prevent her from questioning what she had been told about Homa by the other nurse and the psychiatrist, that Homa is somewhat psychotic and the doctor wants to give her placebos. Therefore, although my efforts to "translate" some of Homa's symptoms from bizarre senseless complaints to symbols which signify important occurrences in her life attracted the attention of the psychiatrist and the two nurses, they were still not influenced enough to criticize their psychiatric categories and labels. They used her symptomatology to work out therapy with placebos, understanding they could better "treat" her with "cold medicines." However, their categories of psychiatric disorders remained unchanged as they continued to see Homa as psychotic and/or depressed with strange symptoms that required an even stranger cure. The psychosocial problems from which she suffers and which they witnessed on previous occasions with house visits, such as her husband beating her, are problems that they are powerless to change. Rather than suggesting to her husband that he see them in the clinic, they concentrate on Homa, who seeks treatment, by giving her placebo medications along with some "real" drugs, since she is the one person of the couple who utilizes the clinic. Undoubtedly, she maintains her relationship with the clinic for the opportunity it presents for sympathy, for sanctioning her illness, and for escaping her husband.

The case of Homa and the therapists does not show failure of therapy. Homa, unlike Menasheh, Monir, and Shira and Habib, looked forward to her sessions with the psychiatrist and nurse, perhaps because the transactions occurred in her home, where she spent her days alone or with her temperamental husband. What this case does show, however, is the failure of the therapists to understand Homa's symptomatology, which they saw as psychotic, as opposed to culturally produced articulations of distress. In addition, the therapists' apparent insensitivity to Homa's discourse and their reluctance to explore the meaning of her symptoms reflect their professional theoretical and empirical knowledge (their orientation toward biological treatments and to symptomatology that fits their explanatory models), social relationships of therapist and patient (the therapists as powerful and controlling, patients as powerless and dependent), and relationships in the society as a whole (Homa's complaints, such as her liver burning, signify the societal stereotype of Iranians being "stupid" or "primitive"). Thus, although the systematic misunderstanding of Homa's symptoms did not provoke misdiagnosis, it did create a therapeutic quagmire: Homa is dependent on the therapists; they treat her biochemically; they do not engage in "talk therapy" because of communicative difficulties; therapeutic encounters continue in Homa's apartment; and Homa's condition remains the same.

The Problem: Culture's Relevance in Clinical Transactions

The cases presented have shown the relevance of culture in clinical transactions. This relevance is twofold: the patients' symptoms—whether backaches or anger or burning liver—are culturally patterned and communicated; and the therapists' culture influences their understanding of patients. Therefore, in cross-cultural situations, such as those between Israeli therapists and Iranian patients, where neither practitioner nor patient grasps one another's symbolic and social realities, clinical communication becomes ineffective and restrained. If understanding, diagnosis, labeling, therapy, and healing concern the interactive manipulation of symbols (cf. Levi-Strauss 1967), then it is no wonder that therapy failed in the cases presented here, where diagnosis and labeling signify interaction with the misunderstood.

Diagnosis and labeling must be seen as symbolic of and symbolic for transactions between practitioners and patients. These transactions are influenced by stereotypes within the society as a whole, psychiatric or medical nosology, patients' behavior, and clinicians' orientations—all of which give meaning to cultural forms while being influenced by and influencing them. Clinical transactions and diagnostic labels—illustrated in this chapter by the cases of Menasheh, Monir, Shira and Habib, and Homa—are socially prompted and culturally buttressed. Accordingly, the difficulties of diagnosis that the Israeli therapists have with their Iranian patients, and the problems that the Iranian patients have with maintaining their therapy, are cultural, not medical, in nature. The cultural misunderstandings that the patients and therapists have of one another preclude the establishment of a suitable psychotherapeutic relationship which is necessary for therapy to succeed. The case studies presented exemplify this predicament. In addition to the influence of culture on therapists' and patients' ideas and behavior, clinical transactions and diagnostic labels are also supported by the therapists' repertoire of professional knowledge. As the following chapter shows, this professional knowledge is often culturally based and biased.

Chapter 9

Conclusion: Culture and Diagnosis

The problems of communication, illness, and diagnosis occur wherever there are sick people who seek treatment. Such problems in medical understanding are enhanced when patients and healers come from different cultural backgrounds and have different ideas about what causes sickness, how one expresses feeling ill, and to whom, and what to do for treatment. In fact, so bound up with our cultural categories are illness expressions and treatment that people are often totally unaware of how their expressions of sickness or concepts of treatment are understood by others. This is the case with Iranian patients and Israeli practitioners today, as much as it was in the mid-nineteenth century when ailing Iranians baffled British diplomats. Robert Binning, who worked for the Madras Civil Service in Iran, wrote in 1857 about being misjudged as a physician by Iranians who sought medical advice:

> I made a hearty breakfast, which was hardly finished, when some of the village people came to pester me for medical advice and physic. Every Frank [foreigner] travelling in the East is, as a matter of course, dubbed a "medecin malgré lui," and as I have had this dignity conferred on me pretty frequently, I took the precaution of procuring at Bombay some boxes of Holloway's Pills, a quack medicine of the universal panacea school, which if it does no good, is not likely to work much harm. To each invalid, I gravely administered six pills to be swallowed immediately; which was done without hesitation—indeed I believe they would each have taken on the spot, the entire contents of a box, had I recommended it. (p. 161–62)
>
> After dinner, three women honoured me with a visit, soliciting advice. They all complained of not being blessed with any family, for certain very satisfactory reasons, which they unfolded at length, in the plainest and broadest terms. Nor were they deterred from speaking thus freely, by the presence of several of the male sex, who crowded into my cell, bound on similar errands, to obtain relief from real or imaginary complaints. One young man, in his turn, quite unabashed by the presence of females, communicated a detail of a weakness, which he laboured under, and which in more civilised societies, a man would be studious to keep concealed. (p. 164–5)

Binning's experiences with sickly or complaining Iranians show the differences in cultural interpretations of sickness. The Iranians attributed to him, as the outsider, knowledge which he had not possessed, but of which he took advantage, most likely to prop his position, and that of his country, as a diplomat. Moreover, the sexual complaints about which Iranian men and women voiced amazed him—that they should admit to such problems in the company of the opposite sex, behavior which would not occur in "civilised societies" such as England. Implied within Binning's autobiographical account are the differences in knowledge, power, and culture which mediate social and medical understanding. Perhaps a bit more discerning, yet still quite incredulous of others' medical beliefs, was C. J. Wills, a young English doctor who, having finished his medical studies in England, seeing an advertisement to work as a physician in Iran, and knowing he would have difficulties opening a practice immediately upon completing his degree, went to Persia for adventure and experience, setting up a clinic in Hamadan. Wills writes (1891:64) about his first day at his clinic:

> Precisely at eleven I proceeded to seat myself; what was my astonishment to find some two hundred people sitting in groups, my two servants vainly endeavouring to keep some sort of order; the noise was great, and practical joking and laughter were in the ascendant. . . .
>
> I soon found that many of the so-called patients had merely come from curiousity, while others had old injuries to complain of, and did not expect medicines, but miracles.
>
> The replies to the question, "what is the matter" were sometimes highly ridiculous, one man informing me that he had a serpent in his inside, while another complained of being bewitched.
>
> Among the ladies . . . the principal request was for aphrodisiacs, drugs to increase *embonpoint*, and cosmetics; while many women of apparently great age were urgent for physic for improving their appearance. Many cases of eye-disease presented themselves, and not a few of surgical injury, which had been treated only in the most primitive manner. It was only by four in the afternoon that I succeeded in getting rid of the rabble-rout that had come to my dispensary.
>
> Rome was not built in a day. As the novelty wore off and the sightseers ceased to come, the sick, who generally amounted from two hundred to two hundred and fifty a day, more or less became more tractable, and my servants better able to manage them.
>
> I made stringent rules as to seeing all in the order of their coming, and separating the men from the women. Although I saw many thousands of patients in Hamadan, yet I found that I made no appreciable addition to my income; those who could pay, didn't; and the only grist that came to the mill my two men absorbed.

Wills, like Binning and other early English and French travelers in Iran (Sanson 1695; Waring 1807; Tancoigne 1820; Fowler 1841; Sheil 1856; Bishop

1891; Lorey and Sladen 1907), found Iranian medical practices and illness expressions peculiar. Like the Israeli internist at Kupat Holim mentioned in chapter seven, Wills regarded a patient's saying he had a "serpent in his inside" ridiculous; unlike the Israeli practitioner, however, Wills did not realize the issue was one of mistranslation, and misunderstanding.

The issues of mistranslation and misunderstanding in the clinical setting have been examined as developments which materialize outside the clinic and then are mirrored within the clinic's walls. Clinical transactions, both illness experience and its clinical explanation, are uninterpretable unless we understand their cultural contexts and individual circumstances. Accordingly, we looked at Iranians in their own sociocultural system and in that of Israel, examining issues which are important to them and which they see as changing, and sometimes making them nārāhat. Furthermore, we saw how the mistranslation that occurs in the clinical setting concerns the disregard of the silent boundaries which generate nārāhati and beget the informal clinical label "Parsitis." These silent boundaries, set up before clinical transactions begin, are social and cultural factors that create separations between people and make communication difficult.

We have seen how Iranian ways of communicating—with intimates and non-intimates, with ta'ārof, with feelings of vulnerability and weakness in a hierarchial system of social relations—are related to both the hierarchical social organization of Iranian society and the ethnopsychological concept of the individual as internally sensitive and externally clever. Silent boundaries between people in Iran (between non-intimates *and* between intimates) are thus fostered by feelings of guardedness, vulnerability, distrust, powerlessness, and insecurity that are forged from the system of social relations and the cultural conceptions of the individual. Accordingly, the nonexpression of one's personal, private nārāhati generates other silent boundaries around the self, whereas the public expression of the differentiated nārāhatis, sadness and anger, abrogates the silent boundaries on the one hand (for sadness), when sad people gain sympathy and support, and aggrandizes them on the other (for anger), when angry people create situations of social detachment and discomfort.

Other silent boundaries emerge when Iranians, with their culturally particular communication patterns, confront the ideologically egalitarian, but culturally and socially differentiated, Israeli society. Ethnic stereotypes emerge due to cross-cultural encounters, and these stereotypes influence interaction and perception of the other. These cultural differences, along with the social changes produced by immigration and accommodation to a new and different social, political, and economic structure, engender sociocultural dissonance among the immigrants. We have seen that, in reaction to the nārāhatis of sociocultural dissonance, some Iranians become ill. These illnesses, due to such stressors as changes in familial roles, financial problems, or work difficulties, are framed in culturally distinctive ways. The dilemmas of diagnosis, therefore, arise when physicians, who are unaware of, or see no relevance in, their patients' social and cultural problems, have to diagnose and treat patients for whom they find nothing pathologically wrong. When dealing with somatizing patients, many biomedical physicians experience a double-bind of being simultaneously powerful medical professionals and powerless medical performers.

Based upon eighteenth-century philosophical concepts of mind/body dualism and twentieth-century biochemical scientific developments, biomedicine is becoming increasingly ineffective to deal with many of the psychosocial problems which are seen in primary care clinics. Because the biomedical model fails to comprehend the interpretive discrepancies in clinical communication, clinicians often fail to diagnose their patients properly, and the therapy which needs straightforward communication for success frequently is foiled because of communicative failure. When communication fails, practitioners and patients are dissatisfied. Patients search for other ways of procuring cures. Practitioners, as do the Israeli clinicians who treat Iranians, either retreat, refer patients elsewhere, give placebos or ineffective tonics, pills, and injections, or suggest that the patients see psychotherapists. The patients seek a label for their troubles, and clinicians are wont to give one.

Labeling in the clinical setting concerns a whole series of social and cultural problems which seemingly have little to do with what occurs behind the closed doors when doctors examine patients. Such silent boundaries materialize throughout the world in various social and cultural systems, but are probably more prominent in the West with Western biomedical physicians and non-Western or immigrant patients, a problem which must be managed due to the increase in international labor migration, refugees from politically troublesome areas, and immigration. Thus, we can expect problems of mistranslation, misdiagnosis and slurred labeling, and difficult-to-diagnose symptoms to exist among German doctors and Turkish workers, among French physicians and North African patients, among British doctors and Indian migrants, among American clinicians and Southeast Asian refugees, Russian Jewish immigrants, or Portugese newcomers.

The silent boundaries, consequently, influence the experiences of patients and practitioners before, during, and after clinical interaction. Most are not aware of the strength and power of these sociocultural factors on their conversations inside and outside the clinic. Many people, clinicians among them, are not fully cognizant how their social system and cultural values operate, and how their own transactions are influenced by "local knowledge" (Geertz 1983), the common sense from which we live our lives, rather than by some genuine value-free reality. Neither the patients nor the practitioners view one another as "inter-actors" within the larger sociocultural context of which the clinic is a part. Consequently, the silent boundaries often impede therapy when the issues are sociocultural ones that the patients and clinicians are locked into, bound by, and of which they are unaware.

In conclusion, we will see that when Rational Men diagnose (to paraphrase Young 1981), they are influenced not only by social organization, relationships inside and outside the clinic, their own culture and that of their patients, and modes of discourse through which they render their patients' articulations into diagnoses, but also by their professional reasoning and knowledge which is, most of the time unknown to them, culturally governed.

Culture, Diagnosis, and Psychiatric Labeling

Although Israeli biomedical and psychiatric clinicians realize that there is something different about Iranians when compared to patients from other immigrant groups—strange bodily complaints, strange expectations from the clinic, difficulties admitting intrapsychic problems, lessening of functioning in one's expected social role—they do not understand how the symptoms and complaints that they see in the clinic are culturally delineated. Nor do they see that their own practices of biomedicine and psychiatry are influenced by cultural norms and beliefs: they are unaware that their diagnoses of patients are influenced by relationships with Iranians outside the clinical setting and by the need to categorize demanded by their profession.

The symptoms presented by Iranian patients are often those physical problems grounded in traditional conceptions of the body and sickness. Among these are chest pains, pains in the back, knees, and arms (related to rheumatism) for Menasheh, and for Homa, rheumatism in the legs, liver problems, and a poorly functioning digestive system. As mentioned in chapter six, rheumatism is a sickness believed to be related to climatic and moisture conditions. The liver is the organ metaphorically referring to feelings of closeness and emotional involvement with others. Digestive problems are often related to an imbalance in consumption of hot and cold foods. Other disorders referred to previously are blood deficiency (kam khuni), weakness, headaches from thinking and worrying, "nerves" (asāb, P.; atzabim, H.), and the sociopsychobiological problem of being angry, asabāni (P.) or its possible Hebrew gloss, atzbani ("nervous").

Not only do Israeli clinicians not know about such traditional Iranian conceptions of sickness and emotions, but they are also not cognizant of the Iranian conception of the person as both emotionally and physically sensitive. Without the knowledge of Iranians' traditional interpretations and expressions of emotional and bodily distress, non-Iranian practitioners interpret the symptomatology in the only way they know how: in their own cultural categories. These categories are derived from the Western concepts of the individual, psychiatric distress, and mind/body dualism, coupled with concepts of patients and practitioners outside the clinical setting. What ensues is the mistranslation of symptoms and the possible failure of therapy.

The cases presented in the previous chapters exemplify Iranian notions of the body, the individual, dysphoric affects, and their translation into psychiatric nosology. A careful perusal of several of these cases exemplifies how misunderstanding gives rise to misinterpretation, creating faulty diagnoses and exacerbating communication difficulties between patient and therapist, which engendered the diagnoses in the first place. For instance, Menasheh's injury in the car accident caused all the somatic complaints for which he expected treatment, first, at the Kupat Holim clinic, secondly, at the mental health center. One could interpret Menasheh's inability to work, due to the aches and pains resulting from the car accident, as exemplifying a continuous relationship between mind and body, both of which, being sensitive, were affected by the accident; one could also take a sociocultural point of view of his symptoms, as designating problems of sociocultural dissonance (such as familial problems, economic difficulties, work complications), which influence him to assume the sick role for aspects of secondary gain, such as manipulating his family, if he does, or getting insurance, which—according to his conversation with me—he does not. Menasheh's preoccupation with his somatic complaints and his inattention to personal, psychological, familial, and social problems engendered the label of "post-traumatic neurosis" and "psychi" from the therapists, and, because he was reticent to talk about his life situations, Menasheh stopped coming to the clinic since it made him more nārāhat than before. Thus, therapy fails.

A more careful look at how diagnoses are made shows how culture is the alien and silent participant in the clinical setting. But it is also a crucial force which must be reckoned with. By looking at three diagnostic categories with which Israeli therapists classify Iranian patients, we can see how culture enters into the clinical setting and molds the conceptions of the practitioners as much as it does the symptoms of the patients. These three categories are "depression," "personality disorders," and "Parsitis."

Depression

Depression, as Lutz (1985) has shown, is a Western ethnopsychological category based upon Western notions of the person and emotions. This is seen in the interpretation of the symptomatology of depression, which may be considered an affective disorder or a psychobiological phenomenon treatable with antidepressant medication. Current psychiatric conceptions of depression in both senses are associated with three types of symptomatology: affective (sadness, irritability, loss of interest); cognitive (guilt, worry, and feelings of loss and hopelessness); vegetative (sleep and appetite disturbances, motor retardation or agitation, loss of energy). These symptoms, described in *DSM-II*, are further particularized in *DSM-III*, which redefines diagnostic categories. Accompanying the reformulation of the various types of depressive disorders are a series of characteristics and symptoms to help clinicians with the diagnosis of depression. Of these, the affective and cognitive elements, which are supposedly universal, are symbolic of Western ethnospychology: dysphoria, usually depression, is the essential feature, "characterized by symptoms such as the following: depressed, sad, blue, hopeless, low, down in the dumps, irritable" (*DSM-III* 1980:213) and combined with such cognitive attributes as "feelings of worthlessness, self-reproach, or excessive or inappropriate guilt" and "recurrent thoughts of death" (p. 214). This individualized psychological focus on the self and the concepts used to express dysphoria are patterned on the Western concept of the individual. What happens, then, when Western therapists, who define depression in these categories, treat patients from non-Western cultures? Does the current Western concept of depression "translate" into other cultural idioms of distress? When dysphoric affects and physical symptoms are patterned in ways that differ from those of *DSM-II* and *DSM-III*, are people expressing depression? Can the somatic, affective, and cognitive symptoms that Iranians manifest in the mental health clinic be diagnosed as depression?

Because Iranians, like the Taiwanese studied by Kleinman (1980), exemplify a "social insight" instead of a "psychological insight" into their personal situations and problems, it is difficult for Israeli therapists to classify them as depressed if the physical or psychological (or social) symptoms expressed are not similar to those which determine the depressive disorders. Iranians consider personal, emotional, and physical sensitivity and various types of social disorders which inspire feelings of weakness or vulnerability (such as familial problems or financial difficulties) as the root of their problems. They frequently somatize their distress with unusual bodily complaints, often with verbal and nonverbal (sulking, not eating) presentations which do not mesh with the psychiatric lexicon utilized for diagnosis. Many patients who, when asked by an Iranian therapist, might complain of nārāhatis of one sort or another, do not, in the Israeli clinical setting, voice psychological perception and often do not elaborate on personal and social problems bothering them. Because the psychiatric definitions of depression do not include social distress, personal and physical sensitivity, anger, or ramifications of nārāhati, many Iranians who might be classified as depressed when questioned by therapists who know about nārāhati and about the family and individual in Iranian culture, are not characterized as depressed in Israel.

The above problem concerning depression among Iranians in Israel raises other questions regarding culture and diagnosis: if Iranians themselves do not utilize the Persian term to refer to depression, *afsordegi*, but rather refer to nārāhati, can we say that depression, as an affective state or major disorder the way it is thought of in the West, exists in Iran? If Iranians do not voice hopelessness and loss concerning innermost feelings, does that mean that they are not depressed and therefore deserve another kind of psychiatric label? Because afsordegi is a literary word not used in colloquial speech, people do not refer to their feelings or their state as being "depressed" through utilization of the term. Nevertheless, the word exists, as meaning "dejection, depression," and, in the original sense, "congelation" (Haim 1958:44)—suggesting a freezing-up, an inability to function. In addition, the terms ghamgini (sadness), ghoseh (sorrow), and asabāni (angry) signify other ways of expressing dysphoria. The first two emotions portray a particular and notable characteristic of Iranian culture (illustrated in poetry, philosophy, religion, and lyrics to songs, as well as in human interaction), and only when a person stops functioning in his or her social role by the nārāhati of sadness or sorrow are these emotions considered detrimental. On the other hand, anger signifies personal and social danger as a pathological emotion representing the individual's feeling, and then being (once anger is enacted), outside the system of social relations. Perhaps what therapists should look for in trying to find an affect most indicative of a depressive-like syndrome in cross-cultural situations is an emotion which is socially dangerous and personally disruptive, an emotion which challenges social relationships, making an individual feel outside the system of social relations and generating difficulties functioning in a normal social role. For Iranians, this emotion is anger. It challenges the norms, customs, beliefs, and system of social relations in Iranian culture. For Americans and Israelis, this emotion is sadness, the nonenjoyment of social relations and withdrawal from social activity. Iranians seek care for anger more than for sadness, and Israeli therapists often misinterpret the symptomatology, diagnose something else, and are thus unable to focus on the social and personal situations which contribute to the problems for which the patient seeks help.

Ways of manifesting the affective, cognitive, and vegetative components of what we in the West define as depression vary cross-culturally, and therapists should be cognizant of culture's influence on emotional expression. In fact, even in the West, the concepts of loss, general hopelessness, irritability, and joylessness are not necessarily the only ways of describing depression, and referral to the changes in definitions of depression in the psychiatric guides, *DSM II* and *DSM III*, indicates the fluidity of the concept even among Western practitioners.

The problem, then, in determining whether or not Iranians are experiencing depression is one of interpretation and knowledge. If the mental health staff expects certain ways of communicating and certain preordained symptomalogy, then the therapists will not "see" depression among Iranian patients. However, if the therapists conceive of the patient as an individual who is part of a social and familial network, all of which undergo transformations of sociocultural dissonance upon immigration, and understand that the person, unable to express verbally certain feelings of nārāhati, resorts to bodily symptomatology to express feelings of discomfort socially or personally, then the clinicians could ask the appropriate questions and perhaps help the patient with therapy. However, without taking into consideration the patients' culture or the culture of Western psychiatric categories, the success of therapy with patients from non-Western cultures, such as that of Iran, is bound to founder.

Personality Disorders

Perhaps more ethnocentric than the category of depression are the so-called "personality disorders" of the psychiatric lexicon. As defined in *DSM II*, personality disorders are "deeply ingrained maladaptive patterns of behavior that are perceptibly different in quality from psychotic and neurotic symptoms" (1968:41). The concept was further refined in *DSM III* twelve years later as traits which are "inflexible and maladaptive and cause either significant impairment in social or occupational functioning or subjective distress" (1980:305). The personality disorders may be part of the symptomatology of another mental disorder, such as Major Depression, warns *DSM III*, and "the diagnosis of a Personality Disorder should be made only when the characteristic features are typical of the individual's long-term functioning and are not limited to discrete episodes of illness" (p. 305).[1]

What the changes in definition and the elaboration of categories of personality disorders show is a basic dissatisfaction with the previous categories and a desire to make the taxonomy of disorders more specific. However, although the elaboration of psychiatric nosology seems more "scientific," it is a guise for the ambiguity of diagnosis and labeling, tricking the clinician into thinking that the label represents a disorder on the one hand, and into blaming the patient for what may be a social or cultural manifestation on the other. For instance, those who exhibit the so-called "antisocial personality disorder" by fighting with others, arguing, brawling, lying, quarreling, drinking too much alcohol, stealing, getting in trouble with authority figures, and being unable to sustain employment could be representing the outcome of a life of poverty and the lack of available resources, whether economic or familial. Defining the person with the personality disorder label disengages the individual from the sociocultural setting which predisposes manifestations of individual behavior and character: personality disorders, as a psychiatric category, are culturally determined; they vary from culture to culture, as does "normal" personality, and when therapists interpret patients from another culture as exhibiting a "personality disorder" they often misconstrue culturally patterned behaviors.

The cultural influence on personality, although part of mainstream American anthropology for years,[2] receives barely a nod from psychiatry. Yet, because of the intricacies involved and the quest for diagnostic labels which legitimate the mental health professions, the nod is a meek one, partially acknowledging culture's effects, partially ignoring them. Therefore, when *DSM II* or *DSM III* defines "compulsive personality" with its various manifestations, the disorder should be considered, although often it is not, a product of sociocultural circumstances. In the United States, for example, the "workaholic" is a folk model of the "compulsive personality" in a positive sense, a person whose desire for success generates behavior of continuous hard work, avoidance of activities which would hinder the work schedule, and so forth, the Protestant Ethic carried to an extreme. However, how would such a person be characterized in a culture where the maintenance of a network of relationships cultivated by conversation and fueled by food and drink several hours a day is of prime importance? The cultural relativity of "personality disorder" labels is thus obscured in the clinical situation when the therapist needs to label. How does this affect Iranian patients in Israel?

Monir was labeled with a series of personality disorders ("immature" and "sociopathic") which were not part of the *DSM II* lexicon in use at the time she was in treatment. This indicates that individual therapists utilize a series of folk or idiosyncratic (individually fabricated) categories which are not in the official psychiatric rubric of disorders but which fill a need to label, the labels often related to the stereotypes that exist outside the clinic. The diagnostic labels characterizing Monir signify the therapist's concepts of what a woman should be—a mother who enjoys mothering. Monir was judged in terms of her being an Iranian mother, and ethnicity and the stereotypic female role were the focus of role-functioning for the therapist. Monir's complaints manifested frustrations with mothering. To the therapist, her complaints did not indicate "depression" or, had he known about it, nārāhati of sociocultural dissonance, of being alone without the extended family to help her, of expectations that she would be able, at some time or another, to continue her education, of seeing how some women work outside the home in Israel whereas she felt stuck in the apartment with three little children, but rather, an "immature" and "sociopathic" personality.

"Personality disorders" are not only an aspect of gender role dysfunction, as were Monir's labels, but they also signify cultural misunderstandings. Therefore, when Monir complains about anger and nervousness hitting her children, this is not seen as something altogether abnormal in the eyes of many Israelis, as people are often nervous. Similarly, when Iranians complain about being angry (P., asabāni) in the guise of "nervous" (H., atzbani) in the Israeli clinics, there is a fundamental misunderstanding, since the Israeli clinicians do not comprehend the destructive concept of anger personally, socially, and physically for Iranian patients. Because neither patient nor therapist can get to the underlying meaning behind the term atzbani, an inherent miscommunication occurs in the clinical setting, and therapy is unsuccessful.

Other terms in the lexicon of "personality disorders" enter into the diagnosis of Iranian patients, such as "passive." Passive in the Israeli context concerns quietness, not taking the initiative, letting others manipulate conversation. Often, Iranians who try to show respect, to ta'ārof, to those of higher status, assume the behavior which in Israel is considered passive. When this respect behavior is manifested in the clinical setting, it is interpreted by the clinicians to be passivity.

Other so-called personality disorders, like those describing Monir, are part of the interplay between the therapist's interpretation of the patient's symptomatology and the categories which the therapist thought most closely fit the patient. Such labels of personality disorders segregate the individual from the social situations which produce the distress that induces them to seek treatment in the first place. The ways they manifest their distress, physically and personally, are culturally patterned. Yet, clinicians consider the presenting symptomatology to be signifying another aspect of "personality disorder" rather than signifying a cultural expression of distress. Therefore, diagnostic labels such as "personality disorders" are culturally relativistic and cannot really be utilized as diagnostic markers for individuals who come from other cultural backgrounds whose symptomatology is influenced by that background. The fact that such diagnoses divorce the individual from the social and cultural situations which engender the presenting symptomatology reinforces the kind of individualization which is the ethnopsychology of the West. When non-Westerners, and even people from Western cultures, are diagnosed with a personality label as if to indicate that the label signifies personal qualities separate from sociocultural influences, the label becomes a heuristic device for the therapist in which the patient is held responsible for something which is frequently sociosomatic in nature.

"Parsitis"

The informal label "Parsitis" or "the Persian syndrome" indicates the frustration that the clinicians encounter with Iranian patients, blaming the patients rather than the situation of biomedical and psychiatric knowledge or sociocultural dissonance. It is an ethnic stereotype posing as a diagnosis. Knowing that someone is Iranian already prejudices practitioners' conceptions of the still-unknown patient as problematic. The stereotypes which characterize Iranians outside the clinical setting—stupid, stingy, suspicious—are transformed within the clinical setting into other stereotypes: multi-complainers who lack understanding of Western medicine and asked the same questions over and over again, doctor-shoppers, bargainers for fees, hypochondriacs, psychologically limited patients who are reticent about expressing their innermost feelings or voluntarily talking about social and personal problems in their lives, who have expectations from the clinic which cannot be met, who do not function in their social and familial roles. Indeed, a few physicans, as noted in chapter seven, commented that Iranians are "primitivim", and several therapists, as reported in chapter eight, commented on the intelligence—or lack of it—of their Iranian patients.

We can now see that the problems of interaction in the clinical setting are influenced by and reinforce the stereotypes held about Iranians in the society at large. The correlation between the societal stereotypes about Iranians and the clinical stereotype subsumed under the label "Parsitis" can be indicated as follows:

Societal stereotype	Clinical stereotype
Stupid	Multi-complainers Hypochondriacs Don't understand physiology Bizarre physical symptomatology Psychologically limited Lack understanding of Western medicine Ask same questions over and over again
Suspicious	Don't believe doctors that nothing is wrong Doctor-shoppers Reticent about expressing feelings or social and personal problems
Stingy	Bargaining for fees (for private biomedical practitioners only)

The clinical label "Parsitis" is influenced by nonclinical factors of social stereotypes and by the patients' expression of symptomatology. The expression of symptomatology, as we have seen, is shaped by cultural ideas of the emotions, the body, sickness, ideas about individual sensitivity, family changes, economic problems, and problems of sociocultural dissonance due to immigration. Moreover, "Parsitis" denotes the clinical phase of biomedicine and psychiatry which represents sickness or disorder as a biological or psychological phenomenon separate from sociocultural forces. The informality of the label and its use as a marker of the "other"—that is, the problematic patient who is difficult to diagnose—does more than blame the patient, however. It also serves to reinforce the social cohesiveness of the practitioners (who come from various cultural backgrounds) as a group, as people who understand that they don't understand. This cognizance of clinical ineptitude, which places the practitioners in positions of powerlessness which only they themselves feel, is then alleviated by the label. Therefore, among themselves they utilize the term "Parsitis," of which the Iranians are unaware, and with some patients they use terms as "depression" and for others, whose symptoms engender "personality disorders," they encourage therapy without labels given to the patient. Thus, patients like Menasheh and Monir, whose symptomatology does not indicate depression for the clinicians, do not know the diagnostic characteristics with which the practitioners characterize them, find "talk therapy" not worth their while personally, economically, or time-wise, anticipate certain expectations from the clinic to help them with the problems of their lives, and, frustrated with the clinical encounter, abandon the therapy which fails them.

Nārāhati and "Parsitis"

The examples of labeling—or of nonlabeling, as the case may be—do not coincide with the labeling theorists' concepts that the patient becomes and then acts the label received. The Iranians in the clinic where I worked did not, for the most part, know the psychiatric labels of their symptomatology, except for Amir who was diagnosed as depressed, and Menasheh who found out through a letter to a potential employer that he was depressed. Since neither knew the psychiatric definition of depression, the label really did not influence them to behave any differently. They did not take on the sense of, or express intrapsychic feelings of, hopelessness and loss, but continued to somatize symptoms of rheumatism or other aches and pains. Yet, on the other hand, the fact that a patient is an Iranian immigrant often does influence the clinicians in their thinking about the patient.

The problem of diagnostic labeling is fundamental for therapy. We have seen how primary care physicians, unable to successfully diagnose their Iranian patients who somatize various problems, were unable to treat them. Psychiatric practitioners, on the other hand, do diagnose the patients, but the labels are symbolic of sociocultural factors of which neither the practitioner nor the patient are aware: transactions between the practitioner and patient in the clinical setting in which negotiations occur with the practitioner assuming an active role of questioner while the patient passively answers; stereotypes about Iranians within Israeli society; social and cultural problems that Iranians have as immigrants, referred to here as sociocultural dissonance; unexpressed, often unrecognized, nārāhati; psychiatric nosology, whose categories and definitions are culturally constituted and vary periodically; therapists' individual orientations and expectations concerning their patients. Consequently, the diagnostic label, whether "Parsitis," depression, or personality disorders, is a symbolic term whose meaning is derived not from the symptomatology of the patients, which the practitioners admit they do not understand, but from relationships, concepts, ideas, beliefs, experiences, emotions, and symbolic means of communication of both practitioner and patient outside and inside and clinical setting.

The diagnostic label, treatment, and relief of their symptoms are what the patients, with their various aches and pains, search for, starting with primary care physicians in an effort to understand what their physical symptomatology is all about. Unsuccessful with biomedical practitioners, those who think psychiatrists, or "nerve doctors," could help them, then go to mental helath clinics searching for the meaning for their symptoms. The mental health personnel, confounded by the presenting symptomatology and by preconceived ideas about Iranians, as citizens and as patients, translate and interpret the problems of their patients into Israeli and Western categories. It is this problem of translation of one cultural category of behavior, that of Iranians, into another, that of the Israeli psychiatric establishment, that is not only problematic for the psychiatric staff at the clinic, but also for the patients who are dissatisfied with treatment. The diagnostic label "solves" the problem that the medical-psychiatric establishment has with Iranian patients: labeling fixes and controls the interaction between clinician and patient for the clinician, creating a semblance of power and efficacy that is absent when a label cannot be given. As the last of a series of medical practitioners to examine Iranians, and by virtue of the fact that everyone could potentially have something wrong psychologically, the mental health clinicians label their patients with terms taken from the official psychiatric lexicon. However, the label is often an artifice, a deceptive momentary appellation of the therapist to make sense out of the misunderstood.

Although the concept of culture is absent from medical and psychiatric knowledge and practice, diagnostic labeling, interaction and negotiation both inside and, as in the case of Homa, outside the clinical setting are mediated by culture. Culture governs emotional expression, concepts of the individual in society, ways of expressing distress and bodily illness, the meaning of illness, perception of symptoms, and how such perception is interpreted and labeled. Accordingly, psychiatric diagnoses, like clinical encounters, are cultural artifacts. They denote both therapist-patient negotiations and social and cultural conditions in the society at large (in this case, education, ethnicity, housing, family structure, religion, immigration status, gender roles, financial problems, the political situation, the structure of health care services), which affect the personal problems of the patient, and the understanding of them by the therapist.

Physicians and mental health practitioners, structurally in the more powerful position of the clinical transactions, can help eradicate or expose the silent boundaries that impede healing and therapy if they understand the influences of culture on both their patients' presentation of symptoms (and discourse, and reactions toward the clinicians' advice) and on their own clinical knowledge and praxis. In order to develop such a sociocultural awareness and understanding, clinicians need to be self-reflexive as well as perceptive of the patient. Perhaps this is too demanding a task for overworked clinicians, many of whom treat either the body or the mind, ignoring the patient's—and their own—cultural background and social situation, which have so much to do with the presentation and interpretation of sickness. With clinical transactions becoming increasingly multi-cultural, it is essential that culture and social stressors be recognized as a key to understanding and healing sickness.

The intent of this book has been an interpretation of the failure of Israeli clinicians to understand and successfully treat their Iranian patients. It is also an attempt to demonstrate the importance of learning how to listen cross-culturally. We have seen that the understanding of those involved in the microsocial transactions which occur in the medical or psychiatric setting signifies the numerous social and cultural constraints which transpire in the society as a whole. The individuals involved in the clinical setting—namely, the patients and practitioners—are products of their own sociocultural experiences and perceptions. They bring these experiences and perceptions into the clinic and communicate them in their transactions. Both carry certain culturally mediated expectations concerning proper clinical transactions: patients want an interpretation and treatment for their physical and/or psychological symptomatology; practitioners, by virtue of their profession, need to interpret in order to treat, to label in order to legitimate their actions. Failure to comprehend the sociocultural factors involved in illness expression, exacerbated when patients and practitioners come from two different cultural backgrounds, contributes to faulty labeling, unsuccessful treatment, frustrated practitioners, unhappy patients, and the failure of therapy. Here the problems of understanding, interpreting, labeling, and treating the Iranian patient by the Israeli practitioner reflect, in the interpersonal encounter which occurs in the clinical setting, the social situation and cultural expressions which arise in Israeli society. Ultimately, this is manifested in the clinical setting by the translation of Iranian patients' *nārāhati* into Israeli practitioners' "Parsitis."

Notes

Chapter 1

1 See Basker et al. (1982) for a critique of the label "Parsitis" and Minuchin-Itzigsohn et al. (1984) for another view of the problem. Both studies exemplify the peculiarities of Persian patients according to Israeli clinicians. Basker interviewed Iranian patients outside a mental health clinic in Jaffa, and read and analyzed files of Iranian and non-Iranian patients of the clinic, showing that the professional notations written in the files did not differentiate the symptoms of Iranians as distinguished from other patients in the way that the clinicians' oral discourse on "Parsitis" would suggest. Minuchin-Itzigsohn et al. interviewed Iranians, Moroccans, and Ashkenazim in several Jerusalem mental health clinics in an effort to understand their discourse and conceptions of mental illness and psychiatric problems, indicating that cultural differences influence their beliefs and symptoms. Although I did not carry out a cross-cultural study among different ethnic groups of patients, I focused on meanings and symptoms of Iranian patients—and nonpatients—referring these to cultural patterns, beliefs, behavior, and human relationships, and to sociocultural transformations that occurred because of immigration. In addition, I show that medical and psychiatric knowledge, diagnosis, and therapy are influenced as much by culture as are the symptoms and beliefs of sick patients, all of which are reflected in the label "Parsitis."

2 Although there are few, if any, holistic (macrolevel and microlevel) sociocultural studies of patients and biomedical practitioners in the West, there are numerous monographs and articles concerning the cultural and social influences on non-Western traditional healers, patients, and healing rituals, such as the following: Levi-Strauss (1967); Turner (1967); Harwood (1977); Obeyesekere (1977); Tambiah (1977); Janzen (1978); Lee (1978); Kleinman (1980); Lieban (1981); Nichter (1981a).

Chapter Two

1 "Forget Your Origin, B-G Tells Settlers," *The Jerusalem Post*, March 26, 1956.

2 For ethnographic accounts of contemporary Jewish communities in Iran, see Fischer (1973), Loeb (1977), and Goldstein (1978).

The historical situation of Iranian Jews does not parallel that of European Jews because of demographic and religious differences between Iran and Europe. Jews were the only major religious minority in European Christian countries (aside from those countries that have had a sizeable Muslim population, such as the Balkan countries and medieval Spain). Whereas European Jews suffered social, religious, economic, and political discrimination and humiliation, in addition to periodic destruction of their communities from the Crusades, the Inquisition, pogroms, blood libels, and lastly, the Holocaust, Iranian Jews have been one of a number of religious minorities in Iran

(Zoroastrians, Armenians, Assyrians, Bahais). This view of Jews as one of a number of Iranian religious minorities, many of whom were persecuted (Fischer 1973), differs from that of Loeb (1977) who, researching contemporary Jewish life in the Shirazi ghetto, did not place Jews within their Iranian context, in which all religious minorities were affected by the mulla-shah struggles and the political economy. He therefore interprets Jews as the only outcaste group.

3 Both Iranian Jews and pre-Revolution Iranian political leaders have employed the relationship between Cyrus and the ancient Jewish community of Iran to exemplify the supposedly good relationships that Jews have had with Iranian political authorities throughout the ages. A fourteenth-century Judaeo-Persian poet, Shahin of Shiraz, uses Cyrus as the hero of his poem *Ardashir-Nāmeh*. Cyrus's relationship to the Jewish community, as a beneficient and just ruler, is resolved in this work by making him the son of Esther the Jewess and Ardashir, the Ahasueros of the Book of Esther, often considered to be Xerxes. For further discussion of Cyrus in prophetic writings and Judaeo-Persian texts, see Netzer (1974).

4 Scholars place Zoroaster, the prophet whose teachings form the bases of the Iranian religion Zoroastrianism, as having lived some time between 1200–1000 B.C. See Boyce (1975).

5 Some of the tenets of the Covenant of Omar: the erection of synagogues and churches that were not in existence in the pre-Muslim period was prohibited; the Qoran was not to be taught to dhimmis; Muslims could not teach dhimmis; dhimmis could not have Muslim slaves or servants; dhimmis could not sell liquor or wine to Muslims; dhimmis were to honor Muslims and stand in their presence, and were not permitted to hit or deceive them; dhimmis were not to prevent anyone from converting to Islam; dhimmis were not to resemble Muslims in clothing or hair; they were not to have Muslim names; they were forbidden to carry arms; they could not ride horses or mules, only donkeys, and sidesaddle; their houses were not to be higher than those of Muslims; dhimmis were not permitted to hold government offices or have positions in which they would have authority over Muslims; the property of the deceased belonged to the Muslim authorities until heirs proved their right to it according to Islamic law. (See "Omar, Covenant of," *Jewish Encyclopedia* 12:1379, Jerusalem: Keter Publishing House, 1972).

6 See Fischel (1949a) for literary relations between Jews and Muslims during the shu'ubiyya movement, in which he stresses the cultural assimilation of Jews in Iranian society. Yet, Fischel seems surprised that Persian was used as the language of Jews of Iran (p. 823): "some early documents come to light which reveal the actual use of Persian by Persian Jews." However, one would expect that any people participating in the society socially, commercially, and politically (at least in devising networks to secure their position), and as urban residents, as have the Jews in varying degrees since before the Babylonian exile, would speak the language of the country in addition to communicating in their own dialects.

7 Of the Persian Jewish poets, two are well-known in the Jewish literati circles: Maulana Shahin of Shiraz (c. 1327–58) and Emrani (c. 1500), the latter having been quite influenced by the former, who used the meter, form, and structure of classical Persian poetry. Shahin's subjects were primarily biblical, to which he gave Persian attire. His best known work is a poetical commentary on the Bible, *Sefer Sharkh Shahin al Ha-Torah*, which was divided into several books: "Book of Genesis," "Moses Book," "Ezra Book," "Ardashir Book," the latter divided in two, Megillat Esther and the story of Shiro

and Mahzad. Shahin was also well acquainted with Islam and the Qoran, in addition to the works of the major Persian poets of his time.

Emrani also used Islamic and Persian sources with biblical accounts, writing poetic versions of Joshua to Kings, *Fath-Nāmeh* (The Book of the Conquest) in 1523 and *Ganj Nāmeh* (The Book of Treasures) in 1536, in which he rephrased poetically the *Pirke Avot* of the Mishnah.

8 For a more thorough description of the *Kitāb-i Anusi* and the status of religious minorities during the Safavid rule, see Moreen (1981).

9 More information exists about the Jews of nineteenth-century Iran than any other previous era. Most accounts were written by Christian missionaries, European diplomats and adventurers, and scouts for Alliance Israélite.

10 See Fischer (1973:409–49) for descriptions and analyses of riots against religious minorities: Jews, Bahais, Christians, Zoroastrians, Ismailis.

11 For example, the Muslim clergy of Hamadan imposed the following regulations on the Jewish community after riots broke out against the Jews in 1892, calling for death to the Jews or their conversion to Islam:

1. It is forbidden for Jews to leave their houses when it snows.
2. Jewish women must appear on public streets with their faces uncovered.
3. She must be wrapped in an *izar* (*chādor*) of two colors.
4. The men cannot wear fine clothes, the only material that suits them is blue cotton.
5. It is forbidden to put on shoes that match.
6. Every Jew must wear a piece of red fabric on the chest.
7. A Jew must never pass a Muslim on a public street.
8. It is forbidden to talk in a loud voice to a Muslim.
9. A Jewish creditor of a Muslim must reclaim his credit in a trembling and respectful tone.
10. If a Muslim insults a Jew, he (the Jew) must lower his head and keep silent.
11. A Jew who buys meat must wrap it and carefully conceal it from a Muslim.
12. He is forbidden to erect beautiful buildings.
13. He is forbidden to have a house higher than that of his Muslim neighbor.
14. He must not whitewash his rooms either.
15. The entrance to his house has to be low.
16. The Jew cannot drape himself with his coat; he will be content to wear it rolled under the arms.
17. He is forbidden to cut his beard, even to trim it with scissors.
18. It is not permitted for Jews to leave the city, or to enjoy the fresh air in the country.
19. Jewish doctors must not ride a horse.
20. A Jew suspected of having drunk liquor must not appear on the streets; if he appears, he is immediately put to death.
21. Jewish weddings must be celebrated in greatest mystery, of such manner that nothing transpires outdoors.
22. Jews must not eat good fruits.

(*Bulletin de l'Alliance Israélite* 1892:49–50)

12 From 1914 to 1916, the first Iranian Jewish newspaper, *Shalom*, was published, followed by *Hageula* in 1920–21 and *Hehayim* from 1922–25, all in Persian with Hebrew characters. The titles are Hebrew. By 1960, Jewish journals were published in Persian with Persian characters—*Alam-i Yahud*, *Israel*, *Rahnamā-i Yahud*, and *Majalleh Sina*.

13 However, tribal leaders, such as some of the Qashqai khans, were persecuted, exiled, and sometimes killed because of their opposition to Reza Shah, and later, to his son.

14 It is interesting to note that there are certain dishes that Muslims prepare for Moharram, such as a sweet pollau (*shirin pollo*) and a rice pudding (*choleh-zard*), that Jews do not make because of their Shi'ite religious connotations. In addition, there are certain regional Jewish dishes in Iran that are not made by non-Jews nor by Jews of other localities.

15 More research and analysis are needed to interpret this ritual to determine its origins (i.e., Baghdadi, Iranian, Sephardic) and its symbolism.

16 Boyce (1968) writes that Zoroastrians performed various rites after death, including the anniversary day called *sāl*. On these days observances and rites for the departed were performed, including offering food and drink, which were partaken by the living in communion with the dead. The Jews commemorate a person's sāl by gathering together all the relatives to hear the Torah read at the home of the deceased's closest relatives and to share in a meal.

17 Most of Israeli anthropology and sociology, spurred by Eisenstadt's seminal study, *The Absorption of Immigrants* (1954), tend to examine the social and cultural problems of Oriental immigrants adjusting to Israeli society, and a disproportionate number of these studies took place on *moshavim* because of their village-like nature affording a community easily studied. See Deshen (1970), Weingrod (1966), Willner (1969), Shokeid (1971), Goldberg (1972), Kushner (1973).

18 With the development of the Zionist movement in Iran, the "Society for the Promotion of the Hebrew Language" was organized. In 1918 they published a text of modern Hebrew, concluding with the Hebrew and Persian texts of *Hatikvah* ("The Hope"), which became the Israeli national anthem. In 1920 the *History of the Zionist Movement* by Aziz ben Yona Naim was published in Judaeo-Persian whose "numerous biblical quotations from Isaiah and the Psalms . . . indicate the strong religious and messianic character of Persian Jewish conception of Zionism" (Fischel 1949a:855).

19 The following is a list of Iranian immigrants in Israel grouped by dates of immigration. The information was taken from "Immigration to Israel, 1948–77," Department of Demography, Central Bureau of Statistics, Jerusalem, 1978. The last two dates come from a worker at the Central Bureau of Statistics who had found for me, by the end of 1980, the statistics on Iranian refugees who came because of the political upheavals in Iran.

Years	Iranian immigrants
1948–51	21,727
1952–54	5,844
1955–57	2,113
1958–60	7,804
1961–64	9,005
1965–68	5,479
1969–71	5,950
1972–77	2,858
1978	920
1979	5,915

20 ORT, the Organization for Rehabilitation through Training, is a trade school system founded and sponsored by the American Joint Distribution Committee to train Jewish youths in occupations for modern society, such as electronics, secretarial science, carpentry, laboratory technology. The schools were established in non-Western societies for the most part in order to ensure that the Jewish population would be able to support itself economically by means other than trade or business, and would thus be integrated within the industrial economy and society.

Chapter Three

1 After reading Good (1977) and having heard people use the term *nārāhati* in various contexts, I became interested in the problem of this emotion and its relationship to Iranian culture and society. Since the focus of Good's 1977 article was not so much on the emotion nārāhati per se but on one of its symptoms, *nārāhati-ye qalb*, "heart distress," I decided to study the *affect* nārāhati and its meaning and expression among Iranians. In 1978 during the political turbulence of the shah's downfall and Khomeini's advent there were many nārāhat people (including myself) and both Iran and later, Israel, became goldmines for case studies. I saw nārāhati expressed and masked in various contexts with various people: inside homes, in streets, in clinics. My interest, after hearing about Israeli doctors' problems with Iranians, thus centered on nārāhati expression. This interest differs from the later works of Good and Good (1982; 1985) who focus on the symbolic meaning of nārāhati. Although we have a different focus, my work complements theirs. Some of my case studies are from clinics, whereas others occur as interaction that I have observed outside the clinic. In addition, the symbolic emphasis which I stress here is the meaning that nārāhati expression has for the people who feel the emotion, as I am looking at the people in the context of relationships with others in the society. This meaning is powerlessness, explained further on.

Although there are many more emotions in Iranian society than nārāhati—such as emotions of happiness, embarrassment, and fear,—I concentrated on nārāhati because of the situation in which I saw people between 1978 and 1981, and because of the medical problems of somatization which occur in Israel and which are due, I postulate, to nārāhati.

2 Among some of the definitions were the following in Hebrew: uncomfortable (*lo noach li; i noach; lo noach*); angry (*mitragezet*); being in a bad mood (*ain li matzav ruach; bli matzav ruach*); not feeling well (*lo margish tov; lo marghishah beseder*); nervous (*atzbani*); someone annoys me (*mishehu matzik li*); feeling restless or untranquil (*margish bekhoser menukhah*); restless (*i sheket*); sickness (*makhalah*); depression (*dikaon*); quarrel (*riv*). In English the following definitions were given: it is an inconvenience; inconvenienced; very upset; bothered; troubled; worried; uneasy; depressed; nervous. In Persian, nārāhati was defined as being sick (*mariz budan*), troubled or distressed nerves (*asāb-i nārāhati*), and one woman interpreted it as "ruined interior" (*vasat-i kharāb*). People rarely mentioned the Persian differentiated terms for negative affects which are subsumed under nārāhati, such as *delvāpasi* (anxiety, concern, understanding), *sarkhordagi* (disillusionment), *delhoreh* (apprehension, worry), *afsordegi* (depression), although *ghamgini* (sadness), *ghoseh* (sorrow), and *asabāni* (angry) were sometimes noted.

3 For a recent study of emotion as a problem of language, see Leff (1981); as a question of universality, which is based upon Darwin's (1872) evolutionary-genetic theory of the

biological innateness of emotion expression, see Tomkins (1962; 1963), Ekman et al. (1972), Ekman (1973), Izard (1971); as socially or culturally veneered biological innateness, see Izard (1980), and for a version regarding differential labeling of a single physiological state, see Schachter and Singer (1962); for an anthropological study of "inner states," see Needham (1981). For anthropological studies of emotions and culture in non-Western societies, see Abu-Lughod (1987); Good and Good (1985); Levy (1973); Lindholm (1982); Lutz (1980); Myers (1979); Obeyesekere (1985); Rosaldo (1980).

4 Ethnopsychology of different peoples has, within the last decade, become a leading subfield of psychological anthropology, replacing the older culture and personality school which viewed cultures as determined by an underlying pervasive motif (see Benedict 1934 and Mead 1935). Among recent monographs on ethnopsychology are studies of Indians and Americans (Shweder and Bourne 1982); Taiwanese (Kleinman 1980); Chinese (Kleinman 1980; 1982; 1985); the Pukhtun of Pakistan (Lindholm 1982); the Bedouin of Egypt (Abu-Lughod 1987); the Ifalukians of New Guinea (Lutz 1980); the Ilongot of the Philippines (Rosaldo 1980); the Pintupi of Australia (Myers 1979); Buddhists of Sri Lanka (Obeyesekere 1985); Iranians (Good and Good 1982; 1985); Moroccans (Crapanzano 1973; 1980; Rosen 1979); Lebanese villagers (Gilsenan 1976); Tahitians (Levy 1973); the Middle East (Gulick 1976); the Chewong of Peninsular Malaysia (Howell 1981).

5 I am not concerned about emotions expressed and/or felt which are due to reactions to biochemical imbalances because of sickness or medication, nor am I here interested in emotions which are "instinctual" survivalistic psychobiological reactions to environmental stimuli, such as certain forms of fear. The latter, however, should be cognized first before the reaction occurs, for what might induce fear in people from one culture might not for people in another, except when life is at stake.

6 For psychobiological studies of emotions in anthropology, see Levy (1973), Kleinman (1980), and Needham (1981).

7 Despite studies of hierarchy and mobility among Middle Easterners, little attention has been given to these issues as they relate to women's relationships to both women and men, aside from women's status determined by (1) religious proscriptions; (2) reproductive cycle; and (3) relationship to others through their relationships to men. The most significant questions concern the extent to which women's relationships of obligation and servitude, domination and subordination (aside from the mother-in-law/daughter-in-law relationship) differ from, or are similar to, those of men, and how these are communicated and acted out.

8 The communication patterns of Iranians, specifically ta'ārof and its sociocultural meanings, have been studied by Beeman (1976a; 1976b; 1977), who delineated interaction in terms of intimate and nonintimate relations, and of equal and unequal status. Beeman's studies are, by far, the most comprehensive analyses of Iranian communication patterns. What needs to be addressed now are the issues of gender differences and social structural problems due to wider societal constraints, and how these are related to communication and interaction. For example, the larger macrosocial context of social hierarchy *and* social mobility needs to be studied as a structural construct while analyzing communication of men *and* women, as do the personality and feelings of interacting individuals which both influence and are influenced by the interaction.

9 See Ajami (1979); Banuazizi (1977); Bateson (1979); Bateson et al. (1977); Beeman (1976b); Binning (1857); Fowler (1841); Hedayat (1979); Lorey and Slayden (1907); Sheil (1856); Southgate (1840); Westwood (1965); Wolff (1861); Zonis (1971).

10 My view of sensitivity among Iranians, from what I have heard and seen while doing research inside and outside of clinics, is similar to the view of Good and Good (1982) where sensitivity is defined as an element of personality, but varies from their analysis of sensitivity as a component of "fright illness" in Iran (1982) and as an etiological aspect of the semantic network of nārāhati (Good and Good 1985). Sensitivity is a very real part of nārāhati, as this chapter explains, but I consider it not to be a "personality characteristic explained in terms of one's childhood" but a part of the ethnopsychology of Iranian character which must be guarded in interaction. Certain relationships and conditions, however, warrant its manifestation.

Both Mary-Jo Good and I have focused on sensitivity as an element of Iranian personality around the same time, in California and in Iran and Israel, respectively, and discussing our work has been helpful in formulating this segment of the chapter.

11 This conversation occurred in Jerusalem with Hebrew as the language of discourse. The Hebrew word for nerve, similar to the Arabic/Persian *asab*, is *atzab*, and the word *atzbani* in Hebrew means "nervous." Iranians tend to use it as a direct translation of the Iranian word for "angry," *asabāni*, hardly ever using the Hebrew word for angry, *ko'es*. Miscommunication in psychiatric clinics occurs because of this mistranslation of concepts (see chapter eight).

12 There seems to be a distinct difference in male and female expression of ghamgini, sadness. Men tend to express sullenness more openly than do women, whereas women are more open verbally about their feelings of sadness. Perhaps the different expressions have to do with different conceptions of the innate character of male and female in Iran, where men are considered, as in the West, rational and reasonable (*'aql*), whereas women are considered emotional and therefore can display, verbally and nonverbally, their emotions more readily and have a different array of forms to do so. Men, as rational creatures bound by society's dictates of appropriate public and private styles of communication and as more involved in the public sector of society, utilize the aesthetic of ghamgini as reflective not only of their feelings, but also of other aspects of the public life: tragedy, sadness, and grief which are expressed publicly, religiously, socially, and politically. Women, on the other hand, bound by home and the intimate relationships of family, can express emotions more readily in various coping styles then can men who have taken on a public cultural aesthetic for expression of sadness. Some of these ideas of male and female differences in sadness expression were discussed with Byron and Mary-Jo Good. Further research and analyses remains to be done.

13 Almost every time I heard a line of poetry recited concerning a person's inner feelings or in relation to an event, the reciters have been men. Several reasons could explain why: (1) men were traditionally educated better than women, and poetry memorization was part of that education; (2) much of the poetry has sexual/mystical connotations, and I was told that schoolgirls should not be taught such subjects; (3) the ideal sensitive Iranian man shows his depth and his profundity by quietness, sadness, and thoughts of the meaning of life, which is expressed by poetry, whereas women are often deemed emotional and not as deep as men, nor concerned with the same issues. In any case, the question as to why more men than women recite poetry at times of nārāhati, and at other times, remains.

14 This sense of the individual not being in control of his own destiny is the theme of a tragic novel by Fereydoun Esfendiary, *The Day of Sacrifice*. The protagonist, Kianoush, is an unemployed middle-class thirty-three-year-old man dependent on his father, who tells him what to do, where to go, how and on what to spend money. Kianoush is angry at his

father for controlling him, but is unable to do anything about it, nor can he express his anger to his father. The father, however, is angry at his son for not obeying him and for not working. Kianoush is asked by his father to contact a revolutionary friend of his to stop an assassination attempt. Although procrastinating to carry out his father's request because of his anger, Kianoush eventually tries finding his friend—only to be in the wrong place at the wrong time. He is jailed as an accomplice in the assassination and is condemned to be executed.

15 For scholars who equate religious dissimulation (*taqiyya*) with present-day impression management, see Bateson (1979) and Zonis (1972).

Chapter Four

1 The case of ethnicity and identity among Jews in Israel does not concern boundary-maintenance systems, as Barth (1969) purports, since intermarriage and intermixing are fostered; specific ethnic identity has not been a way of gaining political hegemony, as Cohen (1968, 1974), Gulliver (1969), and Parkin (1969) write, except for Tami, the new Moroccan political party, or Shas, the new Sephardic religious party, and alignment in the two segments of Ashkenazi and Sephardi, which is a cultural-political-religious split going back to before the state was founded and which is not a measure of political attitudes since there are leftists, rightists, and centrists in both groups; ethnicity in Israel is not "transgenerational" as Parsons (1975) maintains, since native-born Israelis tend to devalue their ethnic heritage in favor of Israeli identity and behavior; nor is it ascribed from birth, as Horowitz (1975) states; Israelis do not at all feel guilty by not associating with their cultural heritage, as DeVos (1975) maintains; nor do symbolic expressions, as mentioned by Keyes (1979), form relationships between different ethnic groups, although they do have aesthetic and traditional value as *minhagim*—cultural-religious customs—and are sometimes exploited by modern politicians, as in the Maimona festival (see last section of chapter).

2 The slant that the term *edot* has for Israeli social scientists is not recognized by the majority of them, who are Ashkenazi Jews. Its meaning has become for everyone in the society synonymous with non-Western immigrant groups and their descendants. In a conference on ethnicity in Israel held at Beersheva in the summer of 1980, people referred to *ha-edot,* literally, "the ethnic groups," as non-Western Israelis. No one spoke of Americans, Russians, Argentinians, French, or any of the other recent or not so recent Western immigrants to Israel, as they are not considered by the society, nor by the academics, to be "ethnic groups."

In this book, I refer to non-Western Jews, those Jews originating from Islamic countries rather than from Christian countries, by a variety of appellations. None of these designations are meant to have any kind of cultural value orientation. Rather, they are general classifications for non-Western Jews who come primarily from North Africa, Central Asia, and the Middle East. The terms used here, aside from the widespread misnomer "Sephardic," are "Middle Eastern" and "Oriental."

3 In Iran I never observed such informal poses in a situation of men and women socializing together. Although the positions of posture might have been informal among peers, such informality as that which exists in Israel—of men *and* women sprawled on the floor together—is, indeed, rare.

4 Israeli schools are either secular or religious, the latter being either modern Orthodox and coeducational or ultra-Orthodox and gender-divided.

5 In Israel there is a very high inflation rate which is exacerbated by monthly cost-of-living increases paid by employers to employees to counteract the rise in cost of basic necessities and to follow changes in currency devaluation. The example of Bob, Anat, and Esther occurred before the lira was devalued and replaced by the shekel as the standard of currency.

6 *Kappara* means atonement, forgiveness, pardon, expiation. Among Orthodox Jews before Yom Kippur, the Day of Atonement, a ritual of getting rid of one's bad health, sins, unwanted traits, and other undesirable characteristics is performed. In this ritual either a white chicken or money is encircled over a person's head while a prayer to alleviate the person from personal, social, or physical afflictions is said. The fowl and/or money then goes to the poor as charity, and is called "*kappara*." In the case of Esther, Bob's saying the money is kappara is an insult: she is neither poor, nor would she want money associated with affliction of others.

7 The Persian phrase, *bāham namak khordim,* literally means "we ate salt together." It is used in the context meaning "They ate in my house," or "I ate in their house." Although the conversation I had with Esther occurred in Hebrew, this phrase, which indicates the close relationship of having eaten together, was said in Persian. In Iran, because of all the social and familial differences and distances, coupled with religious proscriptions concerning whose food is edible, both among Muslims and Jews, eating together is indicative of formulating close social bonds. For Esther, Anat's and Bob's having eaten in her house symbolizes a close relationship which was broken by the quarrel over money.

8 This is a generalization about the situation of the Oriental population in Israel. Of course, there are many Jews of Middle Eastern origin who do not fit this particular situation, who are in the government, active members of the Histradut (the national labor union), professors, store owners, doctors, lawyers, engineers, and other professionals. For further information about Israeli social structure, see Eisenstadt (1967), Heller (1975), Shama and Iris (1977), Smooha (1978), Lewis (1979), Liebman and Don-Yehiya (1982), and E. Cohen (1983).

9 I thank Soleiman Mottahedeh for letting me photocopy the manuscript of his play.

10 See Liebman and Don-Yehiya (1982) and E. Cohen (1983), and the widely talked-about book by Amos Oz (1983).

11 Statistical Abstract of Israel, 1982, No. 33, Central Bureau of Statistics, Jerusalem.

12 Accent can be differentiated, as there is a specific "Sephardic" way of pronounciation which is considered to be the "real" Hebrew since the sounds are similar to Arabic. However, although it is possible to differentiate between socioeconomic class, behavior, and language in Israel as in many other countries, much of the communication is caught up with cultural stereotyping. The lower socioeconomic classes, except for some of the ultra-Orthodox sects of Ashkenazim, have been of the Middle Eastern population, although Iranians, among the Middle Eastern Jews, are not of the lower classes (I have not found statistics on immigration group and socioeconomic class, but talking with Iranians and other Israelis indicates that Iranians are not among the poorest of the society). One interesting note concerns a nouveau-riche class of produce sellers developing in Israel: men and women who sell fruit and vegetables in the outdoor markets are known not to tell the income tax authorities how much they make, and pay little, if any taxes. In a country which taxes more than 50 percent of a person's income, not paying that fifty percent makes men and women comparatively well-off. These produce sellers are primarily Middle Eastern in origin, relatively uneducated, many of whom so far do not value higher

education for their children, and are among the wealthier of Israel's citizens, creating a new socioeconomic class. It will be interesting to see in the future how much political and economic weight this new class will have.

13 The sabras' relative ignorance of Jewish cultures and history in the countries of the Diaspora, and their lack of interest in knowing such information, were an impetus to develop the Museum of the Diaspora in Tel Aviv, which opened in the spring of 1979. It is an educational institution whose audiovisual presentation tells of the history and culture of Jews as they went into exile after the destruction of the Second Temple in 70 A.D.

Chapter Five

1 For studies of psychosocial problems of immigration, see Brown (1980), Pfister-Ammende (1980), Bar-Yosef (1966), Marris (1980), Trimble (1980).

2 Stressors of immigration have been associated with mental and psychosomatic illnesses (Belser 1982; Hertz 1982; Kantor 1965; Verdonk 1977). However, in discussing social stressors and illness, none of these studies delineated the symbolic changes which occur among people socialized in one culture as they acclimate themselves to the social system and cultural categories of another, the conflicts raised, and the ways people cope with or resolve the conflicts.

Theories that immigrants are "uprooted" from their culture of orientation and thus suffer loss of familiar behavioral patterns, environmental conditions, and social relationships (see Coelho and Ahmed 1980; Marris 1980; Nann 1982) are also inadequate: on the one hand, they do not distinguish analytically between the social and the cultural regarding changes that the immigrants experience, and, on the other, they fail to show how the social and cultural are mutually dependent.

3 Iranians in Los Angeles, studied by Good and Good (1985), exhibit reactions to similar stressors: problems they have with the American bureaucracy; fear of being deported; insecurity of living as an immigrant; loneliness; family problems; difficulties relating to American society.

4 Youth Aliya is an established immigrant policy to bring young people without their parents to Israel to work on a kibbutz or to study in schools geared for immigrants to ease their adjustment to Israel.

5 The conversations I had with people on this subject took place in Hebrew or English. The Hebrew word, *bedikaon*, or the slang *medupras* (mas.) and *medupreset* (fem.), from the English "depressed," were the terms used. No one referred to Israelis as nārāhat in this context.

6 Every healthy man in Israel must serve in the army from the ages of eighteen to twenty-one, and then each year for one month or more in the reserves until his late fifties. To be eliminated from reserve duty for physical or psychological reasons, as was Amir, is socially embarrassing and personally demoralizing, since much of men's adult social world—networks, gossip, comradeship, jokes—comes from army connections. Therefore, Amir's being rejected from the reserves is experienced both as a social and personal rejection.

7 *Nida* is the Hebrew term referring to religious injunctions regarding menstrual blood, the menstruating woman, impurity, and something untouchable by men because of contact with menstrual blood which is considered by Orthodox Judaism as polluting. Nida con-

cerns ritually proper sexual relations between husband and wife, which is the wife's duty to maintain. Sexual intercourse is forbidden during menstruation and for a week following it. During the period of nida, some ultra-Orthodox couples sleep on separate beds, do not physically touch each other or, among some sects, even avoid handing objects to one another. A week after mentruation is terminated, the woman goes to the *mikvah*, the ritual bath, to purify herself. She is then reeady to resume sexual relations with her husband. The period of nida acts as the opposite of a natural form of birth control, since the prescribed time to resume sexual relations occurs during ovulation.

8 The concept of "spilling seed" is an interesting religious injunction regarding reproduction, sexuality, gender relations, sibling power, and men's relation to the power and control of sperm. In religious discourse, masturbation is often referred to as "onanism," originating from the biblical story of Onan, son of Judah, who "spilled his seed" rather than impregnating his dead brother's wife. Onanism also refers to coitus interruptus according to the Midrash, and the Talmud considers it to be "unnatural intercourse" or masturbation. The Onan story, according to the *Encyclopaedia Judaica* [1972(12):1396) "is pre-Sinai, and the context makes it sufficiently doubtful whether Onan's sin is his contraceptive act or his frustration of the purpose of the levirate marriage," and "there is a question whether the prohibition against onanism, in any sense, is a prohibition of biblical or rabbinic force." Although the *Encyclopaedia* states, citing a Talmudic source (Tosefot RiD to Yev. 12b), that "the use of a device which smacks of Onan's method but is free of his intent is preferable to abstinence, so that the *mitzvah* [commandment] of marital sex can be continued," many Orthodox Jews, like Amir, consider it sinful.

9 Somatization among Iranian immigrants in Israel is due not only to their particular social and cultural status as immigrants. Rather, there are certain forms and styles of somatization which occur among Iranians in Iran as a way to get sick due to difficulties of social life (see Good 1977 on "heart distress"). Other ways of expressing sickness are explained in the following chapter.

Chapter Six

1 Studies of somatization in the United States and in other societies (Bazzoui 1970; Binitie 1975; El-Islam 1974; B. Good 1977; M. J. D. Good 1980; Katon et al. 1982; Kleinman 1980, 1981; Nichter 1981a, 1981b; Racy 1980; Rosen et al. 1982; Teja et al. 1971) show how people indicate social and personal distress through the idiom of bodily discomfort as a way of coping with dysphoric affects.

Medical and psychiatric research (Barsky 1979; Engel 1959; Leff 1973, 1981; Mechanic 1972; Minuchin et al. 1978) suggests that somatizers are people who have no psychological vocabulary with which to express their emotional or personal problems. However, these studies assume a certain cultural evolutionary bias: those Westernized people with a higher education, presumably the upper and middle classes (including those who do the research), have a psychological orientation toward illness, whereas those who are less educated, "traditional," and working class or lower class somatize more. The cultural evolutionary emphasis within the somatization literature is conspicuous by the notable absence of studies about somatization among the well-educated and upper classes in Western society (except for college students who often form the subjects of experiments): we all know that simply being equipped with a psychological vocabulary does not mean that somatization does not occur. Business executives, lawyers, doctors, scientists, professors, and artists also fall victim to headaches, hyperventilation, fatigue, pains , and so on.

2 See B. Good (1976) for an explanation of the high tradition theory of Galenic-Islamic medicine and its integration into contemporary Maragheh, Iran. Good's findings in Maragheh are here reinforced, as the system of humoral medicine is a vital aspect of thinking of health and illness among Iranian Jews.

3 For a comparison with other cultural systems which also categorize foods into hot and cold qualities, see Opler (1963), Currier (1966), Harwood (1971), Logan (1975), and Kay (1977).

4 Here I am referring to those people who are not the poorest of the poor, among whom purchasing foods high in nutrition is the problem. For the poor the diet consists primarily of bread (neutral quality), yogurt (cold), and perhaps dates (very hot) or some other inexpensive hot and cold foods. For the rest of the population, the diet combines the neutral, hot, and cold foods at each meal to create a diet healthy in proteins, carbohydrates, vitamins and minerals, such as *kalam pollo*, made from rice (cold), cabbage (hot), cooked dried beans (cold), chicken (hot), and spices (usually hot).

5 The linguist Thass-Thienemann (1971:242–43) wrote the following regarding the liver in European folklore:

"The liver as the source of violent emotions, love and hatred was in Shakespeare's mind when he said: 'to quench the coal which in his liver glows.' The words *to glow, gall, gold,* and *yellow,* Old English *geolo,* German *gelb,* are interrelated and developed out of one basic phonemic pattern. The section of the liver, the *bile,* is found in the *gall*. This word, Old English *gealla,* originally meant 'shining yellow,' which is also the quality of gold. This golden-yellow shine explains the *glow* attributed to the liver. It made the liver the seat of 'ardent' passions.

"The bile is secreted into the duodenum; it helps digestion. Thus it became the carrier of the aggressive intention implied in all digestion. Its overflow is a sign of irritation, vexation or anger. If someone becomes irritated, it is said in German: 'something runs over his liver' (*ihm ist etwas uber die Leber gelaufen*). If someone freely expresses his irritation, it is said in German, 'he speaks but of his liver' (*er spricht von der Leber weg*). To be vicious means in Hungarian *rossz maju*—'having a bad liver.' Envy is often characterized as 'yellow' or 'green,' hostility as 'bitter.' Yet it is not the hatred that is yellow or bitter but rather the bile secreted by the stimulation of this hatred. Such expressions suggest that anger may manifest itself in a concomitant increase in the secretion of bile, a biological observation which the early Greeks could hardly have made through experimentation. The bile is normally yellow-green in color: it may turn dark green in the case of accumulation as a result of high emotional irritation. The Greek *melan-cholia* properly 'black bile,' denoted the despondent state as a disgrace of the bile. In this case depression has been correlated with the secretion of the bile."

However, what Thass-Thienemann failed to note was that *melan-cholia's* relationship to depression was a somatopsychic one, and the same with the other emotions in relation to the liver.

Chapter Seven

1 See Shuval et al. (1970) and Antonovsky (1972). Those projects done in Israel on utilization rates concern different immigrant groups, but no mention is made of either

social and cultural differences and difficulties, or concepts of illness in the immigrants' original sociocultural systems.

2 See Shuval (1980) for a study of professional values of Israeli physicians.

According to Yishai (1982:288), 95 percent of the Israeli physicians belong to the Israeli Medical Association (IMA), which was founded in 1912. Of the 6,800 doctors in the IMA, 85 percent are salaried employees working for Kupat Holim or the government. One-third work in hospitals, two-thirds in clinics, 40 percent for Kupat Holim, 60 percent for the state.

The majority of the physicians at Kupat Holim clinics are immigrants. Perhaps this is because the majority of physicians in Israel are immigrants. The majority of sabras who work at Kupat Holim are women: women physicians will accept positions with community-based clinics whereas their husbands, if also physicians, legitimate their higher status positions in the society by procuring employment in hospitals (Shuval 1980; also see Hazelton 1977).

3 Although physicians use the term "functional" in reference to Iranians' complaints, and not the term "illusory", I am adopting it to describe the phenomenon of the dilemmas of diagnosis. The term "functional" places the problem in the hands of the patient, whereas "illusory" connotes difficulties in comprehension for both physicians and patients, as the sickness may be real, or an illusion, and the dilemma is for both.

4 See Antonovsky (1972); Ben-Sira et al. (1978); Eaton et al. (1979); Grewel (1967); Grushka (1968); Halevi (1963); Hes (1958); Honig-Parness (1982); Lerner and Noy (1968); Maoz et al. (1966); Miller (1964); Shuval (1979); Shuval et al. (1978).

For recent studies which do emphasize cultural differences and illnesses among various populations in Israel, see Basker et al. (1982), Bilu, (1979), and Minuchin-Itzigsohn et al. (1984).

5 There are four psychiatric hospitals in Jerusalem. In the south is Talbieh, a Kupat Holim hospital, the only mental hospital in the center of the city. Associated with Talbieh Hospital are two mental health clinics of Kupat Holim, one for children, one for adults. In the north quarter of the city is Ezrat Nashim Hospital, privately funded and government-aided. Affiliated with Ezrat Nashim is one mental health clinic which is divided into child and adult components. Fourteen miles west of Jerusalem is a government-funded hospital, Eitanim. This hospital serves the rural area of Beit Shemesh, a development town west of Jerusalem, as well as outlying western neighborhoods of Jerusalem; two clinics serving child and adult populations are affiliated with Eitanim, one in Beit Shemesh and the other in a Jerusalem neighborhood. The psychiatric department of Hadassah Hospital, a non-profit private institution, is also affiliated with the western segment of the city and is responsible to a subgroup there. In addition, Hadassah provides services for patients with acute physiological problems who are referred from other psychiatric hospitals as well as providing more private psychiatric help for the wealthier Jerusalemites and for university students. Another government-funded institution is Givat Shaul, a hospital which has as patients people who are in rehabilitation programs, tourists, and psychiatric cases from the courts. And, in East Jerusalem is Bethrin, a hospital for Arab patients; associated with this hospital is a children's clinic.

It is interesting to note the background of some of the mental health hospitals in Jerusalem. Each building, except for Hadassah and Ezrat Nashim, which are new, was affiliated with another group of people before 1948 in such a way that they were "outside society" in the Israeli context. Givat Shaul was the Arab village Dir Yassin, whose population was massacred during the War of Independence by the fanatical fighters known as "Irgun Zvei Leumi." After the war, the village became a refuge for immigrants until 1950, when it was transformed into a psychiatric hospital. Eitanim was an orphanage and school for Arab children whose parents were killed in the wars against the Jewish settlers before 1948. It was administered by the Grand Mufti of Jerusalem, who was affiliated with the Nazis, for approximately twelve years. After independence, it became a tuberculosis hospital; between 1956 and 1958 it was used as a children's psychiatric hospital, and afterward became an adult psychiatric hospital. Talbieh was a monestary until 1948, and became a mental hospital in 1951.

6 Among the nonpsychiatric medical facilities are four major hospitals and several minor hospitals. Among the larger teaching hospitals are Hadassah Ein Kerem, built after the War of Independence when the Hadassah Hospital on Mount Scopus was seized by the Jordanians. After the Six Day War when Mount Scopus came under Israeli hands, the Hadassah Hospital on Mount Scopus was rebuilt and now has certain specialized services, among them a rehabilitation center for war and accident victims. Two other large hospitals in Jerusalem are Bikur Holim, an old hospital in the center of the city, and Sha'are Tzedek, in newly built buildings in the southwestern part of Jerusalem. Sha'are Tzedek is directed by the Orthodox community who coordinate *halacha*, Jewish law, with modern biomedical services, taking into account such problems as the use of electricity and ambulances on the Sabbath (Jewish law bars turning on electricity and driving on the Sabbath), the segregation of males and females on wards, the prohibition of autopsies, and other issues which concern the Orthodox communities in hospital situations.

7 When I was looking over medical files in a Kupat Holim clinic, I found copies of notes from physicians for lab tests, x-rays, EKGs, EEGs, etc., which were given to patients, and the results of these tests. These notes were sometimes transliterations of the English letters into their Hebrew equivalents, such as "EKG" being the Hebrew letters "*a*leph, *k*uf, *g*immel." I often found other notes in three Hebrew letters which I also assumed referred to some sort of medical test. The letters, "*b*eit, *m*em, *p*eh," back transliterated into English, are "B.M.P." I never heard of such a test, and asked an American physician I knew to explain it to me. He was not familiar with this procedure. Then a nurse at the clinic told me what the letters stand for—"*bli mamtzot patologit*"—"without pathological findings."

8 Those who refuse to fill out the form were often elderly women, people who were feeling very ill, people who said they could not read the languages of the questionnaire, and those who feared questionnaires, such as Soviet immigrants who still carry the consciousness of living in a police state, and Hassidim who prefer no affiliation with the state and its social policies.

There were other questionnaires which I am not counting among the 285. These are ones that parents had filled out for their little children or ones that were returned half-completed.

9 The four categories were coded by putting together in different columns all the similar reasons for visiting the doctor according to the patients' complaints. The columns were then combined to create the categories as follows:

Somatic malfunctioning—asthma, high blood pressure, gynecological problems, thyroid trouble, heart problems, hemorrhoids, ulcers, emphezema, follow-up for surgery.

Notes or tests—prescriptions, fertility tests, medical notes (excuses to employers, to the welfare organizations, army, school, etc., regarding inability to perform required roles or asking for specific services), consultations, blood tests, examinations (this is included under the rubric of "notes or tests" because some people received notes from their physicians to come for physicals since they had not seen the doctor in several years).

Chronic pains or troubles—rheumatism, back pains, headaches. chest pains (Iranians' heart complaints), pains in the joints, arm pains, stomach pains, "everything hurts," insomnia, pains in the legs.

Acute self-limiting situations—sore throats, influenza, cold, cough, bronchitis, swelling, bladder infection, pregnancy, "angina" (the term used by Israelis to mean chest cold), fractures.

Chapter Eight

1 For studies by labeling theorists who conceive of labeling as a social phenomenon of individual behavioral rule-breaking and of power differences between the labelers and the labeled, see Szasz (1961), Scheff (1966), and Waxler (1974, 1980). Concerning the ambiguity of psychiatric diagnosis and how labeling signifies differences in doctors' orientations and training, see Beck (1962), Katz et al. (1969), Cohen et al. (1975), Morrison and Flanagan (1978), Gaines (1979).

Other researchers, concerned about problems of labeling and psychiatric diagnosis, examined psychiatric classification through experiments with psychiatrists and mental health personnel. Temerlin (1968) demonstrated, through a mock interview with an actor who was labeled psychotic, that there is a strong tendency for mental health professionals who heard the label to agree with his previously designated mental state regardless of his actual condition. Rosenhan (1973) shows, by having students enter psychiatric hospitals with one symptom which could be indicative of psychosis, that the one symptom influenced the staff at the institutions to label every behavior they displayed as evidence of psychiatric symptomatology in spite of "normal" behavior, indicating that psychiatric diagnosis is selectively perceived by the observers rather than being characteristics exhibited by the observed.

2 Thirty-four is not a large sample of the Iranian population at the clinic. Most were charts of patients recommended to me by the secretaries of the clinic who know what ethnic or immigrant groups patients come from. I chose others by searching through the file cabinets for typical Iranian surnames. Since the process of reading Hebrew handwriting was time-consuming for me, I chose to concentrate on reading only files of Iranians. Basker et al. (1982), however, did an interesting comparison of patients and therapists in a mental health clinic in Israel by checking the charts of patients of different immigrant groups, testing for symptomatology, diagnosis, labeling, and supplemental comments by the therapists.

3 Because of the possible confusion of these two terms—"nervousness" or "anger"—by Iranians within the one Hebrew word *atzbani*, I lump the two together. The patients rarely mention the Hebrew word for anger, *ko'es*. The charts and my interviews both contain the Hebrew word *atzbani* (nervous) which is of the same semitic root as the Persian-Arabic word for angry, *asabāni*. Therefore, the context of the situation determines whether the speaker means "nervous" or "angry". I assume, however, that since anger is disapproved of in Persian culture, that the patients refer to anger.

4 According to *DSM-II* and *DSM-III*, there are different types of depression. Notable is major depressive disorder with vegetative symptoms such as sleep disturbances, appetite change, and motor retardation. The physical symptoms could exist with or without dysphoric mood. This varies from certain forms of "reactive depression" or "depressive neurosis" (*DSM-II* terms) or "dysthymic disorder" (*DSM-III* term). These categories of depression designate a more temporary affective disorder due to a reaction to an event, specific problem in life, thought, internal conflict, etc. Individuals experiencing such depression exhibit dysphoria and some of the vegetative symptoms. In addition to the above disorders, there is the affect depression, a depressed mood unaccompanied by the physiological symptoms, which arises as a reaction to a stressor.

This is not intended to be a debate and exposé of the problems of analyzing depression or the philosophy of depression cross-culturally. Many scholars and psychiatrists have written and debated this issue. See Akiskal and McKinney (1975); Bebbington (1978); Binitie (1975); Brown and Harris (1978); Katon et al. (1982); Marsella (1980); Mezzich and Raab (1980); Sethi et al. (1973); Waziri (1973); Weissman and Klerman (1977).

What is of concern here is not the argument that depression varies cross-culturally, as many realize it does, but that certain symptoms are recognized as depression among Iranians by Israeli psychiatric staff, whereas other symptoms are classified as different types of psychiatric disorders.

5 Another label given to patients of a certain ethnic group in Israel by the psychiatric clinicians is "Mea Shearim Disease." This refers to a Jerusalem neighborhood called Mea Shearim, which is inhabited by an ultra-Orthodox anti-Zionist sect called Naturei Karta. The so-called disease is a type of catatonia exhibited by adolescent males who are brought into the clinics by members of the family or religious establishment. It is believed that they are seen and treated by rabbis until they become psychotic and the rabbis can no longer do anything for them. The clinicians consider this catatonic syndrome as resulting from sexual segregation in the ultra-Orthodox communities: the boys studying at yeshivas learn about such sins as masturbation; supposedly they enter the catatonic state so as to refrain from masturbating, which they did before becoming psychotic.

6 Depression as a psychobiological disease seems to be a valid cross-cultural psychiatric category when people express the vegetative symptoms associated with major depressive disorder, whereas the illness depression or style of dysphoria varies from culture to culture: other kinds of symptomatology, both physical and psychosocial, might be exhibited in culturally specific ways, as among Iranians. This is the problem of categorization and understanding that Israeli therapists have with Iranian patients. At the time of my research, *DSM-III*, with its refined definitions of depression, was not in existence. The clinicians did not differentiate symptomatology into different types of depression, as is done now with major depressive disorder, cyclothymic disorder, dysthymic disorder, etc. Rather, they used categories such as "slight depression," "post-traumatic depression," or "severe depression." See the previous section.

7 See Good et al. (1985) for an analysis of Iranians' discourse on depression. Although our data base differ, the discourse of Iranians in California about nārāhati is quite similar to that of Iranians in Israel. Because the Goods' sample were more Westernized and more "at home" in a psychological idiom, they readily spoke about their psychosocial problems and, the Goods write, they did not somatize. Those Iranians with whom I worked in Jerusalem *did* somatize their dysphoric affects and came to the mental health clinic, not

really by their own choosing, but by the recommendation of primary care physicians who were unable to help them. The Iranians in California spoke of their depression—or nārāhati—in a cluster of terms connoting sadness, sensitivity, mistrust, and anger. The Iranians in Jerusalem focused mostly on anger, which they could not control and which was distressing them. Some spoke of sensitivity regarding others in social relations. Few spoke about sadness, and only one of my sample indicated mistrust of others. However, unlike the Iranians in California, those in Jerusalem reported psychosocial problems primarily when prompted to do so by the therapists.

8 See Weissman and Klerman (1977) and Brown and Harris (1978) for studies about depression among women resulting from their social structural position.

9 This comment makes me wonder what the therapist would say about the average American who finishes high school, and often college, without having studied a foreign language.

10 Homa was the first and only person I heard referring to penicillin as cold medicine.

Chapter Nine

1 The kinds of Personality Disorders distinguished in *DSM II* in 1968 were the following: paranoid; cyclothymic; schizoid; explosive; obsessive compulsive; hysterical; asthenic; antisocial; passive-aggressive; inadequate. These disorders evolved into other discrete entities by 1980 in *DSM III:* paranoid; schizoid; shizotypal; histrionic; narcissistic; antisocial; borderline; avoidant; dependent; compulsive; passive-aggressive; atypical; mixed; other.

2 See Benedict (1934); Hallowell (1955); Wallace (1961); Lindholm (1982); Reisman (1983).

Glossary

Although many of the Persian words are derived from Arabic, for the sake of simplicity, the words will be differentiated here according to their usage in the Persian (P.) or Hebrew (H.) language.

āberu (P.) honor, respectability
āblimu (P.) sour lemonade
afsordegi (P.) depression
āghā (P.) gentleman, sir, mister, sometimes used for "father" or "husband"
ahl al-kitāb (P.) people of the book (Jews, Christians, Zoroastrians)
ākhund (P.) clergyman; theologian
aliya (H.) immigration to Israel; lit., "ascent" (pl., *aliyot*)
anderun (P.) inner quarters of a house; women's quarters
asab (P.) nerve (pl., *asāb*)
asabāni (P.) angry
asabāniyat (P.) anger
atzabim (H.) nerves
atzbani (H.) nervous
atzbanut (H.) nervousness
bābā (P.) father (colloquial)
bād (P.) wind
bād-i mafāsal (P.) wind of the joint; rheumatism
bast (P.) sanctuary
bātin (P.) interior; conscience
bāzaari (P.) bazaar merchant
beit meshuga'im (H.) crazy house
birun (P.) outside; the outer public area of a house; men's quarters
chādor (P.) lit., tent; veil covering a woman's body to insure modesty
cheshm-i bad (P.) evil eye
darkon (H.) passport
darvish (P.) person who prefers life of poverty and spirituality to the complexities of social life; the rejecting outsider, in the context of *safā-yi bātin*
dayenu (H.) it would have been enough
dhimmi (P., A.) protected people, living in an Islamic state
dikaon (H.) depression
edot (H.) ethnic groups (sing., *edah*)
edot ha-mizrach (H.) Eastern ethnic groups; Oriental Jews

ehterām (P.) respect
esfand (P.) wild rue
gham (P.) sorrow, grief, sadness
ghamgin (P.) sad
ghamgini (P.) sadness; sorrow
ghoseh (P.) sorrow, grief
ghoseh khordan (P.) lit., eat sorrow; to grieve
gol-i gāv zabān (P.) foxglove
hagirah (H.) immigration to countries other than Israel
hakham (H.) wise man (pl., *hakhamim*)
halutzim (H.) pioneers
hamām (P.) bath
hassās (P.) sensitive
hassāsiyat (P.) sensitivity
hayāt (P.) courtyard
heyf-eh (P.) It's a pity
hoz (P.) pond, basin, fountain
jedid al-Islam (P.) new Muslims; term used to connote Mashhadi Jewish community
jegar (P.) liver
Jegaram misuzad (P.) My liver burns
jeziyeh (P.) capitation tax
jinn (P.) supernatural spirit
kam khuni (P.) blood deficiency
kappara (H.) atonement, forgiveness, pardon, expiation
ketābi (P.) literary language
ketubot (H.) marriage contracts (sing., *ketuba*)
khākshir (P.) London rocket-seeds
khānum (P.) lady, wife
khevreh (H.) group of friends
khoresh (P.) a sauce of meat (or fish) and vegetables or fruit
khun (P.) blood
khutzpah (H.) audacity, impudence
kibbutz (H.) collective farm (pl., *kibbutzim*)
kiddush (H.) the blessing over wine
luti (P.) one who is extravagant materially and also forgiving of others; colloquially, thug; in the context of *safā-yi bātin*, a totally accepting insider
madrasseh (P.) school (used to refer to the Islamic religious school system)
mahalleh (P.) neighborhood, ghetto
makolet (H.) small, usually corner, grocery store
margiz (H.) angers, provokes (third person singular, present tense)
mārpich (P.) spiral; lit., "snake twisting"
mazal tov (H.) congratulations; lit., good luck
mentaliyut (H.) mentality
mezāj (P.) temperament, condition of health, physical constitution

metapelet (H). woman who has private daycare in her home
mezuzah (H.) talisman posted on the doorpost of a religious Jew's house; (pl., *mezuzot*)
milium (H.) annual army reserve duty
minhag (H.) custom (pl., *minhagim*)
mobārak (P.) congratulations
moshav (P.) collective settlement of individually or family-owned farms (pl., *moshavim*)
muezzin (P.) Muslim man who calls people to prayer
mujtahid (P.) clergyman who practices religious law
mulla (P.) clergyman versed in religious law and theology
nabāt (P.) crystallized sugar, rock candy
najes (P.) ritually unclean or impure
nārāhat (P.) uncomfortable, ill-at-ease, upset, worried
nārāhati (P.) an undifferentiated unpleasant emotional or physical feeling
nārāhati-ye asab (P.) nerve distress
nedunya (H.) dowry
nida (H.) Jewish religious injunction regarding menstrual blood and impurity
parnasa (H.) maintenance, support, livelihood
pārti-bāzi (P.) system of patronage or favor-granting, influence
por-rou'i (P.) brash, audacious
primitivim (H.) primitive people
primitiviyut (H.) primitivity
protectzia (H.) system of patronage, favor-granting, influence
psychi (H.) crazy, "nuts"
rāhat (P.) comfortable
sabra (H.) native-born Israeli
safā-yi bātin (P.) inner purity or goodness
sāl (P.) year, often used as name for ritual commemorating anniversary of someone's death
sayyid (P.) one who is a descendant of Mohammad
shomā (P.) you, formal and/or plural
shu'ubiyya (P.) a Persian literary movement of the ninth and tenth centuries
ta'ārof (P.) ritual courtesy, politeness code
tabi'at (P.) nature, temperament
taqiyya (P.) dissimulation
ulama (P.) clergy
ulpan (H.) intensive language class (pl., *ulpanim*)
vatikim (H.) veteran citizens
yishuv (H.) Israel's pre-state social and political organization
za'ef (P.) weakness
zāher (P.) apparent, outward, on the surface, external
za'if (P.) weak, powerless
zerang (P.) clever
zerangi (P.) cleverness

Bibliography

Abu-Lughod, Lila. 1987. *Veiled Sentiments: Honor and Poetry in a Bedouin Society*. Berkeley: University of California Press.

Adler, Elkan Nathan. 1897. *Jews in Many Lands*. Philadelphia: The Jewish Publication Society of America.

Ajami, Ismail. 1976. Land Reform and Modernization of the Farming Structure in Iran. In *The Social Sciences and Problems of Development*. Khodadad Farmanfarmaian, ed. Princeton: Princeton University Press.

Akiskal, Hagop S., and William T. McKinney, Jr. 1975. Overview of Recent Research in Depression. *Archives of General Psychiatry* 32:285–305.

Algar, Hamid. 1969. *Religion and State in Iran, 1785–1906: The Role of the Ulama in the Qajar Period*. Berkeley: University of California Press.

Al-Suyuti. 1962. *Tibb-ul-Nabbi*. C. Elgood, ed. *Osiris* 13:33–192.

American Psychiatric Association. 1968. *Diagnostic and Statistical Manual of Mental Disorders*. (*DSM-II*).

———. 1980. *Diagnostic and Statistical Manual of Mental Disorders*. (*DSM-III*).

Antonovsky, Aaron. 1972. A Model to Explain Visits to the Doctor: With Specific Reference to the Case of Israel. *Journal of Health and Social Behavior* 13:446–54.

———. 1979. *Health, Stress, and Coping*. San Francisco: Jossey-Bass.

Avruch, Keven. 1981. *American Immigrants in Israel*. Chicago: University of Chicago Press.

Banuazizi, Ali. 1977. Iranian "National Character": A Critique of Some Western Perspectives. In *Psychological Dimensions of Near Eastern Studies*. L. C. Brown and N. Itzkowitz, eds. Pp. 210–39. Princeton: The Darwin Press.

Bar-Yosef, R. 1966. Social Absorption of Immigrants in Israel. In *Migration, Mental Health and Community Services*. H. P. David, ed. Pp. 55–70. Geneva: American Joint Distribution Committee.

Barsky, Arthur. 1979. Patients Who Amplify Bodily Sensations. *Annals of Internal Medicine* 91:63–70.

Barsky, Arthur, and Gerald L. Klerman. 1983. Overview: Hypochondriasis, Bodily Complaints, and Somatic Styles. *American Journal of Psychiatry* 140(3):273–83.

Barth, Fredrik. 1969. *Ethnic Groups and Boundaries*. Boston: Little Brown.

Basker, Eileen, Barbara Beran, and Morris Kleinhauz. 1982. A Social Science Perspective on the Negotiation of a Psychiatric Diagnosis. *Social Psychiatry* 17:53–58.

Bassan, I. 1903. Israélites de Perse. *Bulletin de l'Alliance Israélite Universelle*. Pp. 129–40.

Bassett, James. 1887. *Persia: The Land of the Imams*. London: Blackie & Sons.

Bateson, Mary Catherine. 1979. "This Figure of Tinsel": A Study of Themes of Hypocrisy and Pessimism in Iranian Culture. *Daedalus* 108(3):125–34.

Bateson, M. C., J. W. Clinton, J. B. M. Kassarjian, H. Safavi, and M. Soraya. 1977. *Safā-yi Bātin*. A Study of the Interrelations of a Set of Iranian Ideal Character Types. In *Psychological Dimensions of Near Eastern Studies*. L. C. Brown and N. Itzkowitz, eds. Pp. 257–74. Princeton: The Darwin Press.

Bazzoui, Widad. 1970. Affective Disorders in Iraq. *British Journal of Psychiatry* 117:195–203.

Bebbington, Paul E. 1978. The Epidemiology of Depressive Disorder. *Culture, Medicine, and Psychiatry* 2:297–341.

Beck, A. T. 1962. Reliability of Psychiatric Diagnoses: A Critique of Systematic Studies. *American Journal of Psychiatry* 119:210–16.

______. 1967. *Depression: Clinical, Experimental and Theoretical Aspects*. New York: Harper and Row.

______. 1976. *Cognitive Therapy and Emotional Disorders*. New York: International Universities Press.

Beeman, William O. 1976a. Status, Style and Strategy in Iranian Interaction. *Anthropological Linguistics* 18:305–22.

______. 1976b. What is (IRANIAN) National Character? A Sociolinguistic Approach. *Iranian Studies* 9:22–48.

______. 1977. The Hows and Whys of Persian Style: A Pragmatic Approach. In *Studies in Language Variation*. Ralph W. Fasold and Roger W. Shuy, eds. Pp. 269–282. Washington, D.C.: Georgetown University Press.

Beiser, Morton. 1982. Migration in a Developing Country. In *Uprooting and Surviving*. Richard C. Nann, ed. Pp. 119–146. Dordrecht: D. Reidel.

Ben-David, J. 1958. The Professional Role of the Physician in Bureaucratized Medicine: A Study in Role Conflict. *Human Relations* 11:255–74.

Ben-Sira, Z., U. Aviram, I. Stern, and I. Shoham. 1978. A Facet Theoretical Approach to Psychosomatic Complaints. *Israel Annals of Psychiatry* 16:219–31.

Benedict, Ruth. 1934. *Patterns of Culture*. Boston: Houghton Mifflin.

Benjamin, J. J., II. 1859. *Eight Years in Asia and Africa: From 1846–1855*. Hanover: Published by the Author.

Benjamin of Tudela. 1929. Travels of Rabbi Benjamin of Tudela. In *Contemporaries of Marco Polo*. Manuel Komroff, ed. Pp. 252–322. London: Jonathan Cape.

Bilu, Yoram. 1979. Demonic Explanations of Disease among Moroccan Jews in Israel. *Culture, Medicine, and Psychiatry* 3:363–80.

Binitie, Ayo. 1975. A Factor-Analytical Study of Depression across Cultures (African and European). *British Journal of Psychiatry* 127:559–63.

Binning, Robert B. M., Exq. 1857. *A Journal of Two Years' Travel in Persia, Ceylon, Etc*. London: Wm. H. Allen.

Bishop, Mrs. Isabelle. 1891. *Journeys in Persia and Kurdistan*. London: John Murray.

Boyce, Mary. 1968. The Pious Foundations of the Zoroastrians. *BSOAS* 31:270–89.

______. 1975. *A History of Zoroastrianism*. Leiden: E. J. Brill.

Brown, Richard H. 1980. Identity, Politics and Planning: On Some Uses of Knowledge in Coping with Social Change. In *Uprooting and Development*. George V. Coelho and Paul I. Ahmed, eds. Pp. 41–66. New York: Plenum.

Brown, G., and T. Harris. 1978. *The Social Origins of Depression*. New York: The Free Press.

Browne, Edward G. 1893. *A Year amongst the Persians*. London: Adam and Charles Black.

Bulletin de l'Alliance Israélite. 1862. Israélites de Perse.

———. 1892. Israélites de Perse.

———. 1907. Israélites de Perse.

Central Bureau of Statistics. 1982. *Statistical Abstract of Israel*. Jerusalem.

Coelho, George, and Paul I. Ahmed. 1980. *Uprooting and Development*. New York: Plenum.

Cohen, Abner. 1969. *Custom and Politics in Urban Africa*. Berkeley: University of California Press.

———. 1974. *Urban Ethnicity*. London: Tavistock.

Cohen, E., H. Harbin, and M. Wright. 1975. Some Considerations in the Formulation of Psychiatric Diagnosis. *Journal of Nervous and Mental Disease* 160:422–27.

Cohen, Erik. 1983. Ethnicity and Legitimation in Contemporary Israel. *The Jerusalem Quarterly* (28) summer: 111–24.

Confino, A. 1903. Israélites de Perse. *Bulletin de l'Alliance Israélite Universelle*. Pp. 115–28.

Crapanzano, Vincent. 1973. *The Hamadsha*. Berkeley: University of California Press.

———. 1980. *Tuhami: Portrait of a Moroccan*. Chicago: University of Chicago Press.

Currier, Richard L. 1966. The Hot-Cold Syndrome and Symbolic Balance in Mexican and Spanish-American Folk Medicine. *Ethnology* 5:251–63.

Darwin, Charles. 1872. *The Expression of the Emotions in Man and Animals*. London: John Murray.

Deshen, Shlomo. 1970. *Immigrant Voters in Israel: Parties and Congregations in a Local Election Campaign*. Manchester: Manchester University Press.

Deshen, Shlomo, and Moshe Shokeid. 1974. *The Predicament of Homecoming*. Ithaca: Cornell University Press.

DeVos, George. 1975. Ethnic Pluralism: Conflict and Accommodation. In *Ethnic Identity: Cultural Continuities and Change*. G. DeVos and L. Romanucci-Ross, eds. Pp. 5–41. Palo Alto: Mayfield.

Donaldson, Bess A. 1938. *The Wild Rue*. London: Luzac.

Eaton, W. W., Lasry, J.-C., and Sigal, J. 1979. Ethnic Relations and Community Mental Health among Israeli Jews. *Israel Annals of Psychiatry and Related Disciplines* 17:165–74.

Eickelman, Dale F. 1976. *Moroccan Islam: Tradition and Society in a Pilgrimage Center*. Austin: University of Texas Press.

Eisenstadt, Shmuel N. 1954. *The Absorption of Immigrants*. London: Routledge and Kegan Paul.

———. 1967. Israeli Identity: Problems in the Development of the Collective Identity of an Ideological Society. *The Annals of the American Academy of Political and Social Science* 370:116–23.

Ekman, P. 1973. *Darwin and Facial Expression*. New York: Academic Press.

Ekman, P., W. V. Friesen, and P. Ellsworth. 1972. *Emotion in the Human Face*. New York: Pergamon.

El-Islam, M. Fakhr. 1974. Culture-bound Neurosis in Qatari Women. *Transcultural Psychiatric Research Review* 11:167–68.

Esfandiary, Fereydoun. 1959. *The Day of Sacrifice*. New York: McDowell, Obolensky.

Fernandez-Marina, R. 1961. The Puerto Rican Syndrome: Its Dynamics and Cultural Determinants. *Psychiatry* 24:79–82.

Fischel, Walter J. 1944. The Jews of Kurdistan a Hundred Years Ago. *Jewish Social Studies* 6:195–226.

______. 1949. Israel in Iran. In *The Jews: Their History, Culture, and Religion*. Lous Finkelstein, ed. Philadelphia: The Jewish Publication Society of America.

Fischer, Michael M. J. 1973. Zoroastrian Iran between Myth and Practice. Ph.D. diss., Univerisity of Chicago, Department of Anthropology.

______. 1980. *Iran: From Religious Dispute to Revolution*, Cambridge, MA: Harvard University Press.

Fowler, George, Esq. 1841. *Three Years in Persia*. Vol. I. London: Henry Colburn.

Frye, Richard N. 1963. *The Heritage of Persia*. Cleveland: The World Publishing Co.

Gaines, Atwood D. 1979. Definitions and Diagnoses: Cultural Implications of Psychiatric Help-Seeking and Psychiatrists' Definitions of the Situation in Psychiatric Emergencies. *Culture, Medicine, and Psychiatry* 3:381–418.

Geertz, Clifford. 1973. *The Interpretation of Cultures*. New York: Basic.

______. 1979. Suq: The Bazaar Economy in Sefrou. In *Meaning and Order in Moroccan Society: Three Essays in Cultural Analysis*. Clifford Geertz, Hildred Geertz, and Lawrence Rosen, eds. New York: Cambridge University Press.

______. 1983. *Local Knowledge*. New York: Basic.

General Federation of Jewish Labour in Palestine. 1948. The Palestine Workers Health Insurance: Kupat Holim. Tel Aviv. Pamphlet.

Ghirshman, R. 1978. *Iran: From the Earliest Times to the Islamic Conquest*. London: Penguin.

Gilsenan, Michael. 1976. Lying, Honor, and Contradiction. In *Transaction and Meaning*. Bruce Kapferer, ed. Pp. 191–219. Philadelphia: Institute for the Study of Human Issues.

Goldberg, Harvey. 1972. *Cave Dwellers and Citrus Growers: A Jewish Community in Libya and Israel*. Cambridge: Cambridge University Press.

Good, Byron. 1976. The Heart of What's the Matter: The Structure of Medical Discourse in a Provincial Iranian Town. Ph.D. Diss., University of Chicago, Department of Anthropology.

______. 1977. The Heart of What's the Matter: The Semantics of Illness in Iran. *Culture, Medicine, and Psychiatry* 1:25–58.

Good, Byron J., and Mary-Jo DelVecchio Good. 1981a. The Meaning of Symptoms: A

Cultural Hermeneutic Model for Clinical Practice. In *The Relevance of Social Science for Medicine*. Leon Eisenberg and Arthur Kleinman, eds. Pp. 165–96. Dordrecht: D. Reidel.

———. 1981b. The Semantics of Medical Discourse. In *Science and Cultures*. Everett Mendelsohn and Yehuda Elkana, eds. Pp. 177–212. Dordrecht: D. Reidel.

———. 1982. Toward a Meaning-Centered Analysis of Popular Illness Categories: "Fright-Illness" and "Heart-Distress" in Iran. In *Cultural Conceptions of Mental Health and Therapy*. Anthony J. Marsella and Geoffrey M. White, eds. pp. 141–66. Dordrecht: D. Reidel.

Good, Byron J., Mary-Jo DelVecchio Good, and Robert Morado. 1985. The Interpretation of Dysphoria and Depressive Illness in Iranian Culture. In *Culture and Depression*. Arthur Kleinman and Bryon Good, eds. Berkeley: University of California Press.

Good, Byron, Henry Herrera, Mary-Jo DelVecchio Good, and James Cooper. 1982. Reflexivity and Countertransference in a Psychiatric Cultural Consultation Clinic. *Culture, Medicine, and Psychiatry* 6:281–303.

Good, Mary-Jo DelVecchio. 1980. Of Blood and Babies: The Relationship of Popular Islamic Physiology to Fertility. *Social Science and Medicine* 14B:147–56.

Gordon, Cyrus. 1977. The Substratum of Taquiyyah in Iran. *Journal of the American Oriental Society* 97:192.

Grewel, F. 1967. Psychiatric Differences in Ashkenazim and Sephardim. *Psychiatria, Neurologia, Neurochirurgia* 70:339–47.

Gruner, O. Cameron, ed. 1930. *A Treatise on the Canon of Medicine of Avicenna*. London: Luzac.

Grushka, Th. 1968. *Health Services in Israel*. Jerusalem: The Ministry of Health.

Gulick, John. 1976. The Ethos of Insecurity in Middle Eastern Culture. In *Responses to Change: Society, Culture, and Personality*. G. DeVos, ed. Pp. 137–56. New York: D. Van Nostrand.

Gulliver, Philip H. 1969. Dispute Settlement without Courts: The Nedendeuli of Southern Tanzania. In *Law in Culture and Society*. L. Nader, ed. Pp. 24–68. Chicago: Aldine.

Hadassah Medical Organization. 1965–1980. *Statistical Report*. Jerusalem.

Haim, S. 1958. *The Shorter Persian-English Dictionary*. Tehran: Y. Beroukhim and Sons.

Halevi, H. S. 1963. Frequency of Mental Illness among Jews in Israel. *International Journal of Social Psychiatry* 9:268–82.

Hallowell, A. Irving. 1955. *Culture and Experience*. Philadelphia: University of Pennsylvania Press.

Handelman, Don. 1976. Bureaucratic Transactions: The Development of Official-Client Relationships in Israel. In *Transaction and Meaning*. Bruce Kapferer, ed. Pp. 223–75. Philadelphia: Institute for the Study of Human Issues.

Harwood, Alan. 1971. The Hot-Cold Theory of Disease. *Journal of the American Medical Association* 216:1153–58.

———. 1977. Puerto Rican Spiritualism. *Culture, Medicine, and Psychiatry* 1:69–95.

Hazelton, Lesley. 1977. *Israeli Women: The Reality behind the Myth*. New York: Simon and Schuster.

Hedayat, Sadeq. 1979 (1945). *Haji Agha*. Translation by G. M. Wickens. Austin: Center for Middle Eastern Studies.

Heelas, Paul. 1981. The Model Applied: Anthropology and Indigenous Psychologies. In *Indigenous Psychologies*. P. Heelas and A. Lock, eds. Pp. 39–63. London: Academic Press.

Heelas, Paul, and Andrew Lock, eds. 1981. *Indigenous Psychologies*. London: Academic Press.

Heller, Celia S. 1975. Ethnic Differentiation among the Jews of Israel. In *Migration and Development: Implications for Ethnic Identity and Political Conflict*. Pp. 97–111. The Hague: Mouton.

Hertz, Dan G. 1982. Psychosomatic and Psychosocial Implications of Environmental Changes on Migrants. *Israel Journal of Psychiatry and Related Sciences* 19:329–38.

Hes, J. 1958. Hypochondriasis in Oriental Jewish Immigrants. *The International Journal of Social Psychiatry* 4:18–24.

Hillel, David Ben. 1972. *Unknown Jews in Unknown Lands*. Walter Fischel, ed. New York: Ktav.

Hollingshead, A., and F. Redlich. 1958. *Social Class and Mental Illness: A Community Study*. New York: Wiley.

Holmes, T. H., and R. H. Rahe. 1967. The Social Readjustment Rating Scale. *Journal of Psychosomatic Research* 11:213–18.

Honig-Parness, Tikvah. 1982. The Effects of Latent Social Needs on Physician Utilization by Immigrants: A Replication Study. *Social Science and Medicine* 16:505–14.

Horowitz, Donald L. 1975. Ethnic Identity. In *Ethnicity: Theory and Experience*. N. Glazer and D. P. Moynihan, eds. Pp. 111–40. Cambridge, MA: Harvard University Press.

Howell, Signe. 1981. Rules not Words. In *Indigenous Psychologies*. P. Heelas and A. Lock, eds. Pp. 133–43. London: Academic Press.

Ibn Sina. 1930. *A Treatise on the Canon of Medicine of Avicenna*. O. Cameron Gruner, ed. London: Luzac.

Israel Histradut Campaign. 1948. Kupat Holim: Israel's Leading Medical System. Pamphlet.

Izard, Carroll E. 1971. *The Face of Emotion*. New York: Appleton-Century-Crofts.

______. 1980. Cross-Cultural Perspectives on Emotion and Emotion Communication. In *Handbook of Cross-Cultural Psychology*. Vol. 3: Basic Processes. Harry C. Triandis and Walter Lonner, eds. pp. 185–221. Boston: Allyn and Bacon.

Janzen, John M. 1978. *The Quest for Therapy: Medical Pluralism in Lower Zaire*. Berkeley: University of California Press.

Jerusalem Post, The. 1956. Forget Your Origin, B-G Tells Settlers. March 26.

Kanievsky, I. 1947. Methods of Medical Care: In *The Social Health Insurance System of Palestine Workers*. Tel Aviv: General Federation of Jewish Labour in Eretz-Israel (Palestine). Pamphlet.

Kantor, M. B., ed. 1965. *Mobility and Mental Health*. Springfield: C. C. Thomas.

Katon, Wayne, Arthur Kleinman, and Gary Rosen. 1982. Depression and Somatization. *American Journal of Medicine* 72:127–35; 72:241–47.

Katz, Martin M., Jonathan O. Cole, and Henry A. Lowry. 1969. Studies of the Diagnostic Process: The Influence of Symptom Perception, Past Experience and Ethnic Background on Diagnostic Decisions. *American Journal of Psychiatry* 125:937–47.

Kay, M. 1972. Health and Illness in a Mexican American Barrio. In *Ethnic Medicine in the Southwest*. Tucson: University of Arizona Press.

Keddie, Nikki. 1966. *Religion and Rebellion in Iran: The Tobacco Protest of 1891–92*. London: Frank Cass.

Keyes, Charles. 1979. *Ethnic Adaptation and Identity: The Karen on the Thai Frontier with Burma*. Philadelphia: Institute for the Study of Human Issue.

Kleinman, Arthur. 1977. Depression, Somatization and the New Cross-Cultural Psychiatry. *Social Science and Medicine* 11:3–10.

______. 1978. Concepts and A Model for the Comparison of Medical Systems as Cultural Systems. *Social Science and Medicine* 12:85–93.

______. 1980. *Patients and Healers in the Context of Culture*. Berkeley: University of California Press.

______. 1982. Neurasthenia and Depression: A Study of Somatization and Culture in China. *Culture, Medicine, and Psychiatry* 6:117–89.

______. 1983. The Ethnography and Cross-Cultural Comparison of Chronic Somatization. Unpublished NSF Grant Proposal.

Kleinman, Arthur, Leon Eisenberg, and Byron Good. 1978. Culture, Illness, and Care: Clinical Lessons from Anthropological and Cross-Cultural Research. *Annals of Internal Medicine* 88:251–58.

Kleinman, Arthur, and Joan Kleinman. 1985. The Interconnections among Culture, Depressive Experiences, and the Meanings of Pain. In *Culture and Depression*. Arthur Kleinman and Byron Good, eds. Berkeley: University of California Press.

Kushner, Gilbert. 1973. *Immigrants from India in Israel: Planned Change in an Administered Community*. Tucson: University of Arizona Press.

Lakoff, George, and Mark Johnson. 1980. *Metaphors We Live By*. Chicago: University of Chicago Press.

Lee, Richard B. 1978 (1967). Trance Cure of the Kung Bushmen. In *Health and the Human Condition*. Michael Logan and Edward Hunt, Jr., eds. Pp. 195–202. North Scituate, MA: Duxbury Press.

Leff, J. P. 1973. Culture and the Differentiation of Emotional States. *British Journal of Psychiatry* 123:299–306.

______. 1981. *Psychiatry around the Globe: A Transcultural View*. New York: Marcel Dekker.

Lerner, Jacov, and Pinchas Noy. 1968. Somatic Complaints in Psychiatric Disorders: Social and Cultural Factors. *International Journal of Social Psychiatry* 14:145–50.

Lévi-Strauss, Claude. 1967. The Effectiveness of Symbols. In *Structural Anthropology*. Pp. 181–201. Garden City, New York: Anchor.

Levy, Robert I. 1973. *Tahitians: Mind and Experience in the Society Islands*. Chicago: University of Chicago Press.

Lewis, Arnold. 1979. *Power, Poverty, and Education*. Ramat Gan: Turtledove.

Lieban, Richard W. 1981. Urban Philippine Healers and Their Contrasting Clienteles. *Culture, Medicine, and Psychiatry* 5:217–31.

Liebman, Charles S., and Eliezer Don-Yehiya. 1982. Israel's Civil Religion. *The Jerusalem Quarterly*. Spring(23):57–69.

Lindholm, Charles. 1982. *Generosity and Jealousy*. New York: Columbia University Press.

Loeb, Laurence D. 1977. *Outcaste: Jewish Life in Southern Iran*. New York: Gordon and Breach.

Lorey, Eustache, and Douglas Sladen. 1907. *Queer Things about Persia*. London: Eveleigh Nash.

Lutz, Catherine Anne. 1980. Emotion Words and Emotional Development on Ifaluk Atoll. Ph.D. diss., Harvard University.

———. 1985. Depression and the Translation of Emotional Worlds. In *Culture and Depression*. Arthur Kleinman and Byron Good, eds. Berkeley: University of California Press.

Maoz, B., S. Levy, N. Brand, and H. S. Halevi. 1966. An Epidemiological Survey of Mental Disorders in a Community of Newcomers to Israel. *Journal of the College of General Practitioners* 11:267–84.

Marris, P. 1980. The Uprooting of Meaning. In *Uprooting and Development*. G. V. Coelho and P. Ahmed, eds. New York: Plenum.

Marsella, Anthony J. 1980. Depressive Experience and Disorder across Cultures. In *Handbook of Cross-Cultural Psychology*. Vol. 6: Psychopathology. Harry C. Triandis and Juris G. Draguns, eds. Pp. 237–89. Boston: Allyn and Bacon.

Marsella, Anthony J., David Kinzie, and Paul Gordon. 1973. Ethnic Variations in the Expression of Depression. *Journal of Cross-Cultural Psychology* 4:435–58.

Matras, Judah. 1965. *Social Change in Israel*. Chicago: Aldine.

Mead, Margaret. 1935. *Sex and Temperament*. New York: Morrow.

Mechanic, David. 1972. Social Psychologic Factors Affecting the Presentation of Bodily Complaints. *New England Journal of Medicine* 286:1132–39.

———. 1980. The Experience and Reporting of Common Physical Complaints. *Journal of Health and Social Behavior* 21:146–55.

Mehlman, R. 1961. The Puerto Rican Syndrome. *American Journal of Psychiatry* 118:328.

Mezzich, Joan E., and Ernst S. Raab. 1980. Depressive Symptomatology across the Americas. *Archives of General Psychiatry* 37:818–23.

Miller, Louis. 1964. Community Psychiatry in Israel. *Israel Annals of Psychiatry* 2:41–46.

———. 1977. Community Intervention and the Historical Background of Community Mental Health in Israel. *Israel Annals of Psychiatry and Related Disciplines* 15:300–309.

Minuchin, S., B. L. Rosman, and L. Baker. 1978. *Psychosomatic Families: Anorexia Nervosa in Context*. Cambridge, MA: Harvard University Press.

Minuchin-Itzigsohn, S. D., R. Ben-Shaoul, A. Weingrod, and D. Krasilowsky. 1984. The Effect of Cultural Conceptions on Therapy: A Comparative Study of Patients in Israeli Psychiatric Clinics. *Culture, Medicine, and Psychiatry* 8: 229–54.

Moore, Sally Falk. 1975. Epilogue. In *Symbol and Politics in Communal Ideology*. Sally Falk Moore and Barbara G. Myerhoff, eds. Pp. 210–39. Ithaca: Cornell University Press.

Moreen, Vera B. 1981. The Status of Religious Minorities in Safavid Iran 1617–61. *Journal of Near Eastern Studies* 40:119–34.

Morrison, James, and Thomas Flanagan. 1978. Diagnostic Errors in Psychiatry. *Comprehensive Psychiatry* 19:109–17.

Myers, F. 1979. Emotions and the Self. *Ethos* 7:343–70.

Nann, Richard C., ed. 1972. *Uprooting and Surviving*. Dordrecht: D. Reidel.

Nasr, Seyyed Hossein. 1968. *Science and Civilization in Islam*. Cambridge, MA: Harvard University Press.

Needham, Rodney. 1981. Inner States as Universals: Sceptical Reflections on Human Nature. In *Indigenous Psychologies*. P. Heelas and A. Lock, eds. Pp. 65–78. London: Academic Press.

Netzer, Amnon. 1974. Some Notes on the Characterization of Cyrus the Great in Jewish and Judeo-Persian Writings. In *Commemoration Cyrus, Hommage Universal*. Vol. 2. Acta Iranica 2. Pp. 35–52. Leiden: E. J. Brill.

———. 1979. The Zionist Movement in Iran: From the Balfour Declaration to the San Remo Agreement. *Pe'amim* 1:23–31 (in Hebrew).

———. 1980. Diaspora Zionism: Achievements and Problems: Iran. In *Zionism in Transition*. Moshe Davis, ed. Pp. 225–32. New York: Arno.

Nichter, Mark. 1981a. Negotiation of the Illness Experience: Ayurvedic Therapy and the Psychosocial Dimension of Illness. *Culture, Medicine, and Psychiatry* 5:5–24.

———. 1981b. Idioms of Distress: Alternatives in the Expression of Psychosocial Distress: A Case Study from South India. *Culture, Medicine and Psychiatry* 5: 379–408.

Obeyesekere, Gananath. 1977. The Theory and Practice of Psychological Medicine in the Ayurvedic Tradition. *Culture, Medicine, and Psychiatry* 1:155–81.

———. 1895. Depression, Buddhism, and the Work of Culture in Sri Lanka. In *Depression and Culture*. Arthur Kleinman and Byron Good, eds. Berkeley: University of California Press.

"Omar, Covenant of." 1972. *Encyclopaedia Judaica* 12:1379. Jerusalem: Keter.

"Onanism." 1972. *Encyclopaedia Judaica* 12:1396. Jerusalem: Keter.

Opler, M. E. 1963. The Cultural Definition of Illness in Village India. *Human Organization* 22:32–35.

Oz, Amos. 1983. *In the Land of Israel*. New York: Harcourt Brace.

Parkin, David. 1969. *Neighbors and Nationals in an African City Ward*. Berkeley: University of California Press.

Parsons, Talcott. 1951. Illness and the Role of the Physician: A Sociological Perspective. *American Journal of Orthopsychiatry* 21:452–60.

———. 1953. Illness and the Role of the Physician. In *Personality in Nature, Society and Culture*. Second ed. C. Kluckholn and H. A. Murray, eds. New York: Knopf.

———. 1975. Some Theoretical Considerations on the Nature and Trends of Change of Ethnicity. In *Ethnicity: Theory and Experience*. N. Glazer and D. P. Moynihan, eds. Pp. 53–83. Cambridge, MA: Harvard University Press.

Pfister-Ammende, Maria. 1980. The Long-Term Sequelae of Uprooting: Conceptual and Practical Issues. In *Uprooting and Development*. George V. Coelho and Paul I. Ahmed, eds. Pp. 153–73. New York: Plenum.

Pliskin, Karen. 1980. Camouflage, Conspiracy, and Collaborators: Rumors of the Revolution. *Iranian Studies* 13:55–82.

Racy, John. 1980. Somatization in Saudi Women: A Therapeutic Challenge. *British Journal of Psychiatry* 137:212–16.

Reisman, Paul. 1983. On the Irrelevance of Child Rearing Practices for the Formation of Personality. *Culture, Medicine, and Psychiatry* 7:103–29.

Rosaldo, Michelle Z. 1980. *Knowledge and Passion: Ilongot Notions of Self and Social Life*. Cambridge: Cambridge University Press.

Rosen, Lawrence. 1979. Social Identity and Points of Attachment: Approaches to Social Organization. In *Meaning and Order in Moroccan Society*. Clifford Geertz, Hildred Geertz, and Lawrence Rosen. Cambridge: Cambridge University Press.

Rosenhan, David L. 1973. On Being Sane in Insane Places. *Science* 179:250–58.

Said, Edward. 1979. *Orientalism*. New York: Vintage.

Sanson, Mr. 1695. *Voyage ou Relation de l'Etat Present du Royaume de Perse*. Amsterdam.

Schachter, S., and J. Singer. 1962. Cognitive, Social and Psychological Determinants of Emotional State. *Psychological Review* 69:379–99.

Scheff, Thomas. 1966. *Being Mentally Ill*. New York: Aldine.

Sethi, B. B., S. S. Nathawat, and S. C. Gupta. 1973. Depression in India. *The Journal of Social Psychology* 91:3–13.

Shama, Avraham, and Mark Iris. 1977. *Immigration without Integration: Third World Jews in Israel*. Cambridge, MA: Schenkman.

Sheil, Lady. 1856. *Glimpses of Life and Manners in Persia*. London: John Murray.

Shokeid, Moshe. 1971. *The Dual Heritage*. Manchester: Manchester University Press.

Shuval, Judith. 1979. Primary Care and Social Control. *Medical Care* 17:631–38.

———. 1980. *Entering Medicine: The Dynamics of Transition*. Oxford: Pergamon.

Shuval, Judith T., Aaron Antonovsky, and A. Michael Davies. 1970. *Social Functions of Medical Practice*. San Francisco: Jossey-Bass.

Shweder, Richard A., and Edmund J. Bourne. 1982. Does the Concept of the Person Vary Cross-Culturally? In *Cultural Conceptions of Mental Health and Therapy*. A. J. Marsella and G. M. White, eds. Pp. 97–137. Dordrecht: D. Reidel.

Smooha, Sammy. 1978. *Israel: Pluralism and Conflict*. Berkeley: University of California Press.

Southgate, Rev. Horatio. 1840. *Narrative of a Tour through Armenia, Kurdistan, Persia, and Mesopotamia*. London: Tilt and Bogue.

Sykes, Ella C. 1910. *Persia and Its People*. London: Metheun.

Sykes, Percy. 1930. *A History of Persia*. London: Macmillan.

Tambiah, Stanley. 1968. The Magical Power of Words. *Man* 3:175–208.

———. 1977. The Cosmological and Performative Significance of a Thai Cult of Healing Through Meditation. *Culture, Medicine, and Psychiatry* 1:97–132.

Tancoigne, M. 1820. *A Narrative of a Journey into Persia*. London: William Wright.

Tavernier, John Baptista. 1684. *The Six Travels of John Baptista Tavernier, Baron of Aubonne, through Turkey and Persia to the Indies—in the Space of Forty Years*. J. P. London.

Teja, J. S., R. L. Narang, and A. K. Aggarwal. 1971. Depression across Cultures. *British Journal of Psychiatry* 119:253–60.

Temerlin, Maurice K. 1968. Suggestion Effects in Psychiatric Diagnosis. *Journal of Nervous and Mental Disease* 147:349–58.

Thass-Thienemann, Theodore. 1971. *Symbolic Behavior*. New York: Washington Square.

Tomkins, S. S. 1962. *Affect, Imagery, Consciousness*. Vol. 1: The Positive Affects. New York: Springer.

———. 1963. *Affect, Imagery, Consciousness*. Vol. 2: The Negative Affects. New York: Springer.

Trimble, Joseph E. 1980. Forced Migration: Its lmpact on Shaping Coping Strategies. In *Uprooting and Development*. George V. Coelho and Paul I. Ahmed, eds. Pp. 449–78. New York: Plenum.

Turner, Victor. 1967. *The Forest of Symbols*. Ithaca: Cornell University Press.

———. 1974. *Dramas, Fields, and Metaphors*. Ithaca: Cornell University Press.

———. 1977. Process, System, and Symbol: A New Anthropological Synthesis. *Daedalus* 106(3):61–80.

Verdonk, A. L. 1977. Migration and Mental Illness. *Migration News*, no. 4:9–18.

Wallace, Anthony F. C. 1961. *Culture and Personality*. New York: Random House.

Waring, Edward Scott, Esq. 1807. *A Tour to Sheeraz*. London: T. Cadell and W. Davies.

Waxler, Nancy. 1974. Culture and Mental Illness: A Social Labeling Perspective. *Journal of Nervous and Mental Disease* 159:379–95.

———. 1981. The Social Labeling Perspective on Illness and Medical Practice. In *The Relevance of Social Science for Medicine*. Leon Eisenberg and Arthur Kleinman, eds. Pp. 283–306. Dordrecht: D. Reidel.

Waziri, Rafiq. 1973. Symptomatology of Depressive Illness in Afghanistan. *American Journal of Psychiatry* 130:213–17.

Weingrod, Alex. 1966. *Reluctant Pioneers: Village Development in Israel*. Ithaca: Cornell University Press.

Weissman, Myrna M., and Gerald L. Klerman. 1977. Sex Differences and the Epidemiology of Depression. *Archives of General Psychiatry* 34:98–111.

Widengren, George. 1961. The Status of the Jews in the Sassanian Empire. *Iranica Antiqua* 1:117–62.

Willner, Dorothy. 1969. *Nation-Building and Community in Israel*. Princeton: Princeton University Press.

Wills, C. J. 1891. *In the Land of the Lion and Sun*. London: Ward, Lock.

Wilson, Sir Arnold. 1921. *S. W. Persia: A Political Officer's Diary, 1907–1914*. London.

Wolf, Margery. 1972. *Women and the Family in Rural Taiwan*. Stanford: Stanford University Press.

Wolff, Joseph. 1861. *Travels and Adventures of the Rev. Joseph Wolff*. London: London: Saunders, Otley.

Yishai, Yael. 1982. Politics and Medicine: The Case of Israeli National Health Insurance. *Social Science and Medicine* 16:285–91.

Young, Allan. 1981. When Rational Men Fall Sick: An Inquiry into Some Assumptions Made by Medical Anthropologists. *Culture, Medicine, and Psychiatry* 5:317–35.

———. 1982a. The Anthropology of Illness and Sickness. *Annual Review of Anthropology* 11:257–85.

———. 1982b. Rational Men and the Explanatory Model Approach. *Culture, Medicine, and Psychiatry* 6:57–71.

Zonis, Marvin. 1971. *The Political Elite of Iran*. Princeton: Princeton University Press.

Index